PLATE I

Beutenmuller

FIELD BOOK OF
PONDS AND STREAMS

An Introduction to the
Life of Fresh Water

By

ANN HAVEN MORGAN, PH.D.
PROFESSOR OF ZOOLOGY, MOUNT HOLYOKE COLLEGE

With about 330 Illustrations, including 23 plates
in color and black and white

G. P. PUTNAM'S SONS
NEW YORK — LONDON

FIELD BOOK OF
PONDS AND STREAMS

Copyright, 1930
by
Ann Haven Morgan

Sixteenth Impression

Made in the United States of America

To

ELIZABETH ADAMS

PROFESSOR OF ZOOLOGY
IN
MOUNT HOLYOKE COLLEGE

FOREWORD

Minnows and frogs and brown water beetles, scurrying to cover as we approach the shore of a still clear pond, show us that the water has some very lively inhabitants. They swim and dive and paddle in the open until we come, and then they hide from us distrustfully. Theirs is another world than ours. In that world there are strange living creatures in endless variety. There are big and little, swift and slow, strong and weak, graceful and ungainly: all are born to feed and grow and reproduce, to hunt and be hunted, to strive for a livelihood; and in so doing to fill a place in the household of nature.

No one who has lived by clear waters can have failed to see something of their wonderful life: minnows on the shoals; caddis worms dragging their cumbersome portable houses over the brook bed; the young of mayflies clinging to the stones in the riffle, or the adult mayflies in their dancing nuptial flight in the air above the stream; and what could be more interesting?

To make the knowledge of the whole range of life in ponds and streams a little more easy of access is a major purpose of this book. And with that knowledge will come appreciation, and a purpose to aid in keeping the waters free from pollution. Clean waters are always charming; and nothing is more sordid and unwholesome than polluted water. Here is a public service of no small moment. It is all in the interest of a better human environment; better for health, for recreation, for instruction, and for æsthetic pleasures.

A book like this cannot fail to render good service since it tells the simple truth about aquatic creatures in an interesting

FOREWORD

way, illustrates them with good figures, and so enables the
reader to know what they are like and where to go to find
them.

JAMES G. NEEDHAM.

Cornell University, March, 1930.

PREFACE

This book began in ponds where frogs sat on the lily-pads and by swift brooks from which mayflies flew forth at twilight. It originated where water plants and animals live and I hope that it may be a guide into the vividness and variety of their ways. Most of all I hope that it may help toward wider enjoyment and further acquaintance in the field of water biology that offers abundant opportunity to all explorers, both beginners and seasoned investigators.

The work of making it has been done along a trail of friendliness which will not be forgotten. Those who need a way to discover the loyalty and generosity of human nature should write a book about ponds and streams.

I have borrowed freely from the writings of many biologists; some of these are named in the bibliography but lack of space has excluded others whose contributions have not been small. A few figures have also been borrowed and these are acknowledged separately. Dr. J. G. Needham of Cornell University first showed me how to look for things in the water; since that time he has continually given me help and encouragement for finding more. It is a satisfaction to have his foreword here. Mrs. Margaret Tucker Saunders has read all of the manuscript and has given freely of her own clear cut observations, and her first hand knowledge of animals.

Fresh water life is a vast subject and even the simplest account of it must include much which can be mastered only by specialists after years of study. Many who are authorities in their fields have helped generously, by giving suggestions and reading sections of the manuscript. The entire chapter on insects has been read by Dr. C. P. Alexander of Massachusetts Agricultural College; the mollusks by Dr. F. C. Baker, and the worms and sponges by Dr. F. M. Smith, both of the University of Illinois; the Trichoptera by Dr. C. Betten, the crustaceans by Dr. G. C. Embody, the Coleoptera by Dr. W. T. M. Forbes, the amphibians and reptiles by Dr. A. H. Wright and Mrs. Anna Allen Wright, all of Cornell University; the bryozoans by Dr. C. B. Davenport of the Carnegie Institution; the Hemiptera by Dr. H. B. Hungerford of the University of Kansas; the leeches by Dr. J. P. Moore of the University of Pennsylvania; the plants by Dr. F. D. Reed of Mount Holyoke College; sections on water environment by Dr. F. A. Saunders of Harvard University. Special thanks are due to Professor S. H. Gage of Cornell University whose comradeship in finding the facts has done much to make the way to them straight and cheering.

Those familiar with days of college teaching know that there is not much spare time in them. Time to write this book has been largely made possible by my colleagues in the department of zoology at Mount Holyoke College, especially Dr. A. Elizabeth Adams, Dr. Christianna Smith, Bernice Maclean, Kathryn Stein, and Margaret Grierson, who have given me every kind of help. As my special helper in this work, Margaret Grierson has continually contributed her untiring interest and keen insight. And the mainspring of this as of most of the activities of this department has been the enthusiasm of Dr. Cornelia M. Clapp.

Some of the drawings have been made by the author but most of them have been made under her direction by Miss Grierson; Miss L. Krause at Yale University; Mrs. E. L. Beutenmuller at the American Museum of Natural History; Mrs. E. L. Burckmyer and Mr. V. S. L. Pate at Cornell University. I appreciate the accuracy and skill with which they have done their work. I extend my thanks to

PREFACE

Mrs. Elsie Broughton Klots who selected the specimens of insects loaned to me by Cornell University, and helped in directing the drawings that were made there. I am grateful also to Miss Clara M. LeVene and Miss Vera A. Timm, of New Haven, who have read all of the proof.

The mistakes that may be discovered in this book are in no way the fault of those who have read the manuscript. I can only hope that if they occur they may not be too confusing and that they may be reported and finally eliminated.

ANN H. MORGAN.

Mount Holyoke College, March, 1930.

CONTENTS

xi

CONTENTS

CONTENTS

The following illustrations are reprinted by permission from *Fresh Water Biology* by Ward and Whipple, published by John Wiley and Sons, Inc.:

ILLUSTRATIONS

Photographs, from life, by the author

FIELD BOOK OF
PONDS AND STREAMS

CHAPTER I

WATER PLANTS AND ANIMALS AND HOW THEY LIVE

This book tells something about the common plants and animals of fresh water and the places where they live. It tries to show them in their home brooks and ponds and in their native mud.

Different waters hold their own special communities; the dainty glen stream shelters companies of mayflies in its swift riffles; pond shallows and meadow brooks are the homes of lurking dragonfly nymphs; and wayside puddles are populous with mosquito wrigglers and water-fleas. In all these places living things must contend with winter cold and summer drought, with storms and flood waters. In winter the pond populations drop to the bottom, frogs and turtles dig under mud and broken plants, whirligig beetles hide under banks to come out with every warm spell, and fresh water sponges are packed in tough-covered capsules. In summer when its own pool dries up the water boatman flies to some other pond but many caddis worms burrow into the mud bottom and endure the drought as best they can.

How to use this book.—The table on pages 4–6 shows the groups of plants and animals discussed in the chapters of this book. The pictures show some of their representative members and the brief notes beneath tell something characteristic of them. After an animal is located in one of these groups

3

it can then be followed to the chapter where it is described more particularly. Only common names are used here; later, common and Latin names are both given. Following the table is a discussion of water as a home, a chapter on the community life in water, and another chapter on how to find water animals.

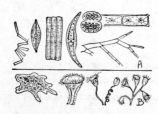

FIG. 1.—Most of these animals 1-celled and microscopic or nearly so. A.—Plant-like, single cells or chains of cells, often in conspicuous green masses; B.—Microscopic, 1-celled animals.

Simpler plants and animals (p. 46).

FIG. 2.—Typical plants with roots and leaves. Flowers often minute, sometimes conspicuous. Submerged in the water, floating on the surface or rising above it.

Higher plants (p. 58).

FIG. 3.—Flattened green or yellowish masses (animal) on submerged stones, sticks, and plants. 1—6 inches across.

Sponges (p. 104).

FIG. 4.—Thread-like, white or green animals hanging from sticks and stones in quiet water. About one-quarter inch long.

Hydras (p. 112).

Fig. 5.—Soft, grayish or black worms. Creeping on under sides of stones. Generally less than one-quarter inch long.

Free-living flatworms (p. 119).

Fig. 6.—Microscopic animals on stones and plant stems or swimming near the surface.

Wheel animalcules (rotifers) (p. 127).

Fig. 7.—Colonies of animals, vine-like on under sides of stones, or rug-like beneath lily pads, or masses of jelly hanging in open water. Colonies one-half inch across up to 15 inches thick.

Moss animalcules (bryozoans) (p. 131).

Fig. 8.—Transparent worms, one-half inch long or less; swarming over muddy bottoms; red worms up to 1–2 inches long, and hair-like worms 1–2 feet long.

Threadworms, hairworms and bristleworms (p. 139).

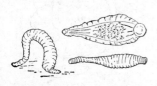

Fig. 9.—Flattened, worm-like animals with a sucker at each end. Clinging to stones and sticks, often on legs of turtles. Mostly 1–3 inches long.

Leeches (p. 148).

Fig. 10.—Many-jointed animals breathing by blood-gills; (a) microscopic, (b) 1 inch, or (c) several inches long.

Water-fleas, fairy shrimps, crayfishes, etc. (crustaceans) (p. 158).

Fig. 11.—Brightly colored, red, orange, spider-like animals running over submerged plants and on the bottom.

Water-mites (p. 175).

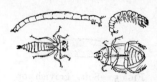

Fig. 12.—Jointed animals of many shapes and sizes, most of them with 6 legs on the thorax even in their immature stages. Young and adult often very different.

Water insects (p. 179).

Fig. 13.—Animals of many sizes bearing a shell, 1-piece and twisted, or 2-piece and hinged.

Snails and mussels (p. 301).

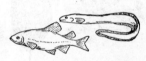

Fig. 14.—Back-boned animals with fins supported by jointed rods of cartilage, breathing by blood-gills throughout their lives. Usually scaly.

Fishes (p. 324).

Fig. 15.—Back-boned animals with limbs provided with fingers and toes; soft-skinned without scales; young breathe by gills, adults have lungs.

Salamanders, frogs, toads (p. 347).

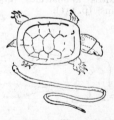

Fig. 16.—Back-boned animals with scaly skin, often covered with bony plates; breathe by lungs throughout their lives.

Turtles and snakes (p. 389).

6

Water and living things.—Plants and animals grow in every brook and pond. The first ones lived in the water and their descendants still dwell there in great beauty and abundance. Water still offers protection and support, and in it plants and animals can secure a livelihood on easier terms than they can on land. Many of them have lived in the water ever since their ancestors started there; others, the aquatic seed plants and insects, tried living on land but went back to the water. Diverse histories lie behind the varied company of plants and animals which now make up aquatic society, but they have all become more or less adjusted to their common experience of water life.

Water environment.—Water is all around us. It covers more than two-thirds of the earth's surface; ocean or streams and lakes and little ponds are almost everywhere. Water has more properties which are beneficial to living things than has any other substance. It is seven hundred and seventy times heavier than air, with a surface film upon which spring-tails can jump, and water striders can walk. This surface film is stronger than that of any other fluid except mercury; and although the water strider's feet bend it down into six dimples, they do not break it. Snails and planarians glide over its underside, and hydras hang head downward from it. The little crustaceans, *Scapholeberis* (Fig. 124), cling to it, ventral side up. On this side they are darkly colored, while their backs are pale, their coloring like their position being just the opposite of that in most animals. The larvæ of mosquitoes thrust their airtubes through the surface film and rest there, tails up and heads down. Like the larvæ of the big diving beetles (Fig. 209), and the pond scorpion, and many others, they are buoyed up by their own air supply.

The greater density of water gives it more supporting power than air, so much so that the fairy shrimp (Fig. 123) and a host of other animals can float motionless in it. All types of animals and many plants have relied upon its support; in water, even the heavy claws of the crayfish take on a lightsome poise (Fig. 133). It is a good transporting agent, too, and even clear riffle-water carries a load of minute organisms on which the net-building caddis worm depends for food (Pl. XVI).

Temperature of the water.—Water is safe to live in, summer and winter, for it does not get so hot nor so cold as air. It is a poor conductor of heat and the changes which occur in a pond are far more gradual than the sudden shifts in the air above it. Ponds have fairly equable temperatures even though they be located in temperamental New England. In general the temperature of the water determines the level which it will occupy in the pond. Cold waters tend to drop to the bottom and warm waters rise to the top, shifts of great import to the hosts of little plants and animals which they carry along with them. As the pond surface cools in summer evenings the top waters fall a little, and when it chills in autumn they drop farther, taking myriads of little organisms downward to winter safety. Water is heaviest when it has cooled to 39.2° F. (4°C.), and then it gradually forms a bottom layer. If the surface water grows colder than that, it becomes less dense, lighter in weight, and stays in the upper levels. At 32° F. (0°C.) it freezes, the ice floats, and the pond is covered with a blanket which keeps its warmth from radiating into the colder air above it. In small ponds spring sunshine melts the ice and gradually warms the water through, even in the bottom layers. In large lakes there is a complicated spring overturn and circulation of the water due partly to changes in temperature and partly to the action of the winds which blow across the surface.

Food content of the water.—The final food supplies of all water organisms are the non-living substances in the water. These are dissolved gases, oxygen and carbon dioxide, and the raw materials of foods, such as carbonic acid and salts— phosphates, silica, calcium carbonate, and nitrates. Their proportions vary in different waters and under diverse conditions. Water absorbs oxygen from the air so that near the surface it is more abundant than in the lower layers. Proof of this can be seen in any bowl of goldfish. Whenever their water supply becomes low in oxygen the fish swim about near the top where there is more of it to be found than in the lower levels.

In their respiration, green plant cells take in oxygen and give off carbon dioxide, just as animals do. But in photosynthesis or food making they take in carbon dioxide and give off oxygen. Photosynthesis can go on only in the light and during the daytime this process is so vigorous that its results overshadow those of respiration. Thus during the day the net result of both processes is that plants give off some carbon dioxide but much more oxygen than they take in, while at night, when respiration alone continues, they give off carbon dioxide only. At night the little crustaceans which live below the surface waters come up to the top to breathe the abundant oxygen which they find there as a result of the day's plant activity, and at the same time they give off carbon dioxide which will be used by the green plant cells next day.

The amount of the carbon dioxide in water is greater in winter than it is in summer, because plants are at a lower ebb of life and do not use so much of it. But spring sunshine starts them into greater activity, which results not only in their increased demand for carbon dioxide, but in the production of oxygen at a period when the animals will need it.

Light in the water.—Water is transparent, but it is well known that even the clearest water is far less transparent than air. It lets the sunshine in upon green plants which can prepare their own food from non-living materials only when they have enough of it. The vast hosts of diatoms and desmids, other simple plants, and even many of the higher ones, could not live on pond and stream bottoms as they do if light did not penetrate through many feet of water. Studies of the distribution of algæ in clear, deep lakes have shown that they cannot get light enough except in the upper fifty or sixty feet of water, and even in the lower levels of that they are very rare. The main population of green plants and animals lives only where light is abundant. Consequently shallow ponds are inhabited down to the bottom, but in large, deep lakes life extends through only a small proportion of the depths.

CHAPTER II

LIFE IN PONDS AND STREAMS

Ponds.—Small bodies of water are sometimes called ponds and the large ones lakes, but properly speaking a pond as here considered is a body of water which is so shallow that rooted water plants can grow all the way across it. It may be a half mile wide; but it is usually not more than twelve or fifteen feet deep, often less than that. Its waters are so shallow that the bottom is well lighted except where the surface is covered by lily pads and duckweeds; but even in such places plenty of light sifts down upon the growing organisms below. Such ponds warm through quickly; an unusually warm winter's day will bring the whirligig beetles up to the surface, and a week or two of spring sunshine will set the whole pond astir. Water and such abundant light and warmth are the only essentials for the growth of diatoms, desmids, and filamentous algæ—the great plant crop of the water, the food supply for millions of small animals which in their turn become food for larger ones like the fishes.

Kinds of ponds.—Many ponds which teemed with life in late winter and spring are dried up and dead looking by August. These transient ponds depend upon the rainfall and the drainage from surrounding hills. They are the uncertain ones in which the fairy shrimps appear, and a host of other little crustaceans which can endure months of drought in their "resting egg" stages, insects like caddis larvæ which dig down into the bottom mud, and water-bugs which can fly to some other place as their own pond dries away. Frogs lay their eggs by thousands in these short-lived ponds and the early summer droughts turn such places into tadpole cemeteries.

Permanent ponds are the ones which hold the greatest variety of water life. They may be big or little, spring-fed or stream-fed, low in the marsh or high on the upland, in the woods or the open; if they only offer water the year round they can support a large population.

Life in ponds (Fig. 17).—In nearly all ponds certain plants grow in more or less clearly defined zones and particular communities of animals are associated with them.

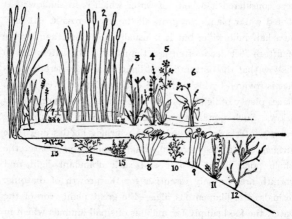

FIG. 17.—Diagram of the distribution of pond plants. In the background are the emergent water plants— 1, pickerel weed; 2, cat-tails; 3, bulrush; 4, bur-reed; 5, water plantain; 6, arrowhead. In the foreground are the floating-leaved plants—7, *Polygonum;* 8, lily pads; 9, spatter-docks; 10, hornwort; 11, eelgrass; 12, pondweed; and the submerged plants—13, *Riccia;* 14, bladderwort; 15, water milfoil.

Closest to shore are the emergent water plants, those which grow with their roots in the water and their stems and leaves in air. Among them are reeds, bulrushes, and marsh grasses, the white-blossomed arrowheads, water plantains, the massed blue spikes of the pickerel weeds, and crowding into every space high standing-armies of cat-tails (Fig. 17). Covering their stems below the water line are the simpler plants, desmids and other algæ, on which swarms of small crustaceans feed. Little plant-eating worms are abundant on them, also, and some of the smaller water beetles.

Beyond this zone are the floating-leaved plants, growing in water knee-deep or a little more. There, the bottom is

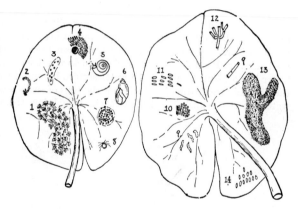

FIG. 18.—Diagram showing the population on the undersides of lily pads: 1, bryozoan colony; 2, midge larva; 3, snail's eggs (*Physa*); 4, beetle's eggs (*Donacia*); 5, snail (*Graulus*); 6, snail (*Physa*); 7, eggs of caddis fly (*Triænodes*); 8, water-mite; 9, tubes of midge larvæ; 10, eggs of water-mite; 11, eggs of damselfly (*Enallagma*); 12, tube of rotifer (*Melicerta*); 13, sponge; 14, eggs of whirligig beetle.

soft and pleasant to walk through and the mud boils up through it with every step one takes. Near shore, lily pads and the ever-present little duckweeds lie on the surface and leaves of the yellow spatterdocks are only half lifted

Pl. II.—1. In the slow meadow streams are diving beetles, nymphs of dragonflies and damselflies, burrowing mayflies, water striders, tadpoles; and leopard and green frogs along the banks. 2. Pond shallows; near shore duckweeds cover the water like a blanket and dot the water surface beyond; here the lily pads are floating hatcheries for the eggs of snails and water insects· sunfishes and sticklebacks hide below them.

Photo. by A. H. Morgan

from it. Sometimes it is gay with the rose-colored flowers of *Polygonum amphibium* (Fig. 73). In the deeper water, the ribbony leaves of pondweeds and fresh water eelgrass stream upward from the bottom. There also may be the submerged meadows of hornwort and just below the surface the little vine-like liverworts, *Riccia* (Fig. 52), and the bladderworts, *Utricularia* (Fig. 82).

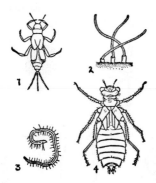

FIG. 19.—Bottom-dwellers: 1, mayfly (*Cænis*); 2, tubes of *Tubifex;* 3, worm (*Nais*); 4, dragonfly (*Libellula*).

The animals which live near shore are even more varied and more numerous than the plants. On the underside of a single lily pad (Fig. 18) are snails, small red water-mites, tube-dwelling rotifers of the genus *Melicerta* (Fig. 102), and numerous midge larvæ. These same lily pads are so many hundreds of floating hatcheries for the eggs of snails, mites, beetles, and other water insects. All the plant stems are coated with a green slime of algæ, the food of pond-snails and countless numbers of little tube-dwelling worms. Colonies of fresh water sponges and bryozoans encircle the stems and spread over the under surfaces of leaves. One sweep of the net will bring up insect carnivores—larvæ of tiger-beetles, water-bugs, dragonfly and damselfly nymphs.

Plant-feeding nymphs of the mayfly *Callibætis* (Fig. 158) dart through the open water. Many of the population have taken to the bottom and when a netful of mud is scooped up or a handful drained through one's fingers, its inhabitants begin to appear—mayfly nymphs, little red worms (*Tubifex*) (Fig. 114), and dozens of other pale worms (*Nais*) (Fig. 111), and midge larvæ, each one squirming enough to be finally discovered. They all find food in this mud mainly from the diatoms with which it is saturated.

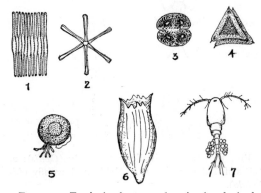

FIG. 20.—Typical plants and animals of plankton society. A. Plants—diatoms: 1, *Fragillaria;* 2, *Asterionella;*—desmids: 3, *Cosmarium;* 4, *Staurastrum.* B. Animals—protozoans: 5, *Arcella;*—rotifers: 6, *Notholca;*—crustaceans: 7, *Cyclops.*

Most small ponds are so shallow that water-lilies and pondweeds grow even in the deepest places. The surface waters of the larger ponds and lakes are occupied by a floating population known as plankton, made up of millions of microscopic plants and animals (Fig. 20). The plant cells are mainly diatoms and desmids, so translucent and minute that thousands of them would go unseen in a glass of drinking water. There are a few kinds of one-celled animals or protozoans, many rotifers, and swarms of diatom-eating crustaceans, the females of the latter often bearing their egg sacs with them. The number of different plankton organisms rises and falls during the year; many species have seasons of special abundance. *Cyclops* (Fig. 126) may predominate at one time, and some other crustacean at another time, their abundance paralleling the increase of one or more diatoms which are their natural food. Plankton organisms have an enormous reproductive capacity. This is especially true of diatoms, which form a staple food crop of the water, comparable to the grass crop on land.

Larger animals of the pond.—Among the lily pads and the water weeds of the shallows, lurk sunfishes, bullheads, mud minnows, and young perch. All of these forage upon snails, crustaceans, and insect larvæ, especially the tempting mayfly nymphs which they find there. Bullfrogs float with their heads just out of water; of all frogs these belong most thoroughly in the pond. Equally at home in it are the painted turtles, and the spotted turtles often found with them (Pl. XXIII). In May and June stumps and floating logs usually carry a load of one kind or the other. They forage in the shallows taking a heavy toll of tadpoles, snails, dragonflies—a miscellaneous bill-of-fare which they always eat under water. Snapping turtles frequent these waters also, catching anything within reach of the lightning-quick thrusts of their heads—fishes, tadpoles, frogs, or crayfishes, as well as the smaller game of insects and worms.

Balance of life in the pond (Fig. 21).—In a pond everything alive is good eating, and even dead and broken fragments do not go unrelished. Swarming millions of tiny crustaceans feed upon the algæ; young fishes devour the crustaceans; and older fishes, turtles, frogs, and even dragonfly nymphs prey upon young fishes. Midge larvæ and mayfly nymphs consume the plant tissues, living and dead; larger insects eat the little wormlike midges; and later, tiger beetles and larger dragonflies feast upon their insect relatives, only to be swallowed in turn by fishes and the other larger water animals.

In a particular year many or very few individuals of a species may be found but seldom does any one species entirely die out. At one time nymphs of dragonflies may dominate the water while mayflies may be hard to find; yet by another

FIG. 21.—Food relations in the pond where large animals eat the smaller ones: 1, adult fish; 2, swarming crustaceans; 3, young fishes; 4, frog; 5, snail; 6, dragonfly nymph; 7, midge larvæ; 8, mayfly nymph; 9, tadpole; 10, painted turtle; 11, young frog.

season mayflies may be gathered with every scoop of the net. In one way or another the balance of life is maintained. Dragonfly nymphs can clutch and bite while mayfly nymphs can do neither; yet mayflies make up for their lack of weapons by their ability to live upon plant food which they can find almost anywhere and by the great number of young which they produce. Some of the pond mayflies like *Callibætis* (Fig. 158) lay eggs when they are less than six weeks old, so that there is time for three or four generations of them to mature and reproduce in one summer. A single female may lay a thousand or more eggs, and as Needham has pointed out, by the fourth generation the possible offspring may number one hundred and twenty-five billions. Even this record hardly equals that of the army of minute crustaceans. These are eaten by many carnivores, yet they have overtopping advantages. Their minute size and their transparency are protections, and like mayflies they feed on plants and have a great reproductive capacity. It has been calculated that in sixty days there might be thirteen billion descendants from one female *Daphnia pulex* (Fig. 124) if no accident befell any of them.

Life in lakes.—Lakes are but larger editions of ponds. In the protected shallows of both, the communities are almost alike. But on the open lake surface where the wind blows unhindered, it sweeps water against the shores. There, clinging forms are found: snails, net-building caddis worms, and at a depth of three feet or more the large burrowing mayfly nymphs, *Ephemera* and *Hexagenia* (Pl. XIII), whose cast skins are often washed up into windrows upon the beaches.

In lakes there are great areas of deep, open water where there are no hiding places for small animals like those provided by the trash and vegetation in shallow waters. But the lake surface harbors a great floating or plankton population, sometimes miles of it, billions of microscopic animals and plants which are not only constantly increasing but also constantly being eaten, or dying and dropping to the bottom. Fishes also live in the open usually a few feet below the surface. They are not minute or transparent like the plankton but they are swifter and stronger than any other water animals. They stay near the top where the foraging is good, though in large lakes this means ten or fifteen feet beneath the surface. Below this depth there is a lonesome reach of water, generally barren of plant and animal life. And finally beneath this is the deep soft ooze of the barely lighted bottom which mud dredgings show to be but sparsely inhabited by a few small worms, mussels, and little red midge larvæ.

In spite of their size large streams do not harbor so many nor such interesting forms as the smaller ones; this is equally true of large rivers as compared with small ones. Rivers travel far, often through soft soil, and their waters gather sand and silt only to drop them again along the way, smothering fragile plants and animals beneath them. Only in sluggish rivers or in the inlets of swift streams is there much shore vegetation where the smaller clamberers can hide. With all its uncertainties in drought and flood time, the small stream still has greater advantages, for it is well lighted even on the bottom, and its waters are generally free from mud.

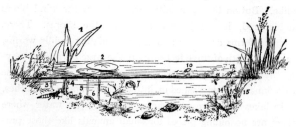

FIG. 22.—Diagram showing the distribution of animals across a slow stream. Plants—1, arrowhead; 2, spatterdock. Animals—3, dragonfly nymph; 4, tube of midge larva; 5, tube of bloodworm; 6, mud-leech; 7, scud; 8, burrowing mayfly, *Hexagenia;* 9, white clam; 10, whirligig beetle; 11, water boatman; 12, water strider; 13, mayfly, *Callibætis;* 14, caddis worm; 15, snail.

Slow streams and marshes (Fig. 22).—A slow stream flows gently and steadily over flat land; its bottom is of fine mud, sometimes of sand; there are no rocks, it has no waterfalls or rapids, and its waters are generally free from mud. Now and then there are inlets crowded with cat-tails, reeds, pickerel weed, and in some regions with water-hyacinth (Pl. II).

Its animal population is very much like that of ponds, especially if higher plants grow along its banks. Where the bottom is sandy there are burrowing mayflies, mussels, snails, and the big dragonfly nymph *Cordulegaster* which lies with its hairy body buried in the sand. In the stretches of muddy bottom are leeches, mussels, and, if the mud is firm enough, little white clams of the family *Sphæridæ* (Fig. 266). There are innumerable midge larvæ, a few of the never-failing

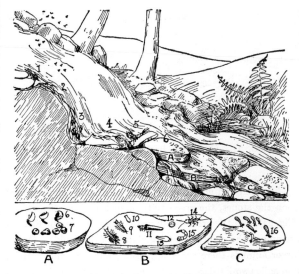

FIG. 23.—Diagram of the distribution of animals in a waterfall. The stones A, B and C are shown enlarged, with their inhabitants; A and C are right side up; B is wrong side up. 1, egg masses of midges; 2, water moss, *Fontinalis;* 3, midge larvæ; 4, alga, *Cladophora;* 5, mayfly, *Chirotenetes;* 6, nets of caddis worm, *Hydropsyche;* 7, pupa cases of caddis worm, *Helicopsyche;* 8, 9, mayflies, *Heptagenia* and *Epeorus;* 10, planarian; 11, caddis worm; 12, water penny; 13, leech; 14, stonefly nymph; 15, caddis worm; 16, black fly, *Simulium.*

crustacean genus, *Asellus* (Fig. 131), and as in the ponds, there are plenty of backswimmers and water boatmen.

Life in the rapids (Fig. 23).—In rapids the water is always falling and jostling, and every plant and animal must constantly clamber, or cling, or glue itself to some holdfast. Water pushes against the flattened stones tilting them so that even when it is all dried out of the stream, they still tell which way the current ran.

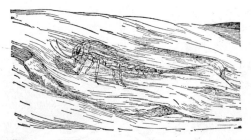

FIG. 24.—Collecting basket of the mayfly, *Chirotenetes.*

The green and golden-green films of desmids and diatoms upon the stones, the green tufts of such algæ as *Cladophora* (Fig. 23), and the green-black water moss *Fontinalis* (Fig. 55) are among the scanty plant population of the rapids. Of the larger animals there are a few fishes, minnows and darters, and agile two-lined salamanders which skulk under the stones. Immature insects predominate—midges, stoneflies, caddis flies, and mayflies, along with leeches, planarians, and a few snails.

Nearly all of these animals of the rapids live upon microscopic food. Net-building caddis worms (*Hydropsyche*) strain their food from the water in their cup-shaped nets which open upstream (Pl. XVI). The mayfly *Chirotenetes* (Fig. 24) carries its own collecting basket to catch plankton from the current. Facing upstream with tail and rear legs firmly braced, it holds its hairy front legs close beneath its bewhiskered mouth-parts and stands ready for whatever food the water may bring to it.

Attached to the rocks by a sucker on the hind end of the body, larvæ of the black-fly *Simulium* (Fig. 233) swing out into the water, spreading their fan-shaped food-brushes to sweep the diatoms and floating algæ into their mouths. If its end sucker loses hold the larva is washed downstream; but even then if it can only get its mouth in contact with a stone or stick it will use some of its silk-like saliva to tie itself down again, swinging upon this till it can once more anchor its sucker.

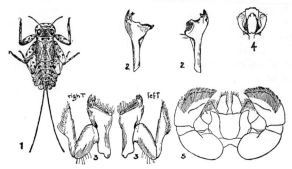

FIG. 25.—*Epeorus*, a mayfly of the rapids, and its mouth parts showing their diatom rakes: 1, nymph; 2, right and left upper jaws or mandibles; 3, right and left lower jaws or maxillæ; 4, tongue; 5, lower lip or labium.

Planarians, snails, and most of the mayflies suck or rake and scrape the green algal slime from the stones and like sheep in a pasture they can get their mouths close down to the smallest growths. The planarian actually swings its sucking proboscis out from the center of its body (Fig. 93); but the mouths of mayflies are beneath their flattened heads and are similarly effective (Fig. 25). Mayflies of the rapids like *Heptagenia*, *Epeorus*, and *Iron*, have horny teeth and

Pl. III.—1. In running water some animals are active all winter; insects, snails, and planarians creep over the stones and salamanders skulk beneath them. 2. Insects emerge from the rapids by hundreds, and the fly-catching phœbes take a plentiful harvest from the air; in the jostling water small animals find safety by holding on or getting under cover.

Photo. by A. H. Morgan

PLATE III

combs on their mouth-parts and using these as diatom rakes they can pull in a good harvest.

Amid the jostling water of rapids small animals find safety only by holding on, by getting under cover, or by being small or slender or flat (Pl. III). Flattest of any of this society are the water pennies (Fig. 215) which cling motionless to the under surface of the rocks, smooth-backed and copper-colored, looking like small pennies but not at all like the young beetles that they really are.

Waterfalls.—In springtime the rocks of waterfalls are green with algæ, but later the water mosses *Fontinalis* and *Hygro-hypnum* often crowd in and cover them. These grow on the straight rock face, well under the waterfall, escaping the dash of the water but kept wet by constant tricklings. Here small clamberers hide among the leaves—case-bearing caddis worms and beetle and midge larvæ. Midges swarm above the falls and lay their eggs in little white skeins upon the wet rock. Adult midges emerge from the waterfalls by hundreds, and the fly-catching phœbe on the branch above gets a plentiful harvest from the air. Large falls are foraging places for swallows which collect the emerging mayflies; even at Niagara they swing into the mist and spray, and when they dart out again their mouths are whiskered with protruding mayflies.

CHAPTER III

COLLECTING AND PRESERVING WATER ANIMALS

Collecting tools (Fig. 26).—For the smaller water animals, crustaceans, insects, and the like, the important collecting tools are a water-net, a white pie plate or saucer, a pair of forceps, a hand-lens, a pail with a cover which fits over the outside, and a few bottles. The water-net should be about eight inches in diameter with a stiff rim to hold the shallow bobbinet bag and a handle not over three feet long. Such nets are sold by supply dealers, or may be made at home. The rim should be so rigid that it will not bend and twist in the handle when the net is pulled through weeds and muck. A strong frame for a water-net can be made as shown in Figure 26, 1 and 2. Two grooves are made at one end of the handle (Fig. 26, 2); one groove is about four inches long and the one opposite is an inch longer. A small hole is bored into the handle at the end of each groove. The heavy wire for the frame is bent as shown in the figure (Fig. 26, 2), and the ends of the wire are fitted down into holes and along the grooves. The whole end is then bound tightly with fine, strong wire or heavy cord. The efficiency of the net depends upon the rigidity of the frame and the tightness of the binding. The net itself should be made of strong bobbinet fastened to tough cotton cloth covering the rim. A pie pan or any shallow white dish holding a little water makes a good background for the field examination of snails, leeches, dragonfly nymphs, and the like, while they

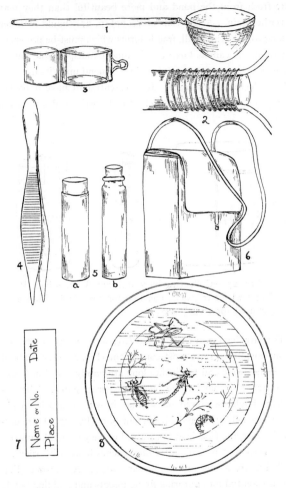

FIG. 26.—Collecting equipment: 1, water-net; 2, method of fastening wire to handle; 3, hand-lens; 4, forceps; 5, a, shell and b, homeopathic vial; 6, knapsack; 7, data label to be put into vial; 8 white pie plate for examining living animals.

27

are fresh from the pond and more beautiful than they may ever be again. A few vials of alcohol (p. 27) should be taken along to hold the small, fragile forms which must be preserved at once. A canvas knapsack is almost indispensable but its size and the arrangement of pockets depend upon its uses and the collector's own taste. It is essential to have a pocket note-book so that observations may be written down on the spot.

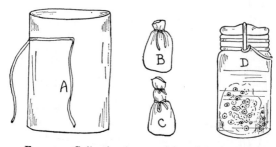

FIG. 27.—Collecting bags and jar: A, open bag; B, bag tied for frogs; C, bag tied for snakes; D, Mason jar used for frogs' eggs.

For carrying larger animals, like frogs and turtles and snakes, stout cotton bags are most convenient (Fig. 27); those about six inches wide and ten inches long are handy sizes but larger ones are desirable for the bigger or fiercer game. The tie-string should be sewed on so that it will always be ready when needed. Covered Mason fruit jars (Fig. 27, D) are use-ful for carrying frogs' eggs in water but they should be uncov-ered as soon as possible after one reaches home with them.

There are a few other necessary tools. An air-net (Fig. 28) is essential for capturing flying insects and a killing bottle for insects (Fig. 28) which are to be preserved dry. The air-net is made like the water-net except that its bag is deep and its frame is about a foot in diameter. For killing bottles both potassium cyanide and carbona are used, the former almost altogether by entomologists. Insects dropped into either of these bottles soon die from the fumes. It is generally advisable to secure cyanide bottles from dealers rather than to prepare them at home since potassium cyanide is a

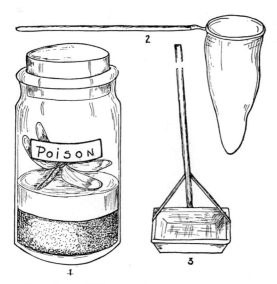

FIG. 28.—1, Killing bottle for insects; 2, air-net; 3, wire sieve-net for pulling up mud and trash.

deadly poison and should be handled with extreme caution. They should always be kept tightly stoppered in order to conserve their deadly fumes for the insects. A few drops of carbona or carbon tetrachloride sprinkled on cotton and put into a tight bottle will kill insects satisfactorily and yet may be safely handled. It usually has to be renewed at each collecting trip but carbona bottles can be made in such a way that they will last much longer. Soak some pieces of old rubber overshoe or inner tube in carbona; put these in a bottle with absorbent cotton packed around them and a piece of cardboard to hold them all down.

Forceps about twelve inches long are almost indispensable for reaching into the water in winter collecting, although many things can be hand picked on the undersides of stones, pulled out of riffles and over-turned upon the bank. Although not essential, a sieve- or trash-net (Fig. 28) is sometimes useful when muck must be ladled up to the bank or into a boat. Sieve-nets can be purchased from dealers; the small ones are best, less than a foot square and two or three inches deep.

FIG. 29.—Glass-bottomed bucket pressed down into the riffles to avoid the distortion at the surface and make the bottom visible.

A wooden bucket with a plate glass bottom (Fig. 29) helps one to see the bottom of shallow rapids. It is simply pressed down into the water so that one can look through it and avoid the distortions made by the uneven surface water. Other useful tools are the cheap wire "lifters" made by soldering a wire to a square of window-screening and used to lift animals from aquaria, hand-bulbs and pipettes or medicine-droppers for picking out frogs' eggs, and a little aquarium net (Fig. 30).

Where and how to collect.— *Near the edge of the pond in* summer, look for flowering plants, bulrushes, reeds, water snakes, bullfrogs and green frogs, tadpoles, water-mites, swarms of springtails, insect larvæ and nymphs, especially those almost ready to leave the water.

Collect with a water-net. For insects and all smaller animals skim the net through the water, scraping it against the vegetation, but do not scoop into the bottom.

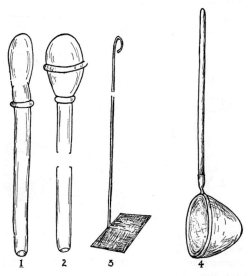

FIG. 30.—Aquarium tools: 1, pipette for picking out frogs' eggs; 2, hand-bulb; 3, wire lifter; 4, aquarium net.

In the shallows.—In the zone of floating leaves are water-lilies, pondweeds, the stoneworts—*Chara* and *Nitella*—water-fernworts, duckweeds, and the liverwort *Riccia;* algæ grow on the submerged stems and "blanket algæ" on quiet water surfaces (Pl. X). The larger animals common there are the spotted turtles, bullfrogs and green frogs, perch, catfishes, pickerel, and several kinds of young fishes; the smaller animals include all types of water insects, bryozoans, snails, leeches, and small crustaceans.

Collect with a water-net, sweeping it through the water and brushing the submerged vegetation. Turn the lily pads for snails, sponges, bryozoans, and insect eggs. Almost any of the plants harbor snails and little crustaceans.

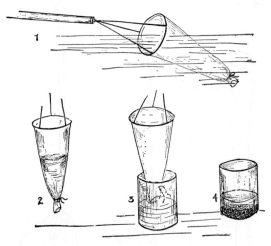

FIG. 31.—Collecting with a plankton net: 1, skimming the surface; 2, draining off the extra water; 3, pouring plankton out of the net; 4, plankton organisms after settling.

In the surface water.—In the open surface water of ponds and lakes are the plankton or microscopic plants and animals —desmids, diatoms, blue-green algæ, protozoans, crustaceans adult and young, and rotifers (Pl. IV).

To collect plankton near shore or in the smaller ponds skim the surface with a long-handled, cone-shaped, plankton net made of silk bolting cloth, trailing the net through the water (Fig. 31, 1) preferably from a boat. After a few minutes' continuous skimming, let the net drain until only a cup or so of water remains, then loose the string letting this through the open end (Fig. 31, 3). Such skimming should be repeated several times. If plankton organisms are abundant they will settle to the bottom of the dish as a brownish or greenish sediment (Fig. 31, 4).

The bottom.—On the pond bottom, in the mud or sand, are mussels, crayfish (in limy regions), an occasional turtle, mud-loving dragonfly nymphs, small mayflies like *Cænis* and *Tricorythus*, big burrowing ones—*Ephemera, Hexagenia*—and a host of midge larvæ and small worms such as *Tubifex* (Fig. 32).

FIG. 32.—A netful of mud with its inhabitants: 1, *Cænis;* 2, *Tubifex;* 3, worm, *Nais;* 4, *Tricorythus;* 5, mud-tubes of midges; 6, nematode worm; 7, snail.

Scoop up the mud and trash in small lots with a strong-rimmed water net. Let the load drain till the animals begin to clamber; then pick them out and drop them in a white dish for examination (p. 27).

Slow streams.—The population of small coves and the side waters of streams is similar to that near the pond shore (Pl. II). Scoop and sweep with a water net as in the ponds but work upstream so the current may take away the muddy water.

Riffles and rapids.—Algæ and water mosses on the stones

are the only plant growths. The animals stay on the under surfaces of the stones, hiding beneath them, or on their lee sides. Among them are a few small fishes—darters and minnows—two-lined salamanders, flattened mayfly and stonefly nymphs, net-building caddis fly larvæ, "water pennies," *Simulium* larvæ, leeches, planarians, and the swift-water snails—*Ancylus* and *Goniobasis*.

Work upstream. Pull stones from the water, turning them over quickly before the stonefly nymphs drop off; examine them carefully, since many of the animals cling tightly and are the same color as the stone. Hold the net against the current, stirring up the stones and gravel above it so that the animals which are dislodged will be caught in it.

Waterfalls.—Water mosses, *Hygrohypnum* and *Fontinalis*, are apt to grow here and clambering animals hide among them—larvæ of caddis flies and the cranefly *Dicranomyia*, crustaceans like *Gammarus* and *Asellus*, small mayfly nymphs and many midge larvæ.

Clear pools.—In gently flowing streams, usually in their clear pools, are beds of little white mussels of the genus *Sphærium*. *Asellus* is common in them and nymphs of the dragonfly, *Cordulegaster*.

Leaf-barriers.—Leaves and trash catch in the riffles forming leaf-barriers which hold their own distinct societies wherein the crustaceans—*Asellus* and *Gammarus*—are prominent, and the largest of the cranefly larvæ, *Tipula abdominalis*.

Springs.—Green algæ spread over spring pools and form "blanket algæ" communities (p. 50). These are populated by minute forms—diatoms, desmids, protozoans, worms, rotifers, crustaceans, and midge larvæ.

On land, by ponds and streams.—Many kinds of animals leave the water but stay in the regions near it. Frogs forage among the grasses along the banks; salamanders hide beneath stones on the wet shores or in drier places nearby. Adults of aquatic insects skulk in the shrubbery, or swarm above the water, and mayflies and caddis flies can often be found in the spider webs on bridges where they have been caught in flight.

Electric lights.—Electric street lamps and the lighted windows near streams or lakes are gathering places for insects, especially on warm humid nights; then caddis flies and craneflies may be picked by dozens from the electric light poles or from the sides of buildings.

When to collect. *Weather.*—In the brook, there is no closed season; even in January the flat stones of the rapids shelter a lively multitude. Sunshiny days are the best ones even for water collecting. Spring sunshine brings out the turtles and all the tadpole tribe, toad, frog, and salamander, and insect visitors crowd into the blossoms of the white water-lilies. Dragonflies and their kin emerge from the water; unlike their dusk-loving mayfly relatives the little *Leptophlebias* swarm forth on quiet sunny afternoons. On misty days or in soft rains flying insects hide under bridges, beneath leaves, or on nearby tree trunks and can be easily picked up by hand.

Time of day.—Many things can be found only at special times, in the morning, or at twilight or night. Mating flights of mayflies and caddis flies occur in late afternoon, mostly at twilight. Animals which hide in the daytime are usually most active at night; such are the mosquitoes, moths, crayfishes, salamanders like *Ambystoma*, the toads, and several of the frogs.

Many water animals lay their eggs at definite times, sometimes almost by the clock. Snapping turtles lay eggs in the forenoon, wood turtles lay in mid-afternoon, and spotted salamanders at night.

Seasons.—In the water as in other places, spring and summer are in general the most active and most populous times. Water organisms join others in the winter retreat to cover; but some of them are easily stirred from their hibernation and others are active all winter (Pl. I). The following list suggests a few of the things which can be found in open spring-fed brooks or beneath pond ice.

In ponds and slow streams October—November	In rapids January—February
Salamanders (*Triturus*) (p. 353)	Green algæ (p. 49)
Bullfrogs and green frogs (p. 385)	Protozoans (*Vorticella*) (p. 57)
Water boatmen, backswimmers (pp. 237, 239)	Sponges (gemmules) (p. 104)
Crayfishes carrying their eggs (p. 172)	Bryozoans (statoblasts) (p. 131)
Nymphs of dragonflies and damselflies, abundant (p. 214)	Planarians (p. 119)
	Snails (p. 304)
	Mussels with young in their gill pouches (p. 318)
Whirligig beetles (p. 271)	Young insects, net-building caddis worms (p. 251)

Care of living animals, life-history cages.—The way to learn most about animals is to watch them in their own homes or to keep them in cages which allow them to behave something like themselves. Such are the life-history cages within which insect nymphs may be kept in their own brooks. The simplest of these rearing cages (Fig. 33), one devised by Dr. J. G. Needham, is made from a piece of wire window-screening measuring about eighteen inches square. The ends are brought together and hemmed over to form a seven inch cylinder. The ends of this are then flattened and hemmed and the cage is pillowed out to give comfortable space within. One end can be easily opened when insects are placed within the cage. In order to secure the different stages of the life-history of water insects like dragonflies or mayflies, capture fully grown nymphs recognizable by their black or very large wing-pads and put them in rearing cages set a couple of inches down into the water of the insects' home stream. Put only one kind of insect in at a time and fasten a tag to the cage, writing name or number with the date, and keep a note-book record of them. Make the cage

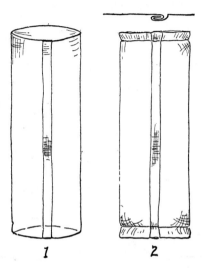

Fig. 33.—Cage for rearing water insects: 1. cylinder of wire window-screening with hem; 2, finished cage with ends folded, detail of hem. (After Needham.)

safe from floods and plunder; visit it every day or two if possible. The winged insect should soon be found at the top of the cage with its cast skin clinging to the cage side below. The cast off skin and the winged insect should be preserved in alcohol as a record of its immature and adult stages. Many quiet-water insects can be kept for a few days in screen-covered dishes within doors. Their changes from nymph to adult will go on equally well there.

Aquaria.—Put a layer of sand in a tumbler, plant a branch or two of *Elodea* in it, fill the glass with water from the pond and then let it settle. Put a couple of pond snails into it— and the aquarium is complete—made simply enough, yet here a snail can live through a sample of its normal daily life

(Fig. 34, 2). The life-history of mosquitoes, larva, pupa and adult (Fig. 34, 1), can be watched in such a simple aquarium; only this one should be kept covered.

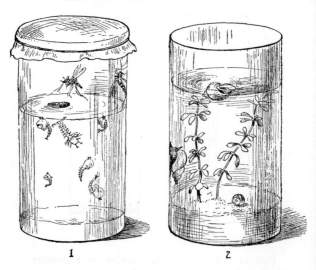

FIG. 34.—Aquaria in tumblers: 1, *Culex* mosquitoes, showing one larva and two pupæ with their air-tubes thrust through the surface film, floating eggs, adults; 2, snails and *Elodea*.

The balanced aquarium (Fig. 35) is just what its name says—a balance between plants and animals. The plants use the carbon dioxide produced by the animals; the animals use the oxygen given off by the plants. A good aquarium plant is one which affords a bountiful supply of oxygen.

The best aquarium dishes are rectangular glass ones which are as wide as they are high. Cylindrical ones distort the vision; deep ones shut out the air so that the water gets little oxygen. In making a balanced aquarium spread a layer of mud over the bottom, being sure that it is free from carnivorous animals; cover this with a layer of sand and gravel.

Water plants should be set in this, good ones for the aquarium being *Elodea*, *Myriophyllum*, and wild celery or *Vallisneria* (Fig. 35). The water should be added gently and then

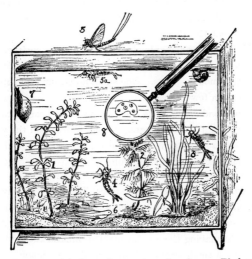

Fig. 35.—A balanced aquarium showing: 1, *Elodea*; 2, *Myriophyllum*; 3, *Vallisneria*; 4, mayfly nymph; 5, adult mayfly; 5a, cast nymphal skin of mayfly; 6, tadpole; 7, snail; 8, snail's eggs seen through reading glass.

·eft to settle for a couple of days. Many things will live well .n such an aquarium if they have plenty of oxygen and a little food. Snails will lay their eggs on the sides of the jar; such pond mayflies as *Callibætis* and *Blasturus*, and dragonflies and tadpoles will thrive here. Do not crowd the animals and do not mix the vegetarians and the carnivores; after such a mixture there will be only one kind left.

It is better to have several small aquaria (e.g., 6 x 3 x 5 inches) than one large one.

If aquaria are made of plate glass, things can be photo-

graphed through the sides.   A reading glass is useful
for observing the very small animals.

If the glass sides and the water become green, it means
that too many algæ are growing there.   The aquarium
should have less light, or there should be more snails
to eat the algæ.

If the gill-bearing animals keep going to the surface, they
need more oxygen; there are too many animals and
not enough plants.   One small aquarium will support
only a few animals.

Scum and bubbles on the top usually mean decaying
material below.   A greasy scum forming on the water
very soon after it is put into the dish is a sign that it
has been treated with alum.

Vivaria.—Salamanders and frogs live well in vivaria.
There are many ways of arranging these so that the animals
have water accessible and yet can climb out on the moist
earth.   In making these as in making aquaria the best way
is to copy a small section of the animals' own home.

Preserving specimens.—There are special methods by which
plant and animal specimens of different groups are best
preserved.   These are suggested in discussions of several
different groups in this book, and are fully described in books
and papers listed in the Bibliography (p. 408).   Animals are
generally preserved in alcohol or formalin, or by drying.
Books which give directions for preserving plants are listed
in the Bibliography.

Killing animals.—Insects such as adult dragonflies and
moths should be killed in a cyanide bottle or with carbona
(p. 29); but aquatic larvæ and nymphs and many other
small forms are best killed by dropping them directly into
alcohol.

Fish, frogs, salamanders and the like should be chloroformed or killed by other methods which common sense may

suggest. If chloroformed they should be enclosed in a tight pail with a little chloroform sprinkled on a cloth.

Occasionally it may be desirable to use chloretone, though not often. This is an anæsthetic which will kill small water animals painlessly and leaves them relaxed and ready to be put into alcohol or formalin. It is sold in crystals which can be dissolved in water to make a saturated solution. Such a stock solution should be kept on hand and a little of it used as needed. The animal should be placed in a little water and drops of chloretone added until it is entirely inert.

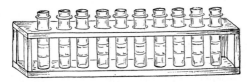

Fig. 36.—Specimen vials and rack for holding them.

Preserving insects and other animals.—Alcohol (ethyl 95%) diluted with about one-fourth water is the best general preservative for sponges, worms, leeches, crustaceans, water-mites, soft-bodied insects, frogs and salamanders and tadpoles, and for mollusks if the soft parts are to be kept. But alcohol is expensive and difficult to secure; and though nothing else is so satisfactory for insects, formalin is much cheaper and often better for other things, especially larger animals like crayfishes, frogs, and turtles. In these a slit should be made in the abdominal wall to let the preservative in upon the viscera. Eggs and larvæ of frogs and other amphibians keep well in a weak formalin solution. Formalin is sold at almost any drugstore and is not expensive; the proper solution may be made by adding one ounce of commercial (40%) formalin to sixteen ounces of water.

Storing specimens in alcohol (Fig. 36).—Small specimens are best kept in well-corked vials. There are several types of vial racks, most of them planned for storage on trays or shelves of closets. Each bottle should have a label giving the name or number of the specimens, the place and the date where they were caught, and the collector's name. These data may be written on regular labels or in soft pencil on a slip of paper placed inside the vial with the writing turned toward the glass; larger animals should have similar labels of heavy paper tied to them.

Some specimens are much better preserved by drying; such are the adult dragonflies, beetles and the like which can be stored: 1, in cotton; 2, in "papers"; 3, mounted on pins; or 4, arranged in "Riker boxes."

1.—Layers of cotton are useful for temporary storage of large lots of adult insects, especially those which have been caught at one time or place. Fit a layer of glazed cotton into a tin box, spread a layer of insects on it, then put in another layer of glazed cotton. When the specimens are packed put the cover on tightly to keep out the insect-eating pests; label with the date and place of collection.

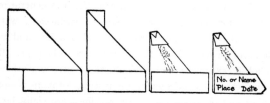

FIG. 37.—Successive steps in folding a storage envelope for insects.

2.—Storage envelopes (Fig. 37) or "papers" are made by folding pieces of paper of about postcard size. One or more specimens are inclosed within these and the data written on the outside. Insects stored like this may be "relaxed" (p. 43) and mounted at any time; the envelopes should be kept in tightly closed pest-proof boxes.

3.—Mounting on pins (Fig. 38) is such a common method

of displaying insects that it should be mentioned here. If the insects have become dried they should be put into a relaxing jar and left there over-night before the mounting process is begun. The relaxing jar may be almost any kind of large covered jar with a layer of damp sand in it overlaid with clean paper. After insects have lain in such a damp jar for a day or two their legs and wings can be moved easily

FIG. 38.—Insects mounted on pins: 1, with pin through the thorax; 2, beetle with pin through the right wing; 3, same in side view with label.

and they are ready for the mounting process. A special insect pin is put through the middle of the thorax or if the specimen is a beetle, through the right wing, and the legs are carefully extended.

If the insect has long wings like a damselfly it should be dried with wings outspread (Fig. 39); and a spreading board must be used. The simplest kind is made of soft wood with a row

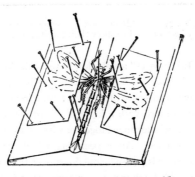

FIG. 39.—Spreading board with damselfly spread upon it, dorsal side down.

of gimlet holes down the center, each about half an inch deep. The specimen is pinned in the regular way and then placed dorsal side down on the board with the head of the pin reaching to the bottom of one of the holes. The wings are carefully outstretched with a piece of paper pinned across each one, and the specimen is then left in a safe place to dry.

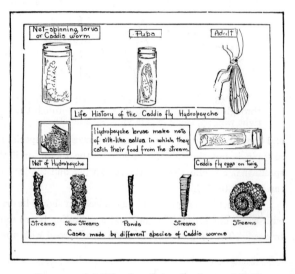

FIG. 40.—A " Riker box " showing how caddis flies may be mounted to show their habits and life history.

4.—" Riker boxes" are shallow boxes with glass covers (Fig. 40). They may be made by hand but it is generally more economical to purchase them ready for use from supply dealers. Each box is fitted with a layer of glazed cotton upon which specimens can be arranged together with whatever descriptions are to be included. After specimens and labels are in position the glass cover is pressed close down over them and carefully sealed on with binding tape, or some other fastening, which will make the box pest-proof. Specimens in " Riker boxes " can be easily examined, handled without fear of breaking and they may be made reasonably safe from insect-eating pests. Groups of specimens with a few explanatory labels thus present good accounts of the habits and life histories of many small animals.

CHAPTER IV

SIMPLER PLANTS AND ANIMALS

Algæ and Protozoans

Water teems with plants and animals invisible to the naked eye, but being microscopic they are outside the general scope of this book. Yet it is upon these organisms that the whole aquatic population ultimately depends for its food; and in a few cases at least one needs no microscope to detect them, for they collect in masses that are conspicuous by their color or odor. Brook beds and water weeds are golden brown with millions of diatoms; the familiar " pond-scum," " green-scum," and the "water-bloom" of ponds and lakes, are made up of microscopic algæ. Certain algæ make reservoir water taste fishy or bitter or make it smell like cucumbers. Pale whitish spots on water-washed stones and fuzzy patches on the legs and backs of water insects are actually colonies of one-celled animals, the beautiful bell-shaped protozoans, *Vorticella* and *Epistylis* (Fig. 51).

Algæ.—Fresh water algæ are simple plants whose form varies from minute rods, stars, crescents, richly patterned microscopic ribbons, slender filaments, single or branched, to the stoneworts (p. 53), so simply built that they are often classed with algæ, yet so large and so much branched that they look like the higher plants. The filamentous algæ grow in long threads or filaments, formed of narrow cells, attached to one another end to end, tandem-wise (Fig. 41). Sometimes these

46

filaments are branched, forming a tuft attached to stones, but they have no structure comparable to a root. Many algæ are single-celled; such are the desmids and diatoms although the constriction around the center of desmids makes them look two-celled, and many diatom cells cling together in spherical and ribbonlike colonies. Marine algæ such as the familiar seaweeds are conspicuously red or purplish or brown; but except for the diatoms most of the fresh-water algæ are green or blue-green. In all algæ the cells contain chlorophyll, the green substance by which plants are able to prepare their own food out of the raw materials of non-living matter. In green algæ masses of chlorophyll are naked within the cells displaying the characteristic green color, but in the diatoms the chlorophyll is cloaked with yellowish-brown diatomin, which gives diatoms their typical color. Fresh water algæ grow in untold numbers in running streams of every description, in lakes, ponds, and pools, and in every little place which holds a few days' stand of soft water.

Six classes of algæ are commonly recognized. They are known chiefly by their colors, red, or brown, or green; these colors except in the green algæ are due to coloring matter which covers the green chlorophyll. Two of these classes are predominantly marine, and the members of one, the yellow-green algæ, are not common or conspicuous enough to be described here.

1. *Blue-green;* filamentous algæ, *Cyanophyceæ.* Mostly in fresh water.
2. *Green;* filamentous algæ, desmids, stoneworts, *Chlorophyceæ.* In fresh and salt water.
3. *Yellow-green; Bacillariaceæ.* Mostly in fresh water.
4. Diatoms, *Diatomaceæ.* In fresh and salt water.
5. *Brown;* brown seaweeds, *Phæophyceæ.* Mostly in salt water.
6. *Red;* red seaweeds, *Rhodophyceæ.* Mostly in salt water.

Blue-green algæ.—During midsummer blue-green algæ (Fig. 41) often become very abundant in lakes, especially in reservoirs where they sometimes form the surface film known as "water-bloom." They are microscopic, one- or many-celled, but commonly form simple chains as in *Anabæna* (Fig. 41). When light is thrown directly through them they look blue-green, but when it merely falls upon them, as it does in ponds, they make the water appear red or purplish. In hot springs blue-green algæ and sulphur bacteria are almost the only living inhabitants and the blues, pinks, and yellows of the silicious deposits around the hot springs of Yellowstone Park are largely due to them.

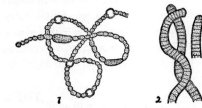

FIG. 41.—Blue-green algæ: 1, filaments of *Anabæna*; 2, *Oscillatoria*; 3, *Rivularia*.

Among the commonest of the blue-green algæ is the free-floating *Anabæna* (Fig. 41), which forms the water-bloom on ponds and lakes and is one of the principal foods of swimming crustaceans. The purplish-black mats of *Oscillatoria* (Fig. 41) cling to the sides of ditches and pools, to rocks and to the stone coping of reservoirs, often becoming detached and floating free at the surface. Under the microscope its filaments exhibit remarkable oscillations, twisting and writhing, coiling and uncoiling, curving to one side and then to another. Gelatinous brown clumps of *Rivularia* (Fig. 41) are common upon stones in rapids, on *Chara*, *Myriophyllum*, pondweeds and broken water-soaked leaves of cat-tails, especially in the fall.

Green filamentous algæ, desmids.—In early spring there is scarcely a pool or runnel that is not brightened by green algæ. They exist in a bewildering variety of sizes and shapes. Among them are the minute single cells of the desmids, hundreds of species fancifully shaped like crescents and stars and triangles, slender interlacing strands of the filamentous algæ like *Spirogyra*, and swimming colonies such as *Volvox* and *Euglena* (Fig. 44), which are animal-like save that they are green with chlorophyll and secure their food by the plant-like method. These organisms are all astride the border between plants and animals. Some of them appear like plants and others more like animals; in classifications we find some of them placed with the algæ and some with the protozoans, their presence in one or the other group depending a good deal on whether a botanist or a zoologist is discussing them. Desmids are single-celled like diatoms; but a living desmid is bright green and a living diatom is golden brown. Many desmids are constricted at the center, as if the cell were partly divided; others, for example, *Closterium*, have a light band across the middle.

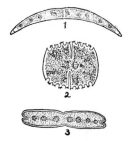

Fig. 42.—Desmids: 1, *Closterium*; 2, *Micrasterias*; 3, *Tetmemorus*.

Desmids are always present in the plankton of lakes, and abundant in clear sunlit ponds. A glass of water from sphagnum pools (p. 65) will often be nile green with them and crescents of the larger species of *Closterium* which grow in such places can easily be seen with a hand-lens.

The dense green mats of "pond-scum" or "frog-spittle" and the "blanket algæ" of early spring are filamentous algæ which grow on the surface of sunny pools and form bubbles of gas as they decay. In such "blankets" *Spirogyra* (Fig. 43) usually predominates, but the threads of *Zygnema* (Fig. 43) and other forms are interlaced with it, as well as a host of desmids, diatoms, and minute animals. In spring pools

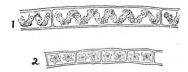

FIG. 43.—Filamentous green algæ: 1, *Spirogyra*; 2, *Zygnema*.

"blanket algæ" flourish all winter, sheltering an extensive community of animals—small mayflies, midges, and crustaceans feed on the algæ and in turn furnish food for predacious animals—young dragonflies, beetles and the like.

The similarity between certain green algæ and animals has already been mentioned. One of the largest of these animal-like algæ is *Volvox* (Fig. 44, 1), whose beautiful spheres of cells are but green dots to the naked eye, though sometimes they

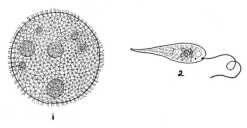

FIG. 44.—1, *Volvox*; 2, *Euglena*.

are so crowded through the water that a glass of it will be colored nile green with them. There are hundreds of cells in each sphere, and each one is provided with microscopic lashing threads whose joint action turns the whole sphere over and over in a slow swimming movement. In midsummer and autumn a smaller green alga, *Euglena* (Fig. 44), covers the surface of pasture ponds and slow streams with a vivid green velvet-like film. Microscopic examination of the smallest particle of this film will reveal hundreds of little whale-shaped *Euglenas*, each with a flagellum waving from its front end.

Diatoms.—Diatoms (Fig. 45) are minute single-celled algæ, estimated to be about one-thousandth of an inch thick. They float free in the water or are attached to leaves and stems; growing in groups or solitary and in myriad shapes and patterns (Pl. IV). They are the most abundant of all organisms in both fresh and salt water. They cover the stems of submerged plants, and most aquatic insects carry hundreds of them hanging upon the hairs of their bodies. In spring they reproduce in enormous numbers, floating upon the surfaces of lakes and covering the stones of stream beds with a film of golden brown.

Fig. 45.—Diatoms: 1, *Meridion*; 2, *Tabellaria*.

All diatoms are enclosed in shells of silica, transparent, colorless, finely lined and patterned. A diatom shell has two parts or valves, the upper valve fitting over the lower one just as a cover slips over a box. The diatoms figured are common ones selected because they suggest the variety and beauty of those which grow in the most ordinary pool (Figs. 1 and 45).

Pl. IV.—Minute plants and animals of pond water. Photograph of part of a model showing life in one-half inch of pond water, magnified one hundred times. Model designed and directed by Roy W. Miner, in American Museum of Natural History. 1, stem and 1 a, traps of *Utricularia* (p. 100); 2, stem and leaves of *Elodea* (p. 79); 3, green algæ, *Spirogyra* (p. 50), and 4, *Chætophora;* 5, desmid, *Closterium* (p. 49); 6, protozoan, *Vorticella* (p. 57); 7, 8, 9, 10, rotifers (p. 127); 11, entomostracan (p. 161); 12, hydra (p. 112); 13, larva of midge caught in trap (p. 291); 14, egg of water-mite; 15, dead leaf. Diatoms and desmids project from the surface of *Utricularia* stem.

Courtesy of Dr. R. W. Miner

PLATE IV

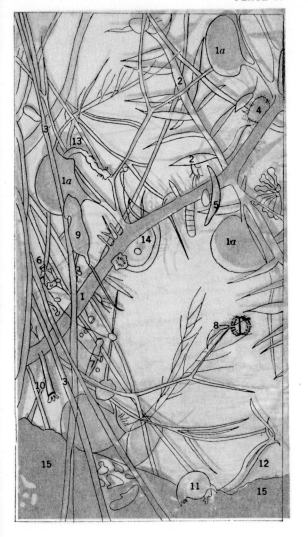

Stoneworts, Family Characeæ

The stoneworts are an intermediate between typical algæ and the higher plants. Their structure is simple and they appear in many ways like specialized algæ; yet they look so much like higher plants that it is difficult not to associate them with that group. They are attached to the pond bottom and usually grow a foot or more high in broad, water-covered meadows. There are two common genera, *Chara* (Fig. 46) and *Nitella* (Fig. 47); several species of *Chara* secrete lime and have been named "stoneworts" because of their hard limy surfaces.

FIG. 46.—Candelabra plant, *Chara fragilis*.

Chara.—Submerged gardens of *Chara* grow in ponds fed by waters from limy soils; the plants are from one to two feet high. Their slender brittle stems consist of nodes, where the branches grow from the stem in whorls, and internodes, an inch or more between. The core of the internode is made up of one cell which extends the entire distance from one node to another. The cores of the branches are also single cells, but are covered by a layer of fine cells like those which surround the central cell of the internode on the main stem.

The fruiting organs are of singular beauty and large enough to be clearly seen with a pocket-lens. They are borne at the

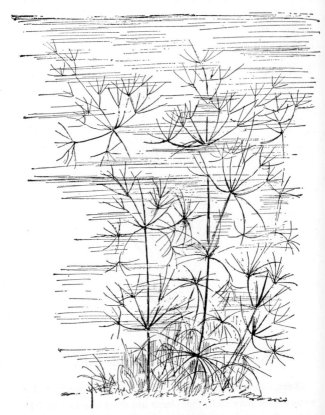

Fig. 47.—*Nitella.*

base of the branches, the pear-shaped ovary with its single egg, and the male organ or spermary beside it looking like a brilliantly colored, microscopic orange. In it are thousands of sperm cells which finally break forth and make their way to the egg. A short time after the egg is fertilized it falls from the branch and later germinates into a new plant.

Chara plants have a marshy odor often distinctly sulphury and feel harsh and brittle to one's fingers. There are many species, but in our flora *Chara fragilis* (Fig. 46) is the common one.

The limy covering of *Chara* stems makes them poor eating and is an effective barrier to all sorts of herbivorous nibblers, but vast numbers of diatoms and desmids settle on them and these provide food for a large population of vegetarians.

Occurrence: Cosmopolitan. July–August.

Nitella.— *Nitella* (Fig. 47) is more delicate than *Chara* but is so similar that it is often called by the same common name, candelabra plant. Its branches grow out from the stem in whorls like *Chara*, but both these and the internodes are naked, not covered by cells and seldom encrusted with lime as in *Chara*. This gives them a translucent delicacy and easily distinguishes *Nitella* from its relative.

Occurrence: Nitella is cosmopolitan, but less common than *Chara*. July–August.

Protozoans

Protozoans are minute animals, living as solitary cells, or in groups, when they are known as colonial protozoans. All of them are microscopic or nearly so (Fig. 1, B); the typical protozoans do not collect in large masses like the algæ, but a few of them are large enough to be seen with a hand-lens.

Protozoans exist in untold numbers in both salt and fresh waters and every pool and brook has its population of them. A few of them are figured here. These are commonly found on the insects or in water which has been brought in from ponds. They are selected because either singly or in clusters they are large enough to be seen through a hand-lens, sometimes even with the naked eye.

FIG. 48.—*Stentor.*

Stentor.—These are trumpet-shaped animals which are transparent blue-green or whitish (Fig. 48). Against a white background the blue-green ones can be seen with the naked eye. They are often very abundant in the water about sphagnum moss.

FIG. 49.—*Spirostomum.*

Spirostomum.—*Spirostomum* (Fig. 49) occurs in shaded, dark-bottomed pools, each animal appearing like a white line about the length of a dash. Large numbers of them sometimes whiten the surface of the water.

Paramœcium.—*Paramœcia* (Fig. 50) show only as white, rapidly-moving particles in dishes of pond water, or as a white edge on the water line when they are crowded together on the surface of dishes of pond trash which have been left standing.

Bell-animals, Vorticella, Epistylis, Carchesium.—Colonies of

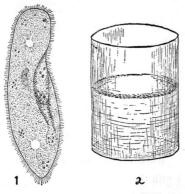

FIG. 50.—1, *Paramœcium;* 2, *Paramœcia* along a water line.

Vorticella or *Epistylis* (Fig. 51, Plate VII) make the fluffy whitish patches which can be found in summer and winter on the bodies of water-insects and crustaceans, or on submerged sticks

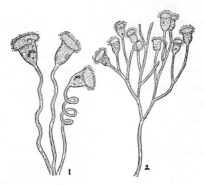

FIG. 51.—1, *Vorticella;* 2, *Epistylis.*

and stones. In some streams scarcely an insect will be found which does not have a crop of these springing, bell-like animals growing upon it. Colonies of *Carchesium* are common upon the undersides of sticks and stones in streams, where they grow nearly an eighth of an inch high.

CHAPTER V

HIGHER PLANTS

Water Mosses and Seed Plants

Compared with the number of higher plants which live on land there are very few which live in the water. Most of these bear their flowers above the surface though their leaves and roots grow beneath it and they make up little groups which are usually but fragments of large families that belong on land. They live only partially in the water and are not truly aquatic like the simpler plants.

In most ponds the rooted plants (Fig. 21) grow from the shore out to midwater and they vary greatly in the degree to which they have taken on the ways of aquatic life. Close to shore the arrowheads and pickerel-weeds (Pl. V) stand upright with leaves and flowers a foot or more above the water. A little farther out are plants which lean upon the water for support; such are the yellow water-lily and the white one, with pads and blossoms floating on the surface. Beyond these plants, often among them, are feathery milfoils, *Myriophyllum* and *Elodea*, and streaming pondweeds, the *Potamogetons*, all of them submerged except for their flowers, which open in the air and depend upon air currents or upon flying insects or upon water to carry their pollen. Although these plants are largely beneath the water, their reproduction occurs in the air. The same thing is true of mayflies and other aquatic insects; they live in the water for a long time but they come out in the air to mate and lay their eggs.

In nearly all ponds are plants which float free, entirely unattached to the bottom; some of them are at the surface, others just below it. They are the duckweeds, with little dangling rootlets, the bladderworts, drifting unanchored, and, in limy water, lush growths of hornwort.

The plants included in this book are only the commonest ones of ponds and brooks with two or three others, like the pitcher-plant, which grow in water-sodden bogs or marshes and are much visited by insects. The animal associations of each plant are briefly mentioned: such partnerships as those of the water-lily and the beetle, *Donacia* (p. 279), and trage-dies like those continually occurring within the leaf traps of pitcher-plants and bladderworts.

Aquatic Liverworts and Mosses—*Bryophyta*

The liverworts and mosses make up the group of *Bryophyta*, green plants closely related to the algæ and in classifications placed just above them. They are small, green, shade and moisture loving plants, which grow crowded in mats and clus-ters. Most of them live in moist places on land; there are a few in ponds but more often they grow in running streams; only a small number can thrive in dry places. They absorb water rapidly but having no storage cells they quickly lose it again. Water goes out of their cells as easily as it does from the skins of frogs and they cannot endure dryness much better.

Liverworts—*Hepaticæ*

Liverworts have some traits like the algæ but though their ancestors may have been aquatic, they are now in general a land group and their forms and habits suggest the mosses. The liverwort has a green leaf-like thallus, which carries on the main work that in flowering plants is done by leaves and roots. If a thallus is thin, chlorophyll develops in all its cells and both sides are green; if it is thick, only the upper surface is green and the lower one bears root-like outgrowths. There are but few aquatic liverworts, commonest among them being the *Riccias* (Fig. 52) which grow in ponds.

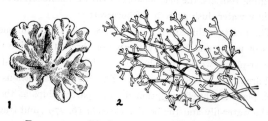

F IG. 52.—1, *Riccia natans;* 2, *Riccia fluitans.*

Crystalworts, Riccia fluitans and Riccia natans.—These sim- ple liverworts float free in the water or grow on the mud along the shores of ponds or quiet streams. *Riccia natans* (Fig. 52) has a lobed thallus and floats on the surface of the water like duckweed. *Riccia fluitans* (Fig. 52) lies just below the sur- face, spreading its slender branched thallus through the water in a bright green network. It often grows among the duck- weeds and broken bits of its thallus are often caught with net sweepings in the shallows. In case the water in which they are living dries away, either of these *Riccias* will grow on damp soil and then the thallus is apt to be reddish or pur- plish. *Riccias* thrive in aquaria and *Riccia fluitans* is very often a stock plant of supply dealers.

Mosses—*Musci*

Mosses can live on the faces of rocks where food and water are scarce, on decaying logs in deep woods, in marshes, and even completely submerged in brooks and shallow ponds. They grow crowded together like the liverworts and lichens with which they are very commonly associated. But their flat green leaves distinguish them from both liverworts and lichens, neither of which bear leaves. The aquatic *Riccias*

(Fig. 52) are examples of the leafless state of the liverworts. "Reindeer moss" and the "red-tipped moss" are common lichens having no leaves but only stubby branches colored gray-green by algæ which grow like a cloak about the white fungus within.

spore capsule with cap removed

cap

sporophyte or spore bearing plant

gametophyte or sex cell bearing plant

rhizoid

FIG. 53.—Diagrammatic outline of parts of a moss plant.

Several kinds of mosses are more or less aquatic. The most abundant of these are the sphagnums, bog mosses, which thrive best when they are soaked with water. Others grow upon the rocks in swift mountain streams and in gorges, where they cover the stream bed with a green-black carpet.

Life history of mosses.—A "fruiting" moss plant (Fig. 53) consists of an upright leafy stem or branch, rootlike organs or rhizoids and a capsule of spores usually borne on a stalk. Carried to the right place by wind or water, the spores will germinate into minute filaments, the protonemata, which make little green patches upon the earth from which the familiar moss plants ultimately grow.

Some moss plants bear female organs, the archegonia, equivalent to the ovaries of an animal; others bear male organs, the antheridia, equivalent to spermaries. In the antheridia there are thousands of minute male cells some of which subsequently fertilize egg-cells borne upon the female plants. The familiar capsule of spores arises from a fertilized egg and is always borne on a female plant. The spores from the capsule mature and are scattered upon the ground and without fusing with any other cell develop into plants which represent the sexual generation. Generally each moss plant is of a different sex, some bearing male, others bearing female organs. Such male and female plants occur in every other generation and hence are known as the sexual generation.

Water Mosses—*Fontinalaceæ*

The water mosses are a family of slender, very dark green mosses with long streamer-like branches, which wave from the stones in swift currents, or grow upon stones and wood on the edges of ponds.

Dichelyma.—The yellowish green masses of *Dichelyma* grow commonly on rotting sticks in and around the edges of ponds and in swampy places. The plants of *Dichelyma capillaceum* (Fig. 54), our only common species, are yellow toward the tips and brownish or black below. The stems are slender, often over three inches long, branched, and usually matted together. The spore capsule matures in summer, its short stem or seta protruding from the leaves that wrap closely around it.

Occurrence.—New Brunswick to Ontario and Pennsylvania Fruits in summer.

Fountain mosses, Fontinalis.—The fountain mosses form dense, dark, olive green covers upon the stones of swift brooks,

Fig. 54.—1, A leafy branch of the common *Diche-lyma capillaceum;* 2, leaves more enlarged. (Grout. From Bry. Eur.)

sometimes in sluggish streams, very rarely in quiet water. Their stems are about three inches long, irregularly branched, with slightly spreading leaves which are absent altogether from the lower part of the stem.

The giant fountain moss, *Fontinalis gigantea* (Fig. 55), very common in cool brooks, can be distinguished by its three-cornered branches which grow several inches long. The other species figured, *F. Novæ-Angliæ* (Fig. 55), is probably our commonest fountain moss.

Occurrence.—Spore capsules mature in summer but they are rarely seen, their stems being so short that they are entirely concealed by the leaves. Cool streams, North America and Europe.

FIG. 55.—Branches of two common fountain mosses: 1, *Fontinalis;* 2, leaf arrangement of *Fontinalis gigantea;* 3, leaf arrangement of *Fontinalis Novæ-Angliæ.* (2 and 3 from Grout.)

Hypnums—*Hypnaceæ*

Water hypnums, Hygrohypnum.—The first part of the word *Hygrohypnum*, derived from the Greek, well names these mosses "wet hypnums." They grow in bright green or yellow green patches on the rocks in and near the beds of swift streams. *Hygrohypnum ochraceum* (Fig. 56), whose branches are 2 to 4 inches long, larger than most of the genus, can be found in almost any mountain brook.

Occurrence.—(*H. ochraceum*)—Northern and central North America. Fruits in spring and early summer.

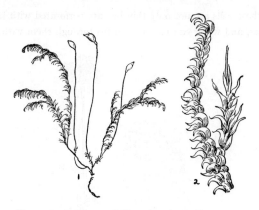

FIG. 56.—1, Plant of *Hygrohypnum ochraceum;* 2, leaf arrangement of same. (Grout. From Bry. Eur.)

Sphagnums or Peat Mosses—*Sphagnaceæ*

Peat moss, Sphagnum.—The sphagnums are pale colored green or pink tinged mosses which grow in big cushiony beds in bogs and marshes. These wet yielding tussocks are made up of the long closely packed plants, their lower ends brown and dead, their stems and rosette-like heads pale green and leafy. This appearance results from their habit of growing at the tips and dying off below.

Their leaves closely overlap each other (Fig. 57). Broad spoon-shaped leaves and thick branches distinguish a number of species called the spoon-leaved peat mosses; those with narrow pointed leaves and slender branches are the acute-leaved peat mosses. Separate species within these groups are very difficult to distinguish.

All of them are remarkable for their power of absorbing water and microscopic examination shows that certain of their cells, narrow ones but normal in their supply of protoplasm and chlorophyll, are surrounded by large thin-walled cells which have entirely lost their protoplasm. The walls of these cells are not only thin but are perforated with large pores, and water can pass to and fro through them with the

FIG. 57.—1, Leafy branches of *Sphagnum*, an acute-leaved peat moss, bearing spore capsules; 2, without spores; 3, spore capsule, enlarged.

greatest ease. These colorless cells account not only for the paleness of sphagnum mosses, but for their extraordinary power of absorbing water. Moist sphagnum has long been used by florists to wrap plants for shipping and during the Great War dry sterilized sphagnum was much used as an absorbent wound dressing.

Seed Plants—*Angiosperms*

The parts of the flower.—Aquatic seed plants have essentially the same structure as their terrestrial relatives and many of them thrive just as well on a damp shore as they do in the water. Most of them have root, stem, leaves and flowers, which function very much as these parts do in typical land plants (Fig. 58).

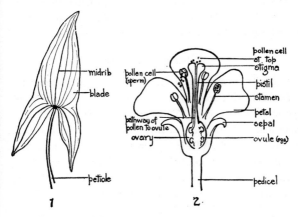

FIG. 58.—Diagrams of 1, the parts of a leaf (*Sagittaria*); 2, a complete flower, cut in section to show its parts, and the pollen cells and their pathway to the ovules.

A complete or typical flower (Fig. 58) is made up of four parts besides the stalk—stamens on which the fertilizing pollen or male cells are produced; pistils which receive the pollen cells and through which they pass down into the ovaries where they fertilize the egg cells; petals which provide a colorful advertisement of these essential reproductive organs; and sepals which protect and hold the other parts together. In the differences of color and form and arrangement of these four parts lies all of the beauty and variety of flowers.

The pistil is usually in the center of the flower. Its enlarged basal part is the ovary containing the enlarged female reproductive cells or eggs; its tip is the stigma. Stamens usually encircle the pistil; a stamen consists of two parts—

the anther, which holds the pollen grains, and a stem-like filament. Pollen grains are deposited upon the stigma of the pistil by wind or by insects, or may simply fall upon it. The process is known as pollination (Fig. 58). Later, the nucleus of the pollen cell fuses with the nucleus of the egg and the fertilized egg with its surrounding cover develops into a seed.

Cat-tails—*Typhaceæ*

Cat-tails are marsh and waterside plants, which grow 4 to 8 feet tall, with creeping root-stocks from which new plants sprout up each spring. These root-stocks grow in all directions and in a few years each parent plant is the center of a colony of cat-tails. Their banner-like leaves, even taller than the flowers, are smooth olive-green, shimmering and silvery when the wind shakes and turns them. The broad-leaved and the narrow-leaved cat-tails are the two well known species in the United States.

Broad-leaved cat-tail, Typha latifolia.—In the broad-leaved cat-tail (Fig. 59) the two sections of the flower spike are closely adjoining. The upper yellower half contains the male or staminate flowers and the lower olive-green part holds the pistillate ones. Pollen of the staminate flowers is wind-carried from one spike to another. The flowers first appear in June. Soon after that the staminate part of the spike shrivels, but the pistillate half fluffs out into the familiar chestnut-brown cat-tail head, about an inch in diameter, which lasts all through the winter, even well into the next spring. But toward spring it loses its trim, clipped surface, and becomes more and more shaggy and unkempt as its quarter million or so of seeds are gradually loosened from the central stalk.

Occurrence.—Although both species are widely distributed, the broad-leaved cat-tail, *Typha latifolia* (Fig. 59), is commoner than the narrow-leaved, *Typha angustifolia* (Fig. 60). It is found throughout temperate North America; frequent

FIG. 59.—Broad-leaved cat-tails, *Typha latifolia:*
1, flower showing staminate and pistillate parts;
2, flower in late summer.

in Massachusetts and Connecticut. Other common names are cat-tail flag, cat-o'-nine-tails, candlewicks. Blooms in June–July. Fruits, August–September.

Animal associates.—An insect population lives upon cat-tails the year around. Plant-lice feed upon the surfaces of their leaves and the leaf-mining moths *Arzama obliqua* and *Nonagria oblonga* tunnel through them. The cat-tail moths, *Lymnoecia phragmitella*, lay their eggs upon the lower, pistillate half of the spike and their larvæ spin silken threads about the flower spike and bind it together. By thus fastening the seeds in place, they preserve them through the winter for their own food and protection. Old flower spikes like these are frayed out two or three times their natural diameter. In winter the larvæ are snugly covered and in spring their cocoons are protected there or in the stems. As many as seventy-six cocoons have been taken from a single pistillate spike. During winter and spring the uninfested spikes lose their seeds entirely but wherever larvæ are present the seeds stay fastened until the following summer when the spikes finally break off.

The larvæ of the snout beetles, *Colandra pertinax*, feed on the starchy core of the root-stock and upon the stalks.

Narrow-leaved cat-tail, Typha angustifolia.—Both leaves and flower-spikes of the narrow-leaved cat-tail (Fig. 60) are more slender than those of the broad-leaved species and the upper staminate section of the flower is conspicuously separated from the pistillate part by a stretch of bare stem.

Occurrence.—This species lives in the same marshes and pond borders with the broad-leaved cat-tails but it is not so widely distributed. Mainly along the coast from Nova Scotia to Florida, often in brackish water. Inland it is locally common around the Great Lakes. Blooms June–July.

Bur-reeds—*Sparganiaceæ*

The bur-reeds are a company of plants which are very similar in looks and habits; they all have reed-like leaves,

FIG. 60.—Narrow-leaved cat-tail, *Typha angusti-folia*.

their fruits are green burs of closely packed nutlets and all grow in marshy pond borders or shallows

FIG. 61.—1, Giant bur-reed, *Sparganium eurycarpum;* 2, branching bur-reed, *Sparganium americanum.*

Giant bur-reed, Sparganium eurycarpum.—Giant bur-reeds (Fig. 61) grow along pond and stream borders among water plantains, arrowheads, and pickerel-weeds. They are from 3 to 6 feet high with very long ribbon-like leaves, about three-quarters of an inch wide. The fluffy balls of their staminate flowers are borne above the larger pistillate heads. The fruits are green spheres of wedge-shaped nutlets packed closely together like the sections of a pineapple.

Occurrence.—In shallow water or on the shore, especially in the larger marshes. Common. Blooms early June–late July. United States, less frequent near Atlantic coast, rare and local in Connecticut.

Branching bur-reed, Sparganium americanum.—The plants are similar to the giant bur-reed, but much more slender and only 1 to 2 feet high (Fig. 61). The flower stems are more or less branching but unbranched forms are often found in the same colony with the others.

Occurrence.—Common in many bogs, borders of ponds and streams. Blooms June–August. Eastern states, south to Florida, west to Minnesota.

Animal associates.—Larvæ of the leaf-beetle, *Donacia*, feed upon its submerged roots (p. 280).

Pondweeds— *Najadaceæ*

The pondweeds are probably more important to the welfare of water animals than any other group of aquatic seed-plants. There are about forty North American species and nearly every one of them flourishes in great numbers, providing either food or shelter for animals. They grow rooted to the bottom and their long shifting leaves fill acres of pond and lake water. Most of them are wholly submerged, except for their flowers; in a few, like *Potamogeton natans* (Fig. 62), the uppermost leaves float on the surface.

Animal associates.—In Lake George, N. Y., pondweeds are known to the local fishermen as "weeds" and the "weed" beds with their population of little clinging organisms furnish shelter and food for most of the smaller fishes of the lake.

Pondweeds are one of the principal foods of wild ducks. They are so vital to animal life, especially to wild fowl, that ponds are planted with them and a growing literature is concerned with their biology and economic importance. Bullheads, perch, and pickerel hide among them and a large snail population, chiefly of *Planorbis*, *Lymnæa*, and *Physa*, gets its living from their leaves.

FIG. 62.—Pondweeds: 1, *Potamogeton natans;* 2, *P. crispus.*

Potamogeton natans.—This is one of the commonest pond-weeds (Fig. 62). Its floating leaves have long stems or peti-oles and oval blades but the submerged ones are incomplete and thread-like, only the petiole being developed.

Occurrence.—In shallow ponds; frequent. Blooms June–September. Almost cosmopolitan in temperate countries.

Brown-leaf or ruffle-leaf pondweed, Potamogeton crispus.— Sometimes called the crisp-leaved pondweed, this species has long, very translucent brown leaves with crisped wavy edges (Fig. 62). The flower stalk bears 3 to 10 small flowers and although each flower has both stamens and pistil these do not mature simultaneously so that pollination occurs only when the wind carries pollen from the stamens of one flower to some other one on which the stigmatic surface of the pistil is ripe.

This pondweed is found in pools and streams, or along lake shores where there is considerable wave action; in such regions its plants are apt to be dwarfed. They usually grow in water from 1 to 5 feet deep; sometimes in depths of 7 to 8 feet. They reproduce asexually by means of "burs" or winter buds, sections of the stems which break off, lie over the winter at the bottom, and sprout forth new shoots in the spring.

Occurrence.—Ponds and lakes, often in brackish water, frequent or common. Blooms June–July. Massachusetts north to Ontario, south to Virginia. Naturalized from Europe.

Animal associates.—Larvæ of chironomids and the moth *Nymphula*, and snails are commonly found feeding on its leaves. Wherever pondweeds are abundant they largely support the chironomids which in turn become important fish food. *Potamogeton crispus* is such a favorite food of wild ducks that game ponds are planted with it.

Sago pond-weed, Potamogeton pectinatus.—Like *Potamogeton natans* this is a very common pondweed especially in brackish water. It is one of the earliest to appear in spring, sprouting forth from tubers early in April. The plants grow entirely submerged in a depth of 1 to 6 feet of water and some of the deep water ones are easily 8 feet long.

Occurrence.—In slow streams and lake borders often in brackish or limy water. Blooms July–September, Quebec to British Columbia, along the coast to Florida, to Pennsylvania, Great Lakes, Kansas, Colorado.

Water-plantains and Arrowheads—*Alismaceæ*

These are border-line plants, which are very adaptable to a changing water supply and show a consequent variation in the form of their leaves. The flowers have 3 white petals, often conspicuous; pistils and stamens may be in the same flower, in different ones on the same plant, or on different plants.

Broad-leaved arrowhead, Sagittaria latifolia.—Arrowheads grow on wet shores or in shoal waters in company with bur-reeds and bulrushes, pickerel-weed, and water-plantains (Pl. X). Broad-leaved arrowheads (Fig. 63) are 6 to 24 inches high with dark green arrow-shaped leaves and delicate, 3-petaled white flowers which are arranged in whorls of threes with the pistillate or female flowers in the lowest cluster. The shape of the leaves in this and other species varies with the depth of water and, in lakes, with their exposure to the action of waves. Plants which grow in deeper water usually have narrower leaves, but narrow and broad leaves are often found on plants only a few inches apart. Arrowheads adapt themselves to either droughts or floods and when submerged they develop narrow ribbon-like leaves. A single plant sometimes has a few narrow grass-like leaves, some broadly ribboned ones, and still others which are arrow-shaped. If a drought has left the plant stranded without water, the narrow water leaves fall off and broad arrow-shaped ones, better suited to work in the air, gradually take their places. Adjustments like these are very common in all the arrow-heads and they live in or out of water with all the ease of frogs.

Occurrence.—This and other species all grow on the margins of quiet streams or in the protected bays of ponds and lakes. Blooms July–August. Very common throughout the eastern states.

Animal associates.—Arrowheads are pollinated by water insects, mainly by damselflies and dragonflies which keep

FIG. 63.—Broad-leaved arrowhead, *Sagittaria latifolia*.

alighting on the flowers, even though they have no appetite for their pollen. Water snails eat the flower petals and sometimes carry pollen from one flower to another.

Water-plantain, Alisma Plantago-aquatica.—Water-plantains (Fig. 64) belong to pond shores and ditches but they also grow commonly in almost every little pool, and with bed·

Fig. 64.—Water-plantain, *Alisma Plantago-aquatica*

straw and swamp milkweeds in the marshes. Like arrow-heads they readily adapt themselves to land life. They are 1 to 3 feet high, and bear strongly veined leaves with long petioles which grow from the root. The 3-petaled white or pinkish flowers are very small, hardly more conspicuous than their branching stems.

When seedling water-plantains are set in pots of earth sub-merged in shallow water, and kept growing there for a couple of months, they will develop into typical water plants, with some floating leaves and others which are narrow and ribbony like those of fresh water eel-grass (p. 80).

Occurrence.—On shores and in shallow water, in muddy ditches and swamps. Blooms July–August. Common throughout the United States.

Animal associates.—Adult syrphus flies which feed on its pollen (p. 299) are its most frequent visitors.

Water-weeds and Eel-grass— *Hydrocharitaceæ*

Water-weed, Elodea canadensis.—*Elodea*, or *Anacharis* (Fig. 65), is a true aquatic, loosely rooted on the bottom or floating free in the water, entirely submerged, and growing so successfully in water that solid beds of it fill many ponds and slow streams. Its branches are crowded with dark green, translucent leaves arranged in whorls of three or more. They have a single, central vein, and are so thin that they become transparent and papery with very little exposure to the air. Stems of *Elodea* are brittle and whenever broken the frag-ments continue to grow independently, rapidly increasing the number of plants. The flowers are inconspicuous; in one species the female ones are borne on very long stems which reach up to the surface of the water; while the short-stemmed male flowers form low on the same plants but break off and rise to the surface, where they meet the female flowers.

Elodea is a beautiful water plant but it spreads with amaz-ing rapidity and crowds out other plants. English botanies make frequent mention of its habits in rivers. In 1848, the curator of the Botanic Garden at Cambridge introduced it into a tributary of the River Cam and by 1852 it had spread

FIG. 65.—Water-weed, *Elodea canadensis.*

into the river, choked the drainage, and even stopped the rowing.

Occurrence.—It is very common in slow streams, in back waters off main channels, and in ponds (Pl. X). Blooms July–August. Eastern states south to Virginia and Kentucky, west to Wyoming. Other common names are ditch moss, choke pondweed.

Animal associates.—Snails find good foraging grounds on *Elodea* leaves and it is not unusual to find a six inch branch loaded with four or five of them (Fig. 34).

Fresh water eel-grass, wild celery, Vallisneria spiralis.— Fresh water eel-grass (Fig. 66) is familiar to canoeists and

waders who often find shallows of lakes and creeks clogged
with its streaming leaves. It is always rooted in the bottom
and the leaves may be a yard or more long though scarcely

Fig. 66.—Eel-grass, *Vallisneria spiralis*.

a quarter of an inch wide, bending with every shift of the
current. The small greenish female flowers are borne singly
on the ends of long spiral stems so supple and springy that
they are not pulled under water when wind ripples its sur-

face. The short-stemmed male flowers develop near the base of the plant, several hundreds of them in each cluster, the separate flowers becoming detached as they mature. A bubble of air in each one buoys it to the top and there it opens and floats along the surface till it meets the female flower. The male flowers congregate in great numbers about the larger female ones to which their sticky pollen finally adheres. After pollination the spiral stem of the female flower contracts and pulls the maturing fruit down into the water.

Occurrence.—Common in quiet waters. August. Eastern states to South Dakota, and Texas; occasional on Atlantic Coastal Plain.

Animal associates.—Fresh water eel-grass is the favorite food of the canvas-back duck and other water birds. It is an excellent aquarium plant, growing easily and providing abundant oxygen for the animals (Fig. 35).

Duckweeds—*Lemnaceæ*

All the duckweed family are very small and all float upon the surface of the water; among them are the *Wolffias* (Fig. 70), the smallest of the flowering plants. They have no true leaves nor stems but the green plant body or thallus is usually called a leaf and it looks very much like one. Minute flowers grow directly out of it, borne from its side or upper surface. The male flower is only a single stamen, and the female flower a single pistil. Both are rare, for duckweeds usually reproduce by "budding off", or division of the thallus into two parts, each of which produces roots and becomes a new plant.

Greater duckweed, Spirodela polyrhiza.—In many regions this species (Fig. 67) is the common duckweed, forming the green water blankets made of thousands of little plants floating on the surface, each with 4 to 16 rootlets hanging from it. The thallus is circular, usually about a quarter of an inch wide, green above and pinkish purple beneath; its 5 to 15 simple veins and a cluster of 5 to 10 rootlets distinguish this species.

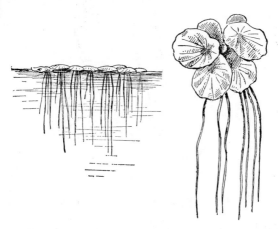

F<small>IG</small>. 67.—Greater duckweed, *Spirodela polyrhiza*.

Occurrence.—Floating on the surface of pools, in marshes and ponds, often very abundant in park and garden ponds. June–early September. Common through most of the United States, except toward the north, less frequent near the coast.

Animal associates.—As their name implies, these plants are a favorite duck food. They grow very rapidly, crowding together in blankets which often so completely shut out the light from the water beneath that the submerged plants die and the herbivorous insects and crustaceans are forced to migrate for food (Pl. II, 2).

Ivy-leaved duckweed, Lemna triscula.—The ivy-leaved duckweeds (Fig. 68) form zigzag chains and lattices floating just below the surface of the water. The thallus is oval or lanceolate; their habit of remaining connected makes the fanciful lattices.

Occurrence.—In ponds and ditches, especially in cat-tail

83

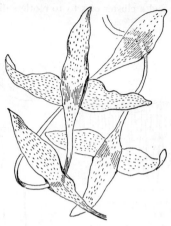

Fig. 68.—Ivy-leaved duckweed, *Lemna triscula*.

marshes. Frequent. Blooms in June–August. Rare near the Atlantic coast but otherwise generally distributed over the United States.

Lesser duckweed, Lemna minor.—In spite of their small size these duckweeds (Fig. 69) also form green blankets on the

Fig. 69.—Lesser duckweed, *Lemna minor*.

water. The thallus is but a small fraction of an inch long, has but one root, and 1 to 5 simple veins.

Occurrence.—Very common, floating on quiet waters of ditches and ponds, sometimes on wet mud. Blooms June–August. Throughout North America except in extreme north.

Wolffia columbiana.—The *Wolffias* (Fig. 70) are the small-est of all the flowering plants. They float just below the surface film, minute green grains often wedged in among

Fig. 70.—*Wolffia columbiana.* (From Britton and Brown.)

the duckweed plants. The thallus is about a millimeter long, and *Wolffias* are easily recognized by this minute size and the entire absence of roots. In autumn they become so laden with their food store of starch grains that they sink to the bottom and winter over there, rising in the spring after they have used up their own load.

Occurrence.—In quiet water, often among duckweeds. Blooms June–July. Occasional. Distributed over the United States, less frequent near the Atlantic coast.

Pickerel-weeds—*Pontederiaceæ*

Pickerel-weed, Pontederia cordata.—Pickerel-weeds are persistent invaders of water territory. Wherever brook-fed ponds are being filled up they are usually in the front ranks of vegetation which is crowding into the water (Pl. V). They grow 1 to 3 feet high with thick, broadly arrow-shaped leaves. Their violet-blue flowers are crowded together in spike-like clusters about 3 inches long; these fade so quickly that comparatively few perfect spikes of flowers can ever be found (Fig. 71).

Pl. V.—The pickerel-weeds (*Pontederia cordata*) are persistent invaders of the water. Dragonfly and damselfly nymphs climb up the stems and shed their skins.

Photo. by A. H. Morgan

PLATE V

FIG. 71.—Pickerel-weed, *Pontederia cordata*, flower spike.

Occurrence.—Common along stream sides and in pond shallows. Blooms June–October. Generally distributed through the eastern states, westward to Minnesota, and southward to Florida.

Animal associates.—Pickerel-weeds are insect-pollinated; their blue anthers being so placed that an insect cannot enter the flower cup without brushing the pollen from them. The mucky waters in which they grow are full of dragonfly and damselfly nymphs which climb up them to shed their skins, often returning as adults to lay their eggs on the stems just below the water surface.

Fig. 72.—Water stargrass, *Heteranthera dubia*.

Water stargrass, Heteranthera dubia.—This is a plant of the muddy shoals with roots in the mud, its grass-like leaves submerged in the water. The small yellow flowers blossom at the surface, growing from leafy thread-like tubes on the sides of the leaf stems. (Fig. 72.)

Occurrence.—In quiet shallows. Blooms July–October. Height, 2–3 feet. Generally distributed in eastern states and westward but rare near the Atlantic coast.

Buckwheats, Smartweeds, Knotweeds—*Polygonaceæ*

Water smartweed, Polygonum amphibium.—Water smartweeds (Fig. 73) have pink or rose-colored flowers sometimes

Fig. 73.—Water smartweed, *Polygonum amphibium.*

very conspicuous by their abundance. The plants grow near shore, in quiet shallows where their smooth, shining leaves float upon the surface. Varieties and closely allied species differ from this one in shape of leaves and depth of the pink and rose flower color.

Occurrence.—Found locally in shallow calcareous water of ponds, usually over sandy, but sometimes mucky bottoms. Height, 3–6 inches. Blooms July–August. Generally distributed through northern states, southward to New Jersey, Kentucky; rare near the Atlantic coast.

Hornworts—*Ceratophyllaceæ*

Hornwort, Ceratophyllum demersum.—Like *Myriophyllum* (p. 99), which it resembles, *Ceratophyllum* (Fig. 74) grows submerged in ponds usually well out from shore. Its narrow

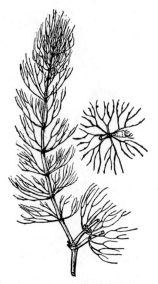

Fig. 74.—Hornwort, *Ceratophyllum demersum.*

thrice-forked leaves are borne in whorls on floating branches a foot or two long and true roots are absent. The seeds germinate on the bottom but when the young plants are about three inches long, they float up near the surface and there they remain. The minute male and female flowers borne at the bases of the leaves never rise above the water but the stamens of the male flowers break off and float to the surface, there shedding their pollen which "rains" down upon the female flowers. *Ceratophyllum's* entire dependence upon water to carry its pollen shows how much more truly aquatic it is than most higher plants of the water. Toward autumn the ends of its branches break off, float about for a time and are finally pulled down to the bottom partly by their own weight and partly by their "living freight of aquatic mollusks, insects, and annelids." Such branches winter over on the bottom but with the return of spring they float up again and grow rapidly.

Occurrence.—Common in ponds and slow streams. June–August or September. Throughout North America except in the extreme north.

Animal associates.—Hornworts grow in ferny beds so thick that they leave no place for any other plants. These hornwort forests are literally animated by a great population of snails, worms, and small animals which feed upon one another or upon the algæ which cover the hornworts.

Water-lilies— *Nymphæaceæ*

Spatterdock or yellow pond-lily, Nymphæa advena.—Although yellow and white pond-lilies often live together the yellow ones (Fig. 75) are commoner and thrive in many ponds where white ones are not found at all. They grow in densely populated shallows where pond-skaters dart about on whatever water they can find, where hundreds of spring-tails make gray-black patches on the surface, and companies of whirligig beetles come swinging in from open water (Pl. II).

Their leaves are stockier and more ovate than those of the white lily. The flower is a yellow or yellow-green cup formed of six overlapping sepals; yellow stamen-like petals encircle the large barrel-shaped pistil and yellow-green stamens are packed closely against its sides (Fig. 75). During the first day of bloom the flower cup opens only slightly but enough

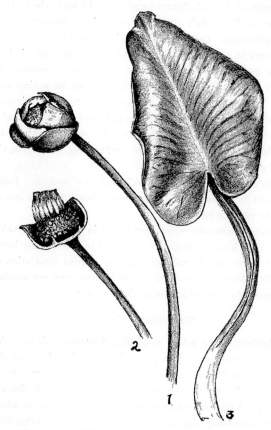

FIG. 75.—Yellow pond-lily, *Nymphæa advena:* I, flower; 2, flower cut to show the barrel-shaped pistil and the stamens surrounding its base; 3, leaf.

to admit insects which come laden with pollen from other flowers, brushing it on to the stigma already ripe to receive it. On the second day the same flower opens wide; its anthers burst with pollen and insects carry this to the stigmata of other half-opened flowers. Thus cross-fertilization is brought about and self-fertilization is prevented.

Occurrence.—Common in quiet waters. Blooms May–September. New York southward and westward. In the northwest and northeast it is largely replaced by a variety whose flowers are partly purple.

Animal associates.—Leaf-miners eat channels through the leaves and the caterpillar *Nymphula* cuts its waterproof tents out of them (p. 258). The leaf-beetle *Donacia* lays its eggs (Fig. 216) on spatterdock pads early in the season, and on the white lily later when water has gone down leaving the stiffer-stemmed spatterdocks high in the air. In winter muskrats feed on the creeping rootstocks.

Small yellow pond-lily, Nymphæa microphylla.—This species is a smaller edition of the common spatterdock. It is a much more slender plant with yellow flowers scarcely an inch wide; the stigma is dark red. Only locally common. Blooms July–August. New England to Pennsylvania and Minnesota.

Pond-lily, Castalia odorata.—Pond-lily (Fig. 76) and sweet water-lily are common names for this plant which is well known to everybody but especially to insects. Its familiar rich green lily-pads, leathery and waterproof on the upper side, often crimson beneath, can withstand heavy rain and the wear and tear of jostling by wavelets (Pl. X). The flowers are pure white or pinkish with rich golden centers; the pungent sweetness of a pond of blossoming lilies fills the neighborhood. Stamens and pistil are in the same flower, but they mature at different times and it is left for insects to transport the pollen from one flower to another. The entertainment offered to them is bountiful but brief; the flowers do not open until the morning sun shines on them, and they close in early afternoon. During that time they are probably

Fig. 76.—Pond-lily, *Castalia odorata*.

visited by a larger company of insects than are any other water flowers.

Occurrence.—In ponds and in slow flowing streams. Blooms June–October. Common. Eastern North America, especially near the coast, west to Kansas.

Animal associates.—The under sides of lily pads are hatcheries for eggs of beetles, snails, the caddis fly, *Triænodes,* and water-mites, as well as the homes and foraging grounds of bryozoans, sponges, and snails (Fig. 18). Minute black insects, known as thrips, abound in the blossoms near shore.

Mustards and Cresses—*Cruciferæ*

Water cress, Radicula Nasturtium-aquaticum.—Among the near relatives of this cress are other water cresses and the

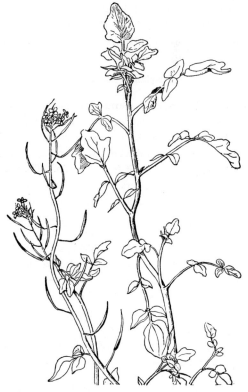

FIG. 77.—Common water cress, *Radicula Nasturtium-aquaticum.*

common horseradish which like water cress is also a table viand.

Water cress (Fig. 77) may grow entirely submerged but in summer it more frequently stands 6 to 8 inches above the surface of shallow water and its branching stems spread out and take root like runners on the bottom. The inconspicuous white flowers have four petals forming the cross, a family characteristic of the *Cruciferæ*. In winter its bushy rosettes make splashes of verdant green in spring-fed brooks.

Occurrence.—Springs and brooks; frequent and locally abundant. Blooms June–July. Generally distributed over the country, in the eastern states southward to Virginia.

Pitcher-plants—*Sarraceniaceæ*

Common pitcher-plant, Sarracenia purpurea.—Pitcher-plants (Fig. 78) grow in peat bogs where their red-green pitchers usually rise out of beds of pale sphagnum moss. Their leaves are true pitchers which hold water and they can generally be found partly full of it from the rain. They are 4 to 8 inches long, green, with dark red veins, streaked with what Schuyler Mathews has called "raw-meat coloring," and have a tough papery texture. The flaring lip of the pitcher is heavily streaked and is covered with stiff hairs which all point toward the water; insects which pass over them fall down into it, finally drown there, and their decomposing bodies are absorbed by the plant. The curiously shaped flower is green and maroon-red, like the leaves. Its 4 or 5 red-lined sepals curve loosely over the green petals that fit about the pistil. This is umbrella-shaped and its stigmatic surface—the inside of the umbrella—is turned upward beneath sepals and petals which protect it from everything but insects.

Common names of pitcher-plants show how playful and how dangerous they have always appeared,—whippoorwill's shoes, Adam's pitcher, fever-cup, sidesaddle flower, and small-pox-plant.

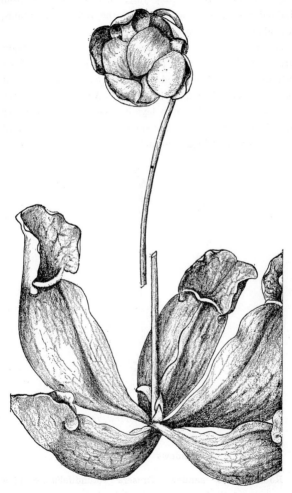

FIG. 78.—Common pitcher-plant, *Sarracenia purpurea.*

Occurrence.—In acid peat bogs, often in water-soaked sphagnum. Like sundews, they are more truly bog plants than aquatics. Bloom May–July. Locally common from Labrador to Florida and west to the Rocky Mountains, abundant near the coast.

Animal associates.—Most associates of the pitcher-plant are flying insects—small flies, moths, and beetles. Their adventures in its leaves end in fatalities except for a few that have become adapted to live there. Among these is the mosquito *Ædes* which even lays its eggs in the fatal water and there the young ones hatch out and live unharmed until they fly out as winged mosquitoes.

Fig. 79.—Round-leaved sundew, *Drosera rotundifolia.*

Sundews—*Droseraceæ*

Round-leaved sundew, Drosera rotundifolia.—Sundew leaves are clothed with long glandular hairs each holding a droplet of a sparkling sticky fluid in which small insects become entrapped and die. The struggles of these captured insects stimulate the glandular hairs to secrete the fluid, and the more they struggle the better the plant can hold them. The leaves of any lusty sundew are covered with shriveled insects whose juices the plant is slowly consuming.

The round-leaved sundew (Fig. 79) grows in a rosette about 2 to 3 inches high, its 5-petaled white flowers rising only a little above the leaves. This is the commonest species but others frequently found are the oblong-leaved sundew which has a leaf 6 to 8 times as long as it is broad, the still narrower thread-leaved and slender-leaved sundews. All of the sundews are bog plants, trapping their insect food upon sticky hairs.

Occurrence.—The round-leaved sundew grows in spring-fed calcareous bogs. Blooms in July. Generally distributed from Labrador, southwest to Florida and California including the Atlantic Coastal Plain.

Water Milfoils— *Haloragidaceæ*

Mare's-tail, joint weed, Hippuris vulgaris.—Mare's-tail (Fig. 80) is a perennial aquatic plant which grows on damp shores or in shallows above which its stout plant stem projects for several inches. It is easily recognized by its whorls of 6 to 12 stiff, stringy leaves. Above the water they are short and stand out stiffly from the stem but beneath it they grow long, flaccid, and drooping. Its minute flowers are arranged in a circlet around the stem at the base of the leaves.

Occurrence.—In ponds and quiet streams, especially in limy or salty waters. Labrador southwest through New England, New York, Minnesota, Nebraska, California.

Water milfoil, Myriophyllum spicatum.—Ferny milfoil gardens are commonly found in slow streams and shallow ponds. Milfoils (Fig. 81) are rooted to the bottom but their long graceful branches reach nearly to the surface and their deep purple staminate flowers project above it. There are several species all of which have finely divided leaves.

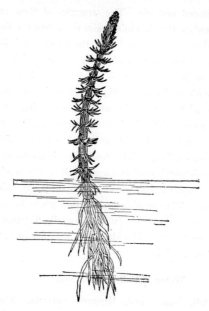

Fig. 80.—Mare's-tail, *Hippuris vulgaris*. (From Arber.)

Occurrence.—In brackish or fresh ponds and slow streams. Labrador to Alaska, south to Connecticut, the Great Lakes region, and the southwestern states.

Bladderworts—*Lentibulariaceæ*

Bladderwort, Utricularia vulgaris.—Although more innocent looking plants than the sundews, the bladderworts (Fig. 82) bear hundreds of death traps for minute water animals. There are several species of them, all delicate, vine-like plants, which float beneath the surface among the stems of water-lilies, and pondweeds. Their presence is the sign of an abundant population of protozoans, nematode worms, roti-fers, and small crustaceans (Pl. IV).

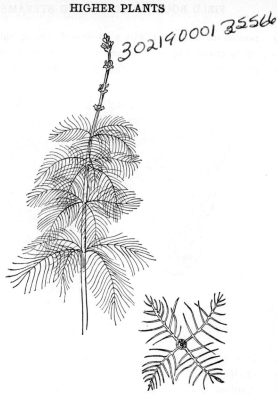

FIG. 81.—Water milfoils, *Myriophyllum spicatum*.

Bladderworts have slender stems which bear finely branched leaves arranged alternately but divided so close to the base that each leaf appears like two leaves growing opposite to each other. On the branches of each leaf are the small bladder-like traps or utricles. There are no true roots but one end of the plant bears green, twig-like rhizoids which perform the work of roots. Air shoots will grow up from the surface when the oxygen supply is low in the water. This bladderwort has yellow flowers on stalks which extend 3 or 4 inches above the water. Each bladder is a slightly compressed sac (Fig. 82, 2) with a slit-shaped opening; this opening is guarded by a valve and the rim of the vestibule is armed with teeth and bristling hairs. Within the bladder

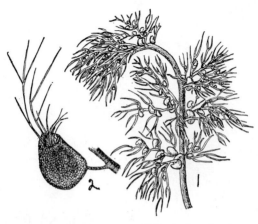

Fig. 82.—Bladderwort, *Utricularia vulgaris*: 1, branch with bladders; 2, bladder more enlarged.

there are more branched hairs, and a digestive secretion is produced from the walls. When little organisms enter the vestibule their movements stimulate the valve to open. Ordinarily the sides of the sac are dented inward (Fig. 82) but as soon as the valve opens the entering water presses its walls from within and at once pushes them outward. This outward movement starts a suction that pulls water and animals with it into the bladder; thus making it at least indirectly the active captor of its prey. By first counting all the animals in a certain number of bladders and then all of the bladders on a stem, Hegner has estimated that all stems taken together on one large plant contained 150,000 living organisms. The bladders which he studied were indented again and "set" for another capture in about 20 minutes after one had taken place.

Occurrence.—Frequent in quiet water containing much organic matter. Blooms July–August. United States southward to Virginia and Texas and in scattered areas westward to Arizona and Lower California.

Animal associates.—These are mainly protozoans, nematodes, rotifers, minute insect larvæ, and crustaceans. If a plant with translucent empty bladders is put into an aquarium well supplied with entomostracans (p. 161), its bladders will soon become darkened by their loads of captured animals.

CHAPTER VI

SPONGES

Porifera

Form and habits of sponges.—To most people the word sponge means bath-sponge. To others it calls to mind the sulphur-sponges of the New England coast or the glassy lacework of the Venus' flower-basket of tropical waters. At any rate it probably suggests salt water and this association is quite natural, for salt water sponges exist in an infinite variety of shape and hue. There are hardly more than 40 to 50 species of fresh water sponges yet known in North America. They are dull-colored, greenish, often moss-like (Pl. X), usually not seen and even if they are noticed, their real identity is not suspected.

Fresh and salt water sponges both consist of colonies of animals which are living together. In close view a fresh water sponge and a piece of bath-sponge look much alike. Both have uneven hubbly surfaces peppered with thousands of holes, the pores which have given the name *Porifera* to the sponge group (Pl. VI, 1). Leading from these pores is a network of canals and chambers in which food and water pass through the soft body tissue of the sponge. All sponges are alike in having a lattice-like supporting framework or skeleton upon which their soft tissues are arranged. This skeleton may be tough and elastic—the spongin of the bath-sponge; glassy—of silicious spicules like the glass sponge;

or it may be a combination of both. In any case it is the hardened secretion of the soft sponge cells. The skeleton of the fresh water sponge is composed of little transparent needles, spicules of silica, the largest of them about one hun-

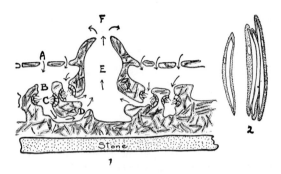

FIG. 83.—1, Diagram of section of a fresh water sponge growing on stone; arrows indicate currents of water through canals and chambers; note spicules in sponge walls: A, incurrent pore or osteole; B, incurrent canal; C, flagellate chamber where food is taken into the cells; D, excurrent canal; E, gastral chamber; F, excurrent pore or osculum. 2, Microscopic spicules greatly enlarged, within cells which form them.

dredth of an inch, straight or curved, smooth or covered with brier-like points, or dumbbell-shaped and sculptured but always hooked or bound together in interlacing chains. In young sponges, grown on glass, bundles of them can be seen projecting through the filmy outer covering (Fig. 86).

The holes on the surface of sponges are of two sizes, small incurrent pores or osteoles (Fig. 83, A) where water comes in and larger excurrent oscula (Fig. 83, F) where it passes out of the sponge. After water has entered the osteoles it is helped onward by the briskly waving flagella in the flagellate chambers (Fig. 83, C). There any food it contains is taken into the sponge cells but most of it passes on through a canal

Pl. VI.—Photographs of living sponges: 1, colony of *Spongilla*, natural size; 2, sponge colony on glass, 7 days after gemmules (dark spots) were taken from the brook.

Photo. by A. H. Morgan

PLATE VI

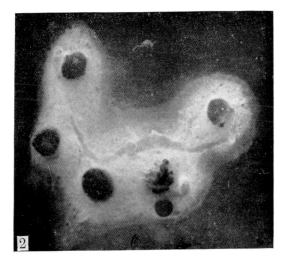

SPONGES

Fig. 83, D) into the gastral chamber (Fig. 83, E). Here it mixes with water from other canals and finally goes out of the osculum (Fig. 83, F), carrying waste matters with it. In a young sponge the oscula are at the tops of chimney-like elevations, and with a lens, waste particles can be seen coming out of these "chimneys" along with the water (Fig. 85). Sponges are wholly dependent upon currents of water for bringing them food and carrying away waste; they may be fed or smothered to death, depending upon whether currents bring clean water supplied with food or water heavy with silt. Sponges cannot move from place to place but their gemmules or winter buds (Fig. 84) have been carried about by birds and by currents of water; and sponges have thus been widely distributed through lakes and streams.

Habitat.—Sponges can live only in clean water. They grow upon water-soaked logs sometimes in large masses, on the leaves of submerged plants, and often with bryozoans on the undersides of stones in riffly brooks. It is not strange that they are abundant on sluiceways and pipes at the outlets of reservoirs, where the water is free from mud and rich in microscopic organisms. Water-pipes are often lined with rough coatings of sponge a quarter of an inch or more thick which hinder the flow of the water and sometimes totally clog the pipes. Occasionally the sponge decays and throws out impurities, giving the well-known "swamp taste" to the water. Sponges and bryozoans are both called "pipe moss" by sanitary engineers. When the Metropolitan Water Works were installed in Boston, an old sixteen-inch pipe was opened which had been laid ten years before. Scattered over the usual coating of rust were numerous patches of sponge as large as the palm of one's hand. These were all growing lustily without any light at all since the unfiltered reservoir water was clean but full of food.

Sponges often live where they are flooded with sunlight and then they are colored green by the chlorophyll of minute

plant cells, the zoochlorellæ, which grow within their ow
cells. It is a common occurrence to find green sponge colonie
on the upper surfaces of submerged logs (Pl. X) and yellowis
or nearly white ones on the under side.

Distribution.—Only 40 or 50 species of fresh water sponge
are known in North America. Two of the commones
Spongilla fragilis and *Spongilla lacustris*, are found in th
eastern states and as far west as Kansas. There are fewe
records of sponges in the southern states and those beyon
the Mississippi River but this is probably due to lack of stud
rather than a scarcity of sponges.

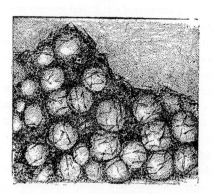

Fig. 84.—Fresh water sponge in winter, gemmules
held among interlacing spicules.

Season.—Colonies are at the height of their growth in Jul
and August. In the early fall most of them begin to shrivel
by October and November they are dead, and only the gem
mules or winter buds remain, held among the interlocke
spicules. These are the only parts of sponges which live ove
the winter; in March and April young colonies begin to grow
from them, first appearing as tiny flecks of white upon sub
merged stones and twigs.

SPONGES

Associates.—Fresh water sponges harbor very inconspicuous little parasites—the six-legged larvæ of Spongilla-flies which descend into the osteoles or pierce their way into the soft sponge cells with their sharp mouth-parts (Fig. 187). They can not only pierce the cells, but they can suck out the contents as conveniently as we can drink through a straw. Each of their slender mandibles is hollowed out on its inner side, and when held closely together they make a perfect tube through which the watery content of the sponge cells is easily drawn. Spongilla-flies have transparent bodies and their stomachs are always so full of sponge that they are literally sponge-colored, inside and out, and a more convincing camouflage would be hard to find. One must search for one of these larvæ with a lens; it will scarcely be noticed unless it is moving and even then it looks like a piece of sponge on legs.

Study and collecting.—It is difficult to distinguish fresh water sponges and in order to identify a species one should know the form of the colony, and the spicules and gemmules as well. When specimens are collected for identification, careful note should be made of the living colony and its habitat and a piece of it scraped off and preserved in alcohol or formalin. Gemmules can be found in late autumn, occasionally in summer, and their general structure can be made out with a pocket-lens, but a microscope is necessary to see the spicules.

A winter study of living sponges.—An interesting winter study of gemmules can be made with only a dish, some pieces of glass, and a pocket-lens for tools. In early winter, gemmules look like so many fig-seeds clustered among the spicules (Fig. 84) and may easily be scraped into water and taken home. Then water, preferably from their own brook or pond, should be poured into a deep pie-plate, a few pieces of clean glass placed in the bottom, the dish set where it will not be jarred, and finally the gemmules dropped onto the glass. They should be left undisturbed for two or three days, at room temperature and out of direct sunlight. A little fresh water should be added so gently that the gemmules will not be shaken. Within a day or two they stick to the glass, no longer rolling with the slightest tremor of the water. This is the first sign of growth, and shows that the soft sponge cells have

FIG. 85.—Sponge colony 3 days old with the gemmules from which it has grown. Note chimney-like elevations.

grown out through the little hole in the gemmule shell, over its side and onto the glass. They make the white plug which shows in the hole and the white drift around the dark gemmule (Fig. 85). By the time the colony has been growing three or four days little elevations will appear on its surface. At first their tips are translucent bulbs but these soon break through and the whole structure becomes chimney-like with

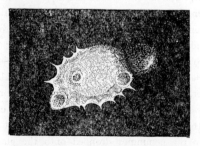

FIG. 86.—Beginnings of the sponge skeleton; the spicules of silica (opal) showing on the edge of a colony 6 days old.

an open osculum at the top. If a bit of finely powdered carmine or starch is scattered on the colony, the particles will be
carried down into the osteoles and will soon be seen coming
out of the larger oscula. If the colony, glass base and all, is
taken from the water for a moment and held up to the light,
the translucent spots and streaks will tell where chambers
and canals have already formed within it (Pl. VI, 2). When
a colony is five or six days old its spicules will prick through
the filmy covering of its transparent border (Fig. 86).

Identification.—Fresh water sponges have been separated
into two groups according to the structure of their gemmules; one contains those in which the opening of the gemmule
is a simple hole, the other those which have it at the end of a
short tube; they have been further classified by their spicules.

Although traits and general form are helpful, for the final
identification of fresh water sponges microscopic study is
necessary. Ward and Whipple's "Fresh-Water Biology"
and Pratt's "Manual of Invertebrate Animals" both contain
illustrated keys to the fresh water sponges.

CHAPTER VII

THE HYDRAS, FRESH WATER JELLYFISHES

Cœlenterata

Form and habits of hydras.—The hydras (Fig. 87) are almost the only fresh water representatives of the great predominantly marine group of *Cœlenterata* to which the jellyfishes, sea anemones, and corals belong. They are soft transparent animals which can stretch themselves until they are

FIG. 87.—Hydras hanging from plants in an aquarium.

half an inch long, or contract till they are as small as pinheads (Pl. IV). When a hydra is extended it looks like a piece of string frayed out at one end. The frayed strands are a circlet of tentacles which surround the mouth, and bring to it any food which they can reach. Its other end is a kind of foot supplied with a sticky secretion, enabling the hydra to hold itself to submerged twigs or even to the underside of the surface film of water. Clinging by its sticky foot it can glide along so slowly that it is hard to realize that it moves at all. Nearly all over its body, especially on the tentacles, there are peculiar stinging cells containing poison sacs. There are

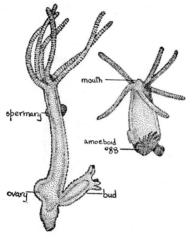

FIG. 88.—Diagrams of hydras (*H. oligactis*) showing bud and reproductive organs.

usually two or three sizes of these and on the tentacles they are arranged in batteries from which their poison sacs are exploded at the slightest touch or invitation. These sacs are to some extent defensive weapons, but they are probably of more value in capturing some of the lively organisms upon which hydras feed.

When feeding, a hydra hangs attached by the foot, swinging its tentacles nonchalantly about in the water until one of them touches something (Fig. 87). If it is a *Daphnia* (p. 165) or something equally appetizing the tentacle will instantly pull it toward the mouth. The other tentacles then contract and

join in the team work of paralyzing and pulling in the prey.
A hydra swallows its food into a capacious central cavity or
cœlenteron, the only cavity in its body. There it is digested
and the useless part cast out of the mouth. Hydras are
gluttonous feeders and they will eat till their bodies swell out
like meal-sacks, the food being clearly visible through their
transparent sides (Fig. 89).

They reproduce both by sex cells and by budding, but the
two kinds of reproduction usually occur at different seasons,

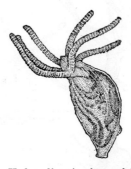

FIG. 89. —*Hydra oligactis* after a full meal.

varying with the species and with their living conditions
(Fig. 88). Buds are most apt to appear when the animals
are well fed. A young hydra bud will stay attached to its
parent for some time after it has a mouth of its own and is
doing its own eating, but the food which the young one eats
may stay in its own cœlenteron or it may pass on into the
parental food cavity. In sexual reproduction thousands of
sperm cells are produced in the spermary, a cone-like eleva-
tion near the base of the tentacles (Fig. 88). Only one egg
is formed in the ovary, the larger swelling near the foot, which
is less often present than the spermary. Spermary and ovary
are sometimes present upon the same animal, as they are in
the green hydra, *Hydra viridissima* (Fig. 90), but in most
species they are found on different individuals. An egg may

be fertilized by a sperm cell from the same animal or from a different one; in any case fertilization occurs while the egg is still attached to the parent's body. There the early development of the young hydra begins under a kind of parental protection.

Hydras tide themselves over dangers of the cold by means of winter eggs which are formed and fertilized in the autumn. Encased in a protective shell, the egg drops from the parent's body, lies dormant over the winter, but resumes its development in the spring. This is a safety device similar to others such as the winter eggs of small crustaceans like *Daphnia*, and of planarians, or the gemmules of sponges.

In the better known hydras like those just described there is only one form of the body; but in certain fresh water jellyfishes to which these hydras are related the individuals of one generation are very different from those of the next. In this so-called "alternation of generations," the hydranths or hydra-like animals of one generation differ greatly from the medusæ or umbrella-like jellyfish of the next generation. In the little known jellyfish, *Craspedacusta*, the hydra-like stage is rarely seen, but the medusa form is occasionally found in great numbers. In September, 1916, millions of little medusæ of *Craspedacusta* were found floating in the waters of Benson Creek about twenty-five miles from Lexington, Kentucky, and again in September, 1924, though none had been observed there between times.

Habitat.—Hydras live in sunlit pools on plant stems and on the under sides of leaves, abundant in early as well as late summer. Dr. J. G. Needham has reported that the "brick-red" hydras were so abundant in early summer at Saranac Inn, New York, that the water was "tinged with red" by them; and Kofoid collected 5335 hydras from a cubic yard of water taken from Quiver Lake in the spring of 1897. Hydras have been reported growing on the walls of filter beds; at Auburn, New York, such a growth of hydra was brilliant pink and occurred in cold weather when there was a lusty population of small crustaceans which are their favorite food.

Food.—Hydras are carnivorous. They thrive on a diet of minute worms and such small crustaceans as *Daphnia*, *Cypris*, and *Cyclops* (Figs. 124, 128, 126), for which they compete with the young fishes. In an aquarium hydras can be seen dangling their tentacles lazily into the water reaching after the *Daphnias* and finally ensnaring them with unbelievable surety. They also swallow young insects and small clams, casting the shells of the latter out of their mouths after the soft parts have been digested. Hickson of the University of Manchester, England, saw a hydra capture and hold a very small tadpole in its tentacles. Another observer saw a hydra swallow a small fish which extended from its mouth after it had been taken in as far as was possible. In 1740 Abbé Abraham Trembley, the pioneer student of hydras, described their capture of baby fishes. In modern times hydras sometimes appear by thousands in hatchery troughs, creating havoc among the very small fry, and they no doubt act the same way in the natural homes of fish fry.

Associates.—Hydras may feed upon young fishes, but it is well known that slightly larger fishes feed upon them. They live on terms of a biological intimacy, known as symbiosis, with at least two organisms. Green algæ or zoochlorellæ live within the body cells of the green hydra as they do in those of fresh water sponges and cause their brilliant green color; and microscopic protozoans (*Kerona pediculus*) live on brown hydras. There are often ten or fifteen of these climbing over an animal at one time, but they are not known to feed upon it nor to do it any harm.

Collecting, aquarium study.—When one is familiar with them hydras can often be seen in still pond water hanging from plant stems like *Nitella* and *Elodea* or from the under sides of lily leaves. But it is usually necessary to gather a few water plants and let them stand in a glass dish of the pond water,

If hydras are present they will soon be hanging out into the water (Fig. 87). They should be kept out of the direct sunlight. Like other animals hydras will have a better chance to live if they get used to water gradually so only a little new water should be given them at a time. Sprays of water plants such as *Nitella*, *Myriophyllum*, or *Elodea* will give off enough oxygen for them and small crustaceans will be their best food. Swarms of these can be dipped out of the water close to the pond shore and hydras will live on them the year round.

In the aquarium their feeding habits can be watched; they will even take a small worm or larva from forceps if it is moved toward them very gently. They will hang from the side of the aquarium, stretching their bodies and tentacles into tenuous slenderness, circling slowly around within a radius of an inch or more. Occasionally, one will attach its tentacles to the glass, loosen its foot and move it over to the tentacles, which are loosened, stretched, and pressed to the glass again; then the foot is lifted again and extended and thus the whole animal moves, looping like an inch worm. Again the same animal may elect to travel by turning slow motion somersaults.

Identification.—The commoner fresh water *Hydrozoa* (Hydras). Animals which have tentacles in a circlet about the mouth and do not form colonies.

Fig. 90—Green hydra, *Hydra viridissima*.

Hydra viridissima (viridis) (Fig. 90).—Green hydra. Body grass-green; about 6 short tentacles; male and female organs on the same individual, usually in summer.

FIG. 91—Gray hydra, *Hydra vulgaris.*

Hydra vulgaris (grisea) (Fig. 91).—Body gray, orange, or brownish; about 6 tentacles; male and female organs usually on different individuals, in summer; 4 kinds of stinging cells.

FIG. 92.—Brown hydra, *Hydra oligactis.*

Hydra oligactis (fusca) (Fig. 92).—Brown hydra. Body brownish, very slender at the proximal (attached) end; about 8 very long tentacles; 3 kinds of stinging cells. Difficult to separate from *H. vulgaris* except by microscopical examination of the stinging cells.

CHAPTER VIII

FREE-LIVING FLATWORMS

Planaria

Most flatworms are parasites. All of the tapeworms which abound in the food canals of fishes, and the host of flukes like those which live on the skin and gills of mud puppies, on the mussel *Anodonta* and within the bodies of turtles, belong to this group. The turbellarians are the only flatworms that are not parasitic. They are small animals whose steady gliding motion is due to thousands of cilia whose turbulent lashings have given the group its name *Turbellaria*. Although turbellarians are generally abundant in fresh water, only the planarians, the largest of them, are familiar; the others being so minute that they are not often discovered. The small ones are mentioned later but nearly all of this discussion refers to the large planarians.

Form and habits of planarians.—Planarians glide over submerged stems and leaves and forage on alga-covered stones. They are soft, gray or velvety black flatworms commonly measuring a half inch or less. They are flattened and look like very small leeches. The shape of the head and body varies but little, earlike flaps, called auricles, being characteristic of many of the family. The mouth is on the end of a short muscular tube, the pharynx, located in the middle of the body. When a planarian is feeding it thrusts its pharynx well out of the body, exploring with it like a kind of feeler, and then sucks the food through it (Fig. 93, 1). At other times it is pulled back into the body through an opening on the under side (Fig. 93, 2). This is visible only from beneath or when a planarian glides upside down under the surface film of the water. Food sucked in through the pharynx goes into the large more or less branched intestine, which often shows as

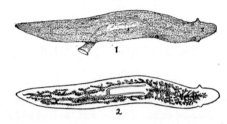

FIG. 93.—Common planarians: 1, upper surface showing the ear-like auricles and the eyes, the cylindric pharynx thrust out from the body as in feeding; 2, diagram of planarian showing its branched food canal and the pharynx pulled back into its sheath within the body.

a vinelike tracery on the backs of planarians. It has only one opening and the waste must go out through the mouth just as it does in *Hydra*.

Planarians are very sensitive to the conditions around them. They appear uncomfortable in bright light, and will try to get into a shadow or into the dark, in the meantime keenly discriminating between small differences in the light. They are responsive to very slight vibrations, especially sensitive to temperature, and must have a sense of taste for they are soon attracted to a crushed snail or any meat juice in the water. With rare exceptions they are hermaphroditic, each animal having a complete male and female reproductive system. Most of them produce thin-shelled transparent summer eggs as well as the thick-shelled winter eggs or "cocoons." But though they are equipped with this elaborate reproductive machinery, all turbellarians depend also upon the simple division of individuals to increase their numbers. The common *Planaria maculata* divides transversely just behind its pharynx (Fig. 94), only a little constriction showing there at first. This grows deeper till the two parts hang together by a mere thread, finally separating and moving away from each other. The head soon grows a new tail,

FIG. 94.—Two individuals of *Planaria* being formed by automatic division of the body.

and the tail region a new head. This kind of division is a very frequent performance among planarians; one often finds a partly divided planarian moving comfortably over a leaf, no longer one animal, yet scarcely two. If planarians are starved or kept in stale water they will divide too often, not getting their growth between divisions, thus producing planarians which remain pigmies as long as the bad conditions exist. This kind of reproduction can be easily imitated artificially by cutting planarians with a knife (Fig. 95). Ways to do this are suggested in the paragraph on aquarium study.

Habitat.—Turbellarians occur in all kinds of fresh water at any time of year, and their presence can be counted upon in almost any aquatic society. Planarians live in shallow pools, in streams, sometimes very swift ones, and in swampy places, often among sphagnum mosses. A pool which at first glance does not seem to have a planarian in it may shelter a population of them hiding on whatever they can find there, stones and trash and water plants. Drooping grasses which trail into the water from the bankside may be black with planarians on their under sides. One of the minute turbellarians, *Stenostomum* (Fig. 96), lives in mats of *Spirogyra* and other green algæ.

Planarians prefer cool, even very cold water, and temperature is quite as important as food in determining where they live. A single species often lives in springs or ponds which are very different in other ways, shallow or deep, rapid flowing or slow, so long as their waters are uniformly cold. The European *Planaria alpina* occurs in the high cold lakes of the Alps, while in lower regions it is not found at all in similar lakes where the water is warm, but only in rapid brooks and in springs whose temperature is more like that of the mountain lakes. Dr. Kathleen Carpenter has suggested that some planarians are relicts of the Ice-Age, animals brought from the north by the great ice-sheet, and left stranded in warmer regions where they are now making the best of it, living only in the coldest places.

Food.—All planarians are carnivorous and often cannibalistic. They thrive on crushed snail-meat and beef-liver, devouring it greedily at night, the time when they are most active. If a hungry *Planaria maculata* (Fig. 98) is turned on its back in a drop of water and a piece of snail-meat held within its reach it will thrust out its pharynx and suck up the meat juice till it is full to bursting. Planarians will gather in groups ten to fifty strong upon pieces of meat which are dropped into their dishes. They will eat hard-boiled yolk of egg. The milky planarian, *Dendrocœlum lacteum* (Fig. 97), will fill its food canal with it till its whole back is yellow.

A few minute turbellarians, the rhabdocœles (Fig. 96), are vegetarians, living on algæ, diatoms, and especially *Spirogyra*, on which they are sometimes abundant.

Aquarium study.—Planarians are easy to collect and can be kept in aquaria for long intervals with very little trouble. They cling to leaves or to stones when these are pulled from the water and they can be easily lifted off with the point of a knife. The aquarium for them should be supplied with a shallow bed of clean sand, a few pebbles, several sprays of *Myriophyllum* or some other water plant, and clean water kept cool and out of bright light. Planarians cannot stand heat or lack of oxygen. If they creep up and form a line along the water's edge it means that their oxygen supply is running low, more plants must be put in the aquarium or fresh water added every day or two. Once or twice a week they should have a meal of crushed snail-meat, or earthworm, or beef-liver, and the water should be changed the day after feeding. Planarians will live for a long time, three months or more, without any food, but they will become smaller and smaller, using up their own bodies nearly to the vanishing point.

To test their power of growing new heads and tails it is only necessary to have healthy planarians, a few small, clean dishes so that each animal can have one to itself, and a knife or a pair of scissors. Place a planarian in a shallow dish of water, and press a sharp knife down across it while it is well extended, or lift it out upon wet paper where it can be cut, paper and all, with scissors. Planarians have no blood or blood vessels to be injured by cutting and branches of the

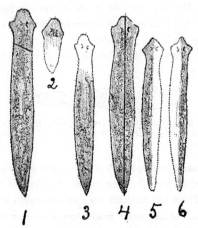

FIG. 95.—Regeneration in planarians: 1, a planarian cut crosswise as indicated; 2, the regeneration of the tail; and 3, the head; 4, a planarian cut lengthwise; 5, the regeneration of the left, and 6, of the right side.

food canal go in all directions making every region capable of digesting food and growing. If a planarian is cut crosswise (Fig. 95) the head will grow or regenerate a new body and the body a new head as they do in natural transverse division. If one is cut lengthwise through the center of the body the right side will regenerate a new left and vice versa. If no food is given to these regenerating animals the growing side will live on the older part and the whole animal will be dwarfed.

Identification.—On the outside of their bodies turbellarians have few external features by which the different species can be separated. Their classification is based very largely upon the sex organs which are undeveloped in all but the fully grown animals and difficult to see at any time. The main groups, however, are divided according to the shape of the intestine, in this case meaning all of the food tract except the pharynx, and often clearly visible through the transparent body wall (Fig. 93, 2). Fresh water turbellarians have a single, blind intestine as in the Order *Rhabdocœlida* or a three-branched one as in the *Triclada*.

1. Turbellarians with a single, blind intestine. Order *Rhabdocœlida*.

Fig. 96.—*Stenostomum leucops*, showing the chain of individuals produced by automatic division of the body.

Stenostomum leucops.—This is a very common species (Fig. 96) which may be here taken as a type of the rhabdocœles. These minute flatworms are common on plants in quiet ponds, but are never more than a quarter of an inch long, so small that they are seldom seen and even less often recognized. They reproduce by budding, a kind of transverse division, and their best recognition marks are the chains of 2 to 4, rarely 9, animals attached to one another, tandemwise.

Occurrence.—Northeastern states, New York, Michigan.

2. Turbellarians whose intestines have three main branches, one running forward through the center of the body and two which turn backward on each side of the pharynx. Order *Triclada.*

3. Turbellarians with one pharynx. *Dendrocœlum, Planaria.*

FIG. 97.—Milky planarian, *Dendrocœlum lacteum.*

Milky planarian, Dendrocœlum lacteum.—These beautiful planarians are creamy white with their food canals showing in a tracery of brown (Fig. 97). Just behind the eyes there is a constricted necklike region which makes the rounded auricles more prominent.

These pale planarians crawl over the stones in shallow streams. An occasional one can be found there throughout the winter (Pl. I). When collected such animals sometimes lay their hard-shelled winter eggs shortly after they are brought into the house. They are about the size of a mustard seed, shiny, chestnut brown and raised on a tiny stalk.

Occurrence.—Eastern states.

FIG. 98.—*Planaria maculata.*

Planaria maculata.—*Planaria maculata* is one of the commonest planarians (Fig. 98). Its body is slender, about one quarter of an inch long, and tapers into a pointed tail. The head is broader than the body, and pointed in front with short auricles. These animals usually pass as common black planarians. Their backs are irregularly spotted with black, and smaller black spots are scattered among the large ones so that the whole surface looks dark, though a light streak sometimes runs along the middle. In summer they reproduce almost entirely by transverse divisions. They live in quiet waters, under stones, among algæ, often in groups of 3 to 5, or 15 to 20.

Occurrence.—Eastern states to Michigan and Nebraska.

4. Turbellarians with several pharynges.

FIG. 99.—*Phagocata gracilis.*

Phagocata gracilis.—These planarians are shiny black or sometimes reddish-brown, one third to 1 inch long. They are round headed and blunt tailed, remarkable in having not one pharynx but twenty-two separate ones, each having a mouth, and opening into the intestine, and all of them extensible through the single opening on the under side of the body (Fig. 99).

Occurrence.—Common in pools, often in brackish water. Massachusetts and Pennsylvania to Wisconsin.

CHAPTER IX

WHEEL ANIMALCULES

Rotifera

Rotifers are transparent microscopic animals which live in fresh or salt water. They abound in the surface waters of great lakes, and swarm through the shallows of ponds and bogs; there is scarcely any stand of soft water, whether transient puddle or rain-barrel or fountain-basin, where rotifers can not be found. They live in ponds and lakes, providing a large part of the food for small crustaceans and worms and are thus indirectly a main source of food for fishes.

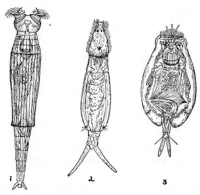

FIG. 100.—Common rotifers: 1, *Philodina*; 2, *Diglena*, which sucks out plant cells; 3, *Euchlanis*, showing shell-like lorica. (From Ward and Whipple.)

Rotifer structures.—Most rotifers are solitary but others are joined together in colonies and while the majority of them move freely through the water, a few are attached to plants or animals. Although they grow in an infinite variety of shapes all of them have circlets of cilia which appear like two rapidly rotating wheels at the front end of the body, hence their name *Rotifera* or wheelbearers. Small as it is, a rotifer has an outer covering, either a soft or a shell-like lorica (Fig. 100, 3), muscles, a food canal, nerves, complicated reproductive systems (Fig. 101).

Seen under the low power of a compound microscope the wheels of the rotifer prove to be the rims of its corona or head region circled with hundreds of cilia waving so fast that they look like two whirling crowns (Fig. 101). By means of

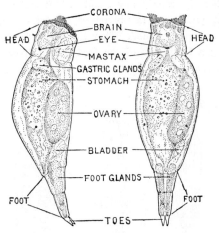

FIG. 101.—Diagram of a rotifer showing circlets of cilia and mastax. (After F. J. Myers.)

these lashing cilia rotifers propel themselves through the water and collect their food. A rotifer's mouth is at the lower edge of the corona and its short œsophagus contains the mastax, a food pouch equipped with three teeth which crush and grind up any delicate alga or protozoan which comes their way. In the plant-eating rotifers the mastax works like a suction pump; the rotifer pierces the cell with its jaws and then pumps it out clean. Cilia and mastax are equally characteristic of rotifers and both keep moving as long as the animal lives. On the moving rotifer the "foot" projects out from behind and would be far better named the tail; it secretes the glue by which the rotifer attaches itself to plants or often to the backs of little crustaceans. Only female rotifers are ordinarily seen and only in them is the characteristic mastax present (Fig. 101). Males are extremely minute; in some species of rotifers the eggs develop without fertilization. In these cases males have not been found and it is pretty certain that they do not exist at all.

Habits, resistance to cold and drought.—Rotifers can live through great extremes of cold and drought. In the fall they produce tough shells and lie dormant in them through the winter months, hatching in spring into the individuals which carry on the race. Some rotifers, *Philodinidæ* (Fig. 100, 1), are dried up, often through long droughts, but are able to keep life going at such a low rate that they can survive and resume their normal living after the crisis is over. They can also regain their activity after being frozen into ice for long periods.

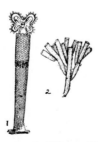

FIG. 102.—The case-building rotifer, *Melicerta*: 1, animal and case; 2, a cluster of cases on lily pad. Visible with hand-lens. (1, from Ward and Whipple.)

There are distinct societies of rotifers; in the open surface water there is a host of minute transparent ones, the plankton rotifers, in the plant-filled shallows near shore is another great company of them which live in the ooze and on the stems and leaves of plants. The agile, swift-moving rotifers feed upon microscopic animals; the larger, slower ones are vegetarians. Many of them eat out the cells of filamentous algæ, and green *Spirogyra* mats are usually full of them.

One of the few rotifers visible to the naked eye is *Melicerta* (Fig. 102) which builds itself a case by cementing together little brown pellets which can be clearly seen through a good hand-lens. *Melicerta* lives on the under sides of lily-pads (Fig. 18) and dozens of them can be found upon almost any branch of hornwort or water milfoil (Pl. IV).

CHAPTER X

BRYOZOANS

Bryozoa (or Polyzoa)

Form and habits of bryozoans.—Bryozoans look so much like moss that they have long been called moss animals or *Bryozoa*. Some species live in colonies growing plant-like in beds (Pl. VII) made up of hundreds or thousands of individuals (zooids) and to the naked eye they appear like delicate stiffened threads; in others these animals are covered with a limy crust, and in a few others like *Pectinatella* (Fig. 107) they are embedded in the surface of solid masses of jelly. In any case, what we see when we pull the colonies from the water are only skeletons or some kind of protecting covers, in which the animals themselves are entirely hidden. The individual animals are minute and visible only with a hand-lens. When undisturbed they constantly rotate their head-like lophophores in the tops of their tubes, or stretch them from pores in the surrounding jelly; but at the slightest jar they snap them down, leaving no sign of life behind them. But if a colony or even a fragment of one is allowed to rest quietly in a dish of water for a few minutes, heads will all rear up again, swinging and nodding back and forth as before. The mouth of each animal is in the center of a circular or horseshoe-shaped wreath of tentacles, this whole "head" region being called the lophophore (Fig. 103). Each tentacle is covered with cilia which wave toward the mouth, whirling along whatever particles get into the current.

The food tube of bryozoans is a U-shaped canal, with the anus opening near the mouth, either just inside or just outside of the circlet of tentacles (Fig. 103). Below the tentacles the body is very flexible and provided with muscles by which the

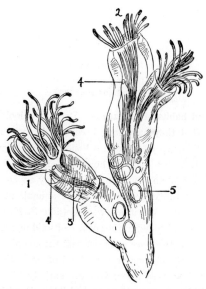

FIG. 103.—Individual animals of *Plumatella:* 1, lophophore with tentacles expanded; 2, with tentacles retracted within the zoœcium; 3, food tube; 4, anus; 5, developing statoblast.

animals can pull themselves, tentacles and all, into their shell-like coverings, the zoœcia, or into surrounding jelly. No one who has witnessed a sudden disappearance of these animal gardens before his eyes can doubt its efficiency in protecting them against nibbling enemies.

The individual bryozoans which start a new colony in spring are themselves produced either from sex cells, or from winter buds called statoblasts (Fig. 103), which are very similar to the gemmules of sponges. Like hydras the fresh water bryozoans have a multitude of relatives in the sea whence they originally came. Their ancestors slowly migrated up the brooks and rivers, or were carried inland by animals, encountering ups and downs of temperature and droughts which they had never met in the ocean. Nearly all fresh water bryozoans have drought- and cold-resistant buds, the statoblasts, each capable of forming a new colony. They are groups of cells which form within the body of an individual bryozoan and are finally set free in the water after the animal has died and its hard outer covering has broken into pieces. Often this does not occur until late winter, although earlier in the year the current may wash away everything which remains of a colony, statoblasts and all. Some statoblasts are enclosed in tough cushions which buoy them up like life-preservers, and armed with hooks which anchor them to twigs and trash (Fig. 107). Thus armed they are carried hither and yon by water and animals, especially by water birds which transport them over long distances into new regions. They usually hatch out in the spring; that they are important safeguards against drought as well as cold is suggested by the fact that some Brazilian bryozoans form statoblasts although they have no winter to endure. They achieve other ends, such as distribution, quite as important to the animal as protection against cold.

Habitat.—Bryozoans live in all kinds of fresh water, in stagnant pools, ponds, and rushing streams. They form delicate traceries on the undersides of flattened stones (Pl. VII), or grow vine-like on logs and boards which have long lain in the water. Furry colonies of *Cristatella* (Fig. 108) grow beneath lily pads in quiet coves, masses of *Pectinatella* (Fig. 107) hang from submerged twigs. The latter and other bryozoans are common in reservoirs.

Food.—They feed upon microscopic organisms, chiefly diatoms (Pl. IV).

Aquarium study and collecting.—Quiet water bryozoans will live for a few days in an aquarium especially if provided with water from their own pond. Bryozoan colonies are beautiful with their nodding lophophores and waving tentacles and the tentacle-wreathed heads of *Cristatella* look like rose colored fountains.

Bryozoans cannot be preserved outstretched unless they are put into an anæsthetic (p. 41) like chloretone, before the alcohol is poured over them. The branching tubes of *Plumatella* keep well in alcohol; but the jelly masses of *Pectinatella* and *Cristatella* shrink into sorry looking remnants.

Identification.—Bryozoans are small and their classification is necessarily based upon microscopic structures. Table of the genera of bryozoans described here; modified from Pratt (see Bibliography, p. 413):

1. Lophophore circular. Order *Gymnolæmata* (mouth not covered).

Family *Paludicellidæ*

Colonies delicate and vinelike, on stones and sticks in ponds and slow streams.

F<small>IG</small>. 104.—*Paludicella ehrenbergii:* 1, colony; 2, branch enlarged.

Paludicella ehrenbergii.—The colony is partly creeping and partly erect, made up of minute club-shaped animals arranged tandem-wise in the branches (Fig. 104). The statoblasts are oval, ringed with a bluish purple band. Creeping on stones in ponds and slow streams, sometimes in water pipes; widely distributed.

Occurrence.—May–August.

2. Lophophore oval, or horseshoe-shaped. Order *Phylactolæmata* (mouth covered).

a, Colony branched, statoblasts without hooks.

Family *Fredericellidæ*

Colonies branching or forming dense clumps, on stones and sticks.

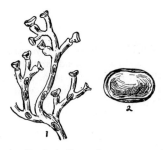

FIG. 105.—*Fredericella sultana:* 1, colony; 2, statoblast.

Fredericella sultana.—Colony partly creeping and partly erect with antler-like branches, sometimes forming dense clumps (Fig. 105). On the undersides of stones and sticks usually in dark places in ponds and streams.

Occurrence.—Common and widely distributed. May–August.

Family *Plumatellidæ*

Colonies of cylindrical tubes either creeping or forming massive clumps.

Plumatella.—Colony made up of brownish or transparent branching tubes which trail vinelike or grow in bushy clumps (Fig. 106). Statoblasts without hooks, sometimes oval, sometimes irregular in shape (Fig. 106). In a variety of places, ponds, streams, water pipes, reservoir sluiceways, preferring

Pl. VII.—1, Vinelike colony of the bryozoan, *Plumatella*, on the underside of a stone; the heads are white and the horny tubes very dark. 2, Half inch of stone surface covered with the protozoan *Vorticella;* the blurred white spots are the moving animals p. 57.

Photo. by A. H. Morgan

PLATE VII

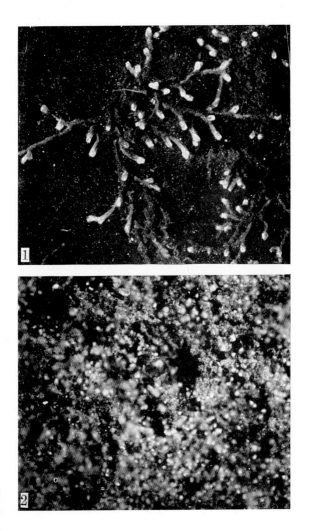

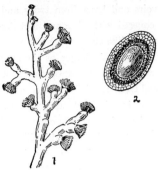

FIG. 106.—*Plumatella polymorpha:* 1, colony; 2, statoblast.

darkness. This is the commonest genus of bryozoans, sometimes so abundant in waterways that it has to be removed with shovels.

Occurrence.—Widely distributed as far west as Montana July–August.

b, Colony massive, secreting a gelatinous base.

Family *Cristatellidæ*

Colonies in compact groups in large spherical masses or flat and rug-like.

Pectinatella.—The colonies are made up of animals clustered on the surface of large masses of jelly which adhere to the

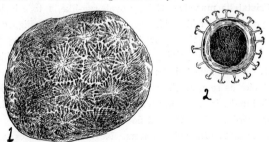

FIG. 107.—*Pectinatella magnifica:* 1, colony; 2, statoblast.

walls of reservoirs and hang from twigs and water plants. They become covered with algæ and look like green grape-fruit. Each rosette-like cluster constitutes one group. The central jelly mass is made larger as the number of animals increases. Toward fall thousands of statoblasts form, and are gradually washed from the jelly surface as the colonies die. They are banded by air-filled cushions and armed with a single row of hooks which catch upon everything with which they come in contact. They float like life-preservers on the surface, and are often piled up in thin brown streaks along the shore line.

Occurrence.—Common. Northeastern states to Illinois and Michigan. August–October.

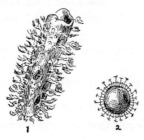

Fig. 108.—*Cristatella mucedo:* 1, colony; 2, statoblast.

Cristatella mucedo.—Colony oval, rug-like, 1 to 2 inches long on the undersides of leaves, especially lily pads (Fig. 108). Toward autumn they grow longer and one colony may be fused with another, giving the effect of a winding, branching mat. When collected the animals will begin to wave their tentacles as soon as the water is quiet; looking down upon their hundreds of waving tentacles is like peering into mini-ature gardens of translucent flowers.

Occurrence.—In quiet waters. Northeastern states and Canada to Illinois. Common in Massachusetts. May–August.

CHAPTER XI

THREADWORMS, HAIRWORMS, AND BRISTLE-WORMS

Nematoda and Oligochæta

Similarity of worms and midge larvæ.—All are not worms which wriggle; nowhere is this more true than in the mucky trash of pond shallows and the weed-grown side-waters of streams where thousands of insect larvæ, almost all of them midges (p. 291), abound in close company with true thread-worms or nematodes and bristleworms or oligochætes. All of these are about the same length, mostly under a quarter of an inch; to the naked eye they look alike, but if they are examined with a hand-lens their differences will at once appear (Fig. 109). The midge larvæ have distinct heads, segmented and almost hairless bodies, usually two fleshy prolegs near the head and two at the rear; such prolegs occur along the abdomen of any common caterpillar. These are never found upon worms. The nematodes are as slender as midge larvæ but they have no heads, their bodies are unsegmented and without an appendage of any kind. Most fresh water oligochætes are either little transparent bristly worms or small aquatic earthworms easily recognized as such. They have no heads and their bodies are divided into segments bearing horny bristles that are used as feet. The midge larvæ along with the nematodes and the smaller oligochæte worms constitute a great host of minute animals which are constantly devouring plant tissues, especially soft ones, continually cleaning up the refuse in the water and in turn becoming the food of larger insects and young fishes. Except for the aquatic earthworm they are all small animals; few are more than an inch or two long, most of them less than half an inch; many are

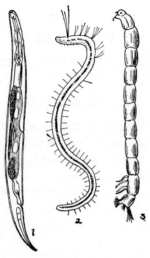

FIG. 109.—1, nematode worm; 2, oligochæte worm; 3, midge (chironomid) larva. (1, after Jagerskiold.)

microscopic. Although their size is insignificant their numbers are so enormous that they play an important and constructive part in water life.

Threadworms—*Nematoda*

Form and habits of nematodes.—The threadworms are slender, strikingly smooth, unsegmented worms, seldom more than a few millimeters long, very often microscopic. They are almost inconceivably abundant in pond and stream and ocean as well as in the soil. Great numbers of them live in the bodies of aquatic mollusks, crustaceans, and worms, in addition to the swarms which inhabit the bottom mud, the surfaces of plants, and everything else in the water. They are constantly moving through its lower levels and even city tap water sometimes contains them. Although many of them are parasites and their ranks include the well-known hookworm, there are also great numbers of them which are harmless and free-living.

Nematodes are very active, constantly lashing their bodies to and fro; this habit and their smoothness and small size will usually identify them (Fig. 109, 1). The mouth is at the blunt end of the body; the other end is pointed. Aquatic members of this group are uniformly minute and difficult to distinguish, except the allied hair snakes or *Gordiacea* which may be a foot or more long.

Hairworms—*Gordiacea*

Form and habits of hairworms.—Although hairworms are generally classed as allies of the nematodes they are in many ways so different from them that they cannot be considered as very closely related.

Hairsnakes or wireworms lie like twisted roots or loose-coiled wire, on the bottom of brooks, springs, ponds, troughs, and rain-barrels. They look like coarse horse-hairs, and about them clings the well-known story that a hair will "turn to life" if you leave it in water over night. Their bodies are entirely covered with a thin layer of horny brown chitin, which stiffens them so that in their slow coiling and uncoiling they seem to be so much living wire. The front end of the body tapers to a point but the rear end is split into two or three parts, the number varying in the two sexes and in different species (Fig. 110).

The adult hairworms that live in the water are a foot or two long (Fig. 110). They lie on the brook bottom, often singly but sometimes a half dozen are twisted together like a snarl of twine. They lay their eggs in long strings hung upon submerged water plants; these later break up into short pieces from a fraction of an inch to an inch long.

Although the life histories of many hairworms are unknown, those of certain species have been studied and the main facts discovered. In *Gordius robustus*, the egg hatches into a minute larva which goes swimming about in the open water and after a time drops to the bottom and bores its way into any animal which it can reach. Hundreds of these young hairworms squirm over the pond bottom, most of them are probably lost, yet many of them manage to get inside the bodies of aquatic insects. A few of them wriggle out of the water and on to the wet soil of the shore, and are there eaten by grasshoppers which come to the water's edge in search of food. Occasionally they are eaten by crickets; both kinds of insects take animal as well as vegetable food. Within a grasshopper the hairworm grows, finally reaching maturity. When thus fullgrown its problem is to reach the water again and if the grasshopper frequents the water's edge at this time, the fullgrown hairworm will burrow out of its body. Whether it is influenced by the moisture is not known but this seems probable. Once in the water the hairworms mate and lay eggs that hatch into larvæ which begin the cycle all over again. Obviously but few hairworms which enter the bodies of grasshoppers ever get back to the water. Most of them must perish because the grasshoppers are not about the water at the right time or more often fail to go near it at all. Yet this and other species of hairworms produce so many eggs that the race is kept going in spite of the great mortality which befalls its members.

Two common hairworms.—Two of the most widely distributed hairworms are *Paragordius varius* and *Gordius villoti* first called *G. aquaticus* by Montgomery; these are common through most of the United States (Fig. 110). Males of *P. varius* are nearly 14 inches long, over 2 inches longer and more slender than the female, the hind end of the body is bi-

lobed in the male, and tri-lobed in the female (Fig. 110).
Their larvæ have been found in two species of crickets.
The males of *G. villoti* are up to 26 inches long and the females

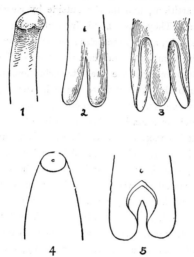

FIG. 110.—Adult or water stage of hairworms:
1, *Paragordius varius*, side view of head; 2, bi-lobed
tail of male; 3, tri-lobed tail of female; 4, *Gordius
villoti*, head of male; 5, tail of male. (Montgomery.
From Ward and Whipple.)

are as long or longer. The tail is bluntly bi-lobed in the male
but blunt and single in the female (Fig. 110). The larvæ
live in various species of grasshoppers.

Bristleworms—*Oligochæta*

Form and habits of bristleworms.—The fresh water bristleworms or oligochætes are either bristle-bearing worms about
half an inch long, or small aquatic earthworms easily recognized as such. Their bodies are segmented and like the
leeches they belong to the great Phylum *Annelida*, which
contains all of the annulate or "ringed" worms. They
are built like earthworms and behave like them, overturning

the ooze of pond bottoms as thoroughly as earthworms over-turn the topsoil of the land. Their slender, cylindrical bodies are divided into segments set off on the inside by muscular partitions, and on the outside by clearly defined constrictions. They have no fleshy outgrowths along the sides of the body, and no tentacles such as are found on their relatives, the clamworms and the tubeworms of the seashore. Their only appendages are the setæ—chitinous rods which prick through the skin, and are borne in varying numbers upon their segments. In the common earthworm, *Lumbricus terrestris*, such setæ can be pulled down into the skin so that they are partly concealed, and can be felt only when the worm is stretched out at full length. All the little fresh water oligochætes, especially the family *Naidæ*, have such con-spicuous setæ that the whole group of them are called bristle-worms; many are transparent. Common types are *Dero* (Fig. 113), which makes a floating tube from bits of plant stems, and other naids (*Naidæ*) which live among the latticed branches of floating algæ. Another family, the *Tubicidæ*, commonly called "bloodworms," are colored blood-red and are very active tube-builders on the bottom mud.

Habitat.—Bristleworms frequent the still water of coves, and stagnant, muddy, or marshy pools, where submerged and decaying vegetation is plentiful. Many species hide on plants in the society of snails, planarians, caddis worms, and hundreds of midge larvæ; the mud of polluted waters is often literally astir with them (Fig. 19). They can live with but little oxygen. *Tubifex* have been taken from the depths of Lake Mendota, Wisconsin, in waters which are low in oxygen for three months at a time.

Food.—Most oligochætes live on decayed organic matter, especially plants; they are constantly cleaning up the pools and they are largely responsible for the quick disappearance of dying algal mats (p. 50) in the fall. Charles Darwin's famous "Vegetable Mold and Earthworms" portrays how the surface of the earth is being continually passed through the bodies of earthworms, how they have literally overturned it again and again. Just as important work is done by their fresh water allies. The little red *Tubifex* (Fig. 114) dig their heads an inch or more down into the bottom mud, and feed there in a layer containing but little oxygen, and where but for them decomposition would go on very slowly. But as they feed, the waste matter from their bodies is cast out from the ends projecting above the mud and thus they make a constant overturn of the mud very like the other one continually being made on land.

Collecting and aquarium study.—Hundreds of threadworms and bristleworms can be found by simply rinsing freshly gathered algæ and water plants in a dish of clean water. Those which live on the bottom can be collected in large numbers by screening mud through a fine-meshed net or sieve (p. 29).

Despite their importance in the economy of nature, bristleworms are not interesting to the general collector. They are too small to be seen easily and their features are monotonous when visible; their chief interest lies in their works.

Identification.—In most of these worms only the most prominent structures can be seen with a hand-lens. A few of the best known forms are here figured.

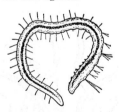

FIG. 111.—*Nais*, one of the commonest bristleworms.

Nais.—There are several species of these transparent little worms (Fig. 111). They are all similar, some of their setæ

145

are short, others long and hairlike; new individuals are produced by budding. They are very common, in mud or on plants, in standing or flowing water.

FIG. 112.—*Chætogaster diaphanus*, a common bristleworm which feeds upon cladocerans.

Chætogaster.—*Chætogaster diaphanus* (Fig. 112) is a half inch long, much longer than most bristleworms, and feeds on little crustaceans, especially the cladocerans (p. 164) *Chydorus* and *Sphæricus*.

FIG. 113.—*Dero*. (Walton. From Pratt.)

Dero.—The lively little *Dero*, hardly a quarter of an inch long, slips in and out of its tube or changes ends within it. It is common on floating leaves from lily-pads to duckweed (Fig. 113).

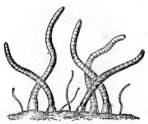

FIG. 114.—*Tubifex tubifex*, tube-building worms with their heads in the mud, and tails pointed upward. (From Needham.)

146

Tubifex.—These are slender, red or brownish worms about an inch and a half long, living in tubes with their tails sticking up above the surface of the surrounding mud (Fig. 114). They often form reddish patches on the mud, which in close view look like waving fringes due to the constant motion of the tails. *Tubifex* depends on abundant decaying organic matter, needing only a moderate amount of oxygen.

CHAPTER XII

LEECHES

Hirudinea

Leeches possess much more beauty and interest than their reputation credits them with. Most of them are marked with concealing colors and patterns, browns, greens, and blacks, picturing upon them the broken shadows and water-soaked leaves of their natural background and hiding them in it. They are sensitive to the slightest vibration of the water, to shadows passing over them, and to small changes in the flavor of the water around them. Their whole set up is one of exquisite efficiency for their mode of living.

Form and habits of leeches.—The external features most essential to a leech are the strong muscular suckers at each end of its body and the sucking mouth which may or may not be armed with jaws (Fig. 115). Leeches are segmented worms like bristleworms and common earthworms and belong to the Phylum *Annelida*. Each segment of the body is creased by two to sixteen superficial wrinkles. These are not easy to distinguish from the true furrows which separate the segments, especially since the number of these superficial rings varies in different parts of the body, there being more in the middle segments and fewer in those near each end of the animal (Fig. 115).

Leeches are hermaphroditic, and like the earthworms, pairs of animals mate even though each one has complete male and female organs within its own body; thus the eggs of one animal are fertilized by the sperm cells of another. They lay their eggs in spring and summer, some species continuing to produce them for five or six months at a stretch. The eggs of all leeches except the family *Glossiphonidæ* are surrounded by a horny capsule cr cocoon, sometimes with several eggs in one case, and glued to stones, plants, or trash, or buried in damp

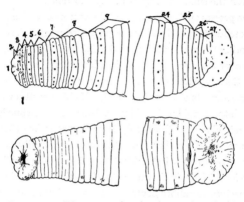

FIG. 115.—Diagrams of a leech: 1, dorsal side showing the eyes, segments numbered above; 2, ventral side showing the mouth opening and the clinging suckers. (From Moore, after Nachtrieb.)

earth. But the family *Glossiphonidæ* carry their eggs in capsules attached to their ventral sides; there the young ones hatch out and cling to their parent with their heads hanging free (Fig. 118).

Leeches are easily recognized. Their habits are well known and their medical use is of such long standing that the phrase "stick like a leech" has been included in the dictionaries. If one only knows one kind of leech it is easy to recognize others. Leeches are nearly all aquatic; only a few live on land. They are curiously varied in their eating habits: a single leech may feast on snail-meat at one meal and suck turtle blood at its next one. Those of the same species will sometimes be found feeding on snails or insect larvæ, and again clamped to the body of a frog and lustily sucking its blood. As a group they appear to be wavering on the edge of parasitism, but not wholly committed to it, and while certain species are permanent parasites others are only predatory.

They are acutely sensitive to vibrations in the water and to even the smallest amount of any substance dissolved in it. If one presses one's finger against the bottom of a dish containing leeches, they will at once begin to creep around, restlessly exploring the whole surface of the dish and if they happen to pass over the finger print, their agitation makes it quite evident that they detect its odor. They are also quickly excited by the movements of water in a pond. If either cattle or persons wade into a pond inhabited by the American medicinal leeches, *Macrobdella decora* (Fig. 119), they will soon swim out into the open water and gather about the intruders, finally attaching themselves to their legs. That they do not rely wholly upon an odor of flesh is shown by the fact that they will attach themselves to rubber boots almost as readily as to bare legs. Wading into leech-infected ponds either with or without boots is a good way to collect them. Leeches are also very sensitive to light and in different species there may be one or several pairs of eyes on the head segments as well as a circlet of light-perceiving organs in each segment (Fig. 115).

Leech bites.—The only American blood-sucking leeches belong to the genus *Macrobdella;* the well-known blood-sucker of ponds and swimming pools is *Macrobdella decora* (Fig. 119). Our other blood-sucking leech is the European medicinal leech *Hirudo medicinalis.* The latter was imported from Europe for blood-letting, and has become established in some regions of New York. It is about 4 inches long, usually greenish colored on its dorsal side with four to six brown stripes. Although most leeches are not thorough-going blood-suckers they are all more or less bloodthirsty. The structures which make them such successful blood-suckers are their toothed jaws and their suction bulb pharynx or throat cavity (Fig. 116). When a blood-sucking leech finds a satisfying skin surface it attaches its hind sucker and swings its head end about, exploring the region. If possible it selects a spot where the skin is broken or is particularly well supplied with blood. It then presses down its anterior sucker, pushes its three jaws into the flesh and makes a wound which is at first perfectly painless, but may later itch intensely. As the jaws enter the flesh, a small amount of hirudin, the leech's saliva, pours into the wound and mixes with the blood. Hirudin acts precisely like mosquito saliva, preventing coagulation of the blood and keeping it thin so that it can be easily sucked up. Like a mosquito bite the leech bite will itch worse if the leech is removed soon after it makes the wound; but there will be almost no itching if it can keep on sucking and finishes its meal. During the first part of the meal the irritating hirudin fills the wound, but near the completion it has been sucked out. An American medicinal leech will take about two and a half times its own weight in blood, which amounts to about half an ounce. This is possible because the fluid part of the blood is drawn off through the kidneys of the leech even while it continues to suck from the wound. Leeches produce some good preservative for their food, for it will keep in their stomachs if not used up for nearly a year. They have been kept in aquaria without food for fifteen months. Leech bites are not dangerous to human beings except through accidental infection of the wound, or in the rare case of a "natural bleeder," suffering from hæmophilia, when persistent hemorrhage will follow the bite. Leeches often attack frogs and turtles in such numbers that they literally suck the life blood out of them but painted turtles carry three or four of them without seeming to feel any ill effects.

Habitat.—Leeches abound in ponds, especially those of the northern states; a few live on stones and boards in swift streams, but most of them prefer quiet water. Sluggish ditches swarm with them. The writer attended a country school near which there was such a ditch, and one of our charming pastimes was that of capturing leeches and "putting them down" each other's necks. Many of the family *Glossiphonidæ* (p. 154) are partial parasites, part of the time clinging to the thin skin behind the legs of turtles and to the bodies of frogs and salamanders, and part of the time foraging for snails and insects over leaves and submerged trash.

Food.—Most leeches will suck blood, if it is available, but even the good blood-sucker, *Macrobdella*, feeds upon worms and larvæ in its youth. When fullgrown it lives mainly on vertebrate blood, preferably human or cattle blood, but lacking these it will satisfy itself with frogs, turtles, and tadpoles. Some species feed upon worms and snails; a few are cannibals, and others are scavengers on dead animals.

Associates.—No very definite information is available concerning the enemies of leeches, but carnivorous fishes—trout, sunfish, yellow perch, and black bass—are known to be important consumers, as well as various wading birds.

Collecting, aquarium study.—Leeches are easily collected and those from quiet water can be kept indefinitely in aquaria. If they are found sticking to boards it is best to slide a knife under them, then let them drop into the collecting dish. They

FIG. 116.—Mouth regions of leeches showing: 1, the mouth which is but a small hole in the oral sucker; 2, the large mouth occupying the whole cavity of the sucker.

are easy to feed, needing only one meal of ground-up meat, beef-liver, earthworms or snail-meat once in a few weeks. When hungry they are very sensitive, and if one even moves one's hand over a dish of hungry leeches so that its shadow falls across them, they will at once begin swinging their heads about exploring for food.

Identification.—Table of the families of leeches represented here, modified from Moore's key to North American fresh water leeches (see Bibliography, p. 414).

1. Mouth a small pore in oral sucker from which a muscular proboscis may be protruded; no jaws.

Suborder *Rhyncobdellæ*.

Body not divided into two regions; usually much flattened; eyes near median line; typically each segment contains 3 rings; eggs within capsules and young fixed to the mother's body.

Family *Glossiphonidæ*, p. 154.

Body divided into a narrow anterior and a wider posterior region; little depressed; eyes when present usually well separated; chiefly parasites attached to the fins and gills of fishes. No representative is included here.

Family *Ichthyobdellidæ*.

2. Mouth large, occupying entire cavity of sucker; pharynx not forming a proboscis; jaws often present.

Suborder *Gnathobdellæ*.

Eyes typically five pairs on segments II–VI; complete segments five-ringed; toothed jaws usually present.

Family *Hirudinidæ*, p. 155.

Eyes three or four pairs (rarely absent), usually one or two pairs on II and two pairs at sides of mouth on IV; no jaws. Predacious.

Family *Herpobdellidæ*, p. 156.

Family *Glossiphonidæ*

Several genera and many species live in shallow water among plants or under stones, or attached to fishes, salamanders, frogs and turtles. They are poor swimmers but good creepers. When disturbed they roll up into balls and drop to the bottom. They carry their eggs and young on the ventral side of the body, undulating their bodies in order to secure more oxygen for them (Fig. 118). When carrying a large family the parent's body is usually humped up a little and its edges are inrolled so that the young leeches are well protected.

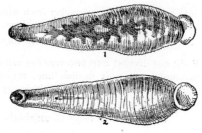

Fig. 117.—Turtle leech, *Placobdella parasitica:* 1, dorsal; 2, ventral.

Turtle leech, Placobdella parasitica.—*Placobdella parasitica* is one of the most abundant American leeches, most often found clinging to the skin at the base of the hind legs of painted and snapping turtles (Fig. 117). When rearing their young these leeches leave the turtles and feed on snails and worms. In early spring before and during the period of reproduction they gorge themselves with blood; at other seasons they may be kept for months without food. The body is broad and flat, with a smooth surface, greenish colored, striped and blotched with yellow; one pair of compound eyes.

Length: very large individuals may be 3–4 inches long when extended.

Glossiphonia complanata.—This is a common leech in running water, on the undersides of stones where it feeds upon snails and clinging insects. Its body is very flat; its dorsal surface is mottled, greenish spotted with yellow (Fig. 118). The eggs are laid in large gelatinous capsules which are at-

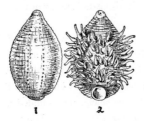

FIG. 118.—A common brook leech, *Glossiphonia complanata:* 1, dorsal; 2, with brood of young leeches attached to ventral side.

tached to the ventral surface where the young are later carried (Fig. 118).

Family *Hirudinidæ*

Members of this family live in ponds and swimming holes. Besides sucking blood they are greedily predacious upon aquatic worms, larvæ, insects, and each other. They are powerful swimmers, moving through the open water in undulating curves.

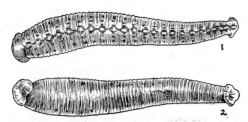

FIG. 119.—Blood-sucker, *Macrobdella decora:* 1, dorsal; 2, ventral.

Common blood-sucker, American medicinal leech, Macrobdella decora.—This and closely related species are the widely

distributed common blood-suckers of shallow water (Fig. 119).
It conceals itself under stones, lying in wait for wading animals
which may come into the pool. It attacks fishes, frogs, turtles,
cattle, and man; it also eats larvæ, worms, and great numbers
of frogs' eggs.

It is dull green or olive green, with a row of about twenty red
spots through the middle of the back and a row of black spots
near each side; the lower surface is reddish orange. This leech
is usually about half an inch wide and so flattened that the
edges of its body are sharp, not rounded as they are in the
horse-leech, *Hæmopis* (Fig. 120). Length, 3–6 inches.

FIG. 120.—Horse-leech, *Hæmopis marmoratis:* 1,
dorsal; 2, ventral.

Horse-leech Hæmopis marmoratis.—The horse-leech (Fig.
120) lives in the mud by the sides of pools, ditches, and
streams, feeding on aquatic worms and mollusks; whenever it
has a chance it will suck blood from the legs of wading animals. Much larger related species occur in the lakes and ponds
of the northern states; other species burrow in the mud.

Its body is smooth and very soft; the ground color is generally some shade of olive green, blotched with irregular spots of
lighter grays and darker browns and black. Length, 4 inches.

Family *Herpobdellidæ*

Several genera and species of these worm leeches abound in
ponds and streams under stones and among plants where they

feed chiefly on worms, insect larvæ, and decayed matter, but also suck blood.

FIG. 121.—The best known worm leech, *Herpobdella punctata:* 1, dorsal; 2, ventral.

Herpobdella punctata.—This is the largest and best known member of the family, others in the group have similar characteristics (Fig. 121). The adults are 1 to 4 inches long and vary in color from a light chocolate brown to a pure coal black. They are widely distributed, common in New England, in small glacial ponds near Woods Hole and in the Charles River.

CHAPTER XIII

CRUSTACEANS

Crustacea

Crustaceans include the lobsters, crabs, and shrimps which are well known to every one in one way or another. But for each of these familiar ones there are thousands that are entirely unknown to most persons. They belong to the *Arthropoda*, the phylum of animals which also includes myriapods, insects, and the spiders and mites. Many of these are land animals; such are the millipeds and centipeds, the spiders, and nearly all of the adult insects. But crustaceans have remained predominantly aquatic, and their habits and shapes are interlocked with the necessities of water life. Fresh water contains only a small part of them; the majority live in the sea.

Form and habits of crustaceans in general.—With their many differences all crustaceans still have a similar pattern of body. They have an outer shell or exoskeleton, which may be thick and limy as in crayfishes or delicately transparent as in *Daphnia* (p. 164) and many other smaller crustaceans. This is the hardened secretion of skin cells, and is molted and renewed as the animal grows, or as it changes from its young to adult form.

Crustaceans seldom have anything like a neck region, and in most of them the head is so fused to the thorax that it cannot be moved at all. Like all other arthropods they have jointed bodies and jointed appendages, antennæ, legs and even mouth parts being segmented. In the larger forms like the crayfishes the body segments show most clearly on the abdo-men (Fig. 122).

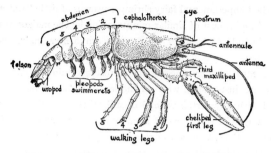

FIG. 122.—Diagram of the crayfish, a higher crustacean.

The jointed appendages are the most diversified and yet the most characteristic structures of crustaceans, big or little. Legs, swimmerets, and mouth parts are all built on a ground plan so uniform that they can be compared part with part, yet they have the most varied functions—feeling, eating, walking, swimming, and reproduction. Their shapes tell how their owners live, what the crayfish eats, and how the fairy shrimp swims. They are good examples of the zoological saying that the outside of an animal tells where it has been.

Nearly all crustaceans breathe by means of gills; in crayfishes these are attached on each side of the thorax, protected by the carapace, the shell covering the head and thorax, where water continually flows over and between them (Fig. 122); in fairy shrimps they are on the ventral side of the body (Fig. 123).

The male and female organs are in different individuals and the young develop from fertilized eggs, but in many forms, like the common little *Cyclops* (p. 166), there are periods and seasons when the young are produced parthenogenetically, from eggs which have never been fertilized by male cells.

Two main groups of crustaceans.—There are two main

groups of crustaceans; very small ones, the *Entomostraca*, and the large ones, the *Malacostraca*. Among the entomostracans are the temperamental fairy shrimps, swarms of little "water-fleas," and a host of similar minute animals; the malacostracans include such larger ones as the crayfishes, scuds, and sow-bugs.

A great host of crustaceans are microscopic animals. Many more are just visible with a hand-lens but cannot be recognized with any certainty; and in still others, like the water-flea, *Daphnia*, their general identity can be made out pretty clearly. Except in considering their general importance in water life this book does not attempt to deal with things which are too small to be seen with the naked eye or through a pocket-lens. The great group of minute crustaceans can be given only slight consideration, and the largest and commonest have been chosen in the hope that these may at least usually be the ones which are found. Habits, food, and associates of crustaceans will be mentioned under separate groups, only the most important of which are here named.

Identification.—Key to orders of crustaceans described here, modified from Pratt (see Bibliography, p. 407).

Subclasses of *Crustacea*

Small, often minute crustaceans without abdominal appendages.   1. *Entomostraca* (p. 161).

Larger crustaceans usually with abdominal appendages.   2. *Malacostraca* (p. 168).

1. Orders of *Entomostraca*

Thoracic appendages flattened and leaflike. *Phyllopoda* (p. 161), suborders *Branchiopoda* (p. 161) and *Cladocera* (p. 164).

Animals minute; body elongate and segmented with cylindrical thoracic appendages.   *Copepoda* (p. 166).

CRUSTACEANS

Animals minute, entirely enclosed in bivalve shells.

Ostracoda (p. 168).

2. Orders of *Malacostraca*

Carapace absent, body flattened laterally, very often jumping animals. *Amphipoda* (p. 169).
Carapace absent (Fig. 131), body flattened dorsoventrally.

Isopoda (p. 171).
Carapace present (Fig. 133), covering the entire thorax.

Decapoda (p. 172).

Subclass *Entomostraca*

Fairy Shrimps, Water-fleas, Copepods, Ostracods

These are small, often minute crustaceans which have no
appendages on the abdomen. The three most important orders
of fresh water entomostracans are the phyllopods, copepods,
and ostracods.

Phyllopods—*Phyllopoda*

The Order *Phyllopoda* includes the Suborder *Branchiopoda*,
the fairy shrimps (p. 163), which are an inch or more long, and
the Suborder *Cladocera*, the water-fleas (p. 164), which are
minute.

Fairy shrimps, Branchiopoda.—Fairy shrimps are about
an inch long, varicolored, red, blue, green, and bronze. They
are the largest of the entomostracans, distinguished from all
the rest by the leaflike appendages which have given them
the name *Phyllopoda* or leaf-footed ones (Fig. 123). These
"leaf-feet" are really gill-feet, combined breathing and swimming organs borne on the body segments posterior to the head,
and although they are true respiratory organs, they are remarkable in having "chewing bases" which help manipulate
the food. Fairy shrimps always swim on their backs and the
waving plumes of their gill-feet are the most conspicuous part
of them. The hind part of the body is slender and with-

out appendages but brightly colored by the blood, red with hæmoglobin as it is in fishes. Their backs are so transparent that it is often possible to see the beating of the long tubular heart.

In all species of fairy shrimps females appear to be much more abundant than males, in some kinds no males are known and the young develop from eggs which have never been fertilized by male cells. Mating fairy shrimps swim about together, the male holding the female to his ventral side with the peculiar claspers which are parts of his antennæ modified as mating organs, the most conspicuous features on the face of the male fairy shrimp (Fig. 123, 2). Just behind his gills, on the eleventh segment of the body, are the tube-like appendages by which he transfers the sperm cells to the female. In *Eubranchipus* (Fig. 123, 1) the female carries the eggs in her conspicuous brood-pouches, sometimes until the young shrimps hatch.

Habitat, season.—Fairy shrimps live in small, often temporary ponds, particularly in cold waters, and are widely distributed over the United States. They swim on their backs through the ice-cold waters of early spring pools but their coming is fraught with uncertainty. For five years they may come round like the seasons, then they may not appear at all no matter how right the conditions and in spite of the fact that earlier they have been too common to be appreciated.

While they are active and full of vitality in the spring they produce resting eggs which fall to the bottom and lie dormant in mud either wet or dried. These eggs can endure drying for long periods; some even appear to need drying before they will hatch. Eggs of fairy shrimps kept in dried mud are reported to have developed when they were put into water after a drying period of fourteen years.

Food.—Fairy shrimps live on microscopic organisms—the protozoans, floating diatoms, and other algæ—which populate the open waters of ponds. These are gathered in a sort of food-trough between the "chewing bases" of the gill-feet and passed on toward the mouth by their movements.

Associates.—Fairy shrimps have few enemies, for their season comes before most animals are active and hungry. Wood frogs and spotted salamanders are laying their eggs then in the same ponds but neither of these groups has yet come into possession of its regular appetite.

Identification.—Fairy shrimps are entomostracans with long (about 1 inch) distinctly segmented bodies, without a carapace; (Fig. 123) the thoracic appendages are flat and leaflike.

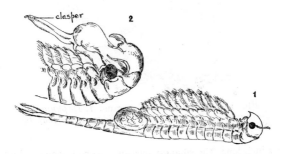

FIG. 123.—Fairy shrimp, *Eubranchipus vernalis:* 1, side view; 2, head of male showing claspers which hold the female.

A common fairy shrimp, Eubranchipus vernalis.—Like all fairy shrimps *Eubranchipus* constantly swims on its back with its eleven pairs of gill-feet waving above it. Its body is semi-transparent, stout and large, about an inch long. The large frontal appendages or claspers of the male (Fig. 123, 2) are his most conspicuous features. Females can be distinguished by the absence of claspers and by the presence of an egg-sac borne on the ventral side of the body.

This and allied species are locally abundant in pools during late winter and early spring, but live over the summer as resting eggs. Eastern North America.

Water-fleas, Cladocera.—Water-fleas are minute crustaceans which swarm through the water in amazing numbers (Fig. 124). Their short bodies are completely covered by a transparent carapace. By far the largest of them, the beautiful and fierce carnivore, *Leptodora*, is less than three-quarters

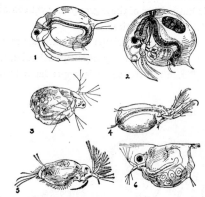

FIG. 124.—Common cladocerans: 1, *Daphnia;* 2, *Bosmina;* 3, *Simocephalus;* 4, *Sida;* 5, *Latona;* 6, *Scapholeberis.*

of an inch long; the smallest measures scarcely one one-hundredth of an inch. Several even average-sized cladocerans can be held in one trap of the bladderwort *Utricularia* (p. 102). Yet every one of them has ten legs and highly organized systems for digestion and reproduction and the like. They are beautifully transparent under a microscope, with every detail of their structure showing distinctly without any tools or preparation except a glass slide and a drop of water, and they have long been favorite animals for study. In 1669 the Dutch naturalist, Swammerdam, described the common water-flea (Fig. 124) as *Pulex aquaticus arborescens*—the water-flea with the branching arms—and "water-flea" it has remained ever since.

Cladocerans and copepods (p. 166) are the staple food of young fishes. Their importance is obviously not due to their size, but to their enormous reproductive capacity. One water-flea (*Daphnia pulex*) produces a brood of eggs every two or three days and with its descendants it is said to produce 13,000,000,000 in sixty days. Like many other entomostracans, this little water-flea has two kinds of eggs—thin-shelled eggs produced all through the summer which develop without fertilization, and thick-shelled eggs produced in autumn. These autumn eggs are regularly fertilized by male cells. Their shells are thickened and sometimes provided with air cells like the statoblasts of the bryozoan, *Pectinatella* (Fig. 107), and they are finally enclosed in a saddle-like cover, the ephippium, which forms around them.

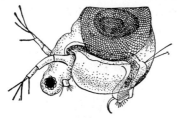

FIG. 125.—A water-flea, *Ceriodaphnia reticulata*, carrying resting egg in the ephippium.

Ceriodaphnia carries the ephippium about on her back for some time, but eventually it falls off and drops to the bottom or the animal dies. Such resting eggs will live through the winter or long droughts, and then develop into daphnids which go on with routine life again.

There is a large cladoceran population in the open water, which feeds on floating diatoms and algæ of the plankton (p. 51) and constitutes a large part of plankton society. They are abundant through the summer, at night feeding close to the surface of the water and in the daytime dropping to a little lower level. Cladocerans can easily be seen swarming near shore and thousands of them can be dipped up in one cup of water.

Copepods—*Copepoda*

There is scarcely a pond to be found without copepods. The little water-hoppers of the genus *Cyclops*, the commonest of all entomostracans, are in every pond and ditch which offers them a semblance of habitation. To the naked eye *Cyclops* is only a little white speck jerking through the water. It has a pear-shaped body tapering into a forked tail, a pair of long antennæ, outspread like antlers and helping it to skip through the water, a single eye in the middle of its head, and four pairs of swimming-feet on the thorax. If it is a female *Cyclops* the pair of egg-packets hanging from her sides will be visible as far as the animal can be seen. The copepods are very uniform in their general shape and habits and *Cyclops* is typical of them all (Fig. 126).

Fig. 126.—A water-flea, *Cyclops;* female carrying a pair of egg packets.

When they are mating the male *Cyclops* clasps the female with his antennæ and they swim about together for long periods during which enough sperm cells to fertilize several clutches of eggs are transferred to the body of the female. Like other entomostracans, they produce two kinds of eggs— summer ones which form in rapid succession and develop quickly, insuring large additions to the copepod race; and the resting eggs usually formed in seasons of cold and drought, which can lie dormant even through years of drying.

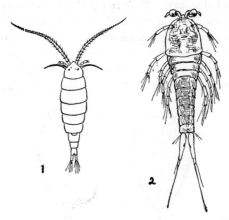

FIG. 127.—Common copepods: 1, *Diaptomus*, often found in spring-pools; 2, *Canthocamptus*.

Copepods eat as much of as many kinds of food as their small size will permit. They feed upon microscopic organisms, and they will devour any kind of decayed matter, but preferably decomposing plant tissue. Those which live among the plankton (p. 19) on the surface of open water are apt to be transparent and slender while those which live in the weeds near shore are shorter and often dark colored. Some species of *Diaptomus* (Fig. 127) are red, blue or purple. The greatest numbers of copepods are found from May to early November.

Aquarium study.—*Cyclops* is easy to keep in an aquarium and is very useful there, being a natural food for small animals such as the brown and green hydras which flourish on it (Fig. 87). The bladderwort, *Utricularia*, catches large numbers of them in its traps (p. 102).

Ostracods—*Ostracoda*

The ostracods have two-valved shells, hinged at the back like clam shells, between which their slender tails kick rapidly backward (Fig. 128). Their two shells are held together by a transverse muscle as they are in clams, essentially the same in its function as the muscles which we eat as fried scallops. The ostracods constitute another army of minute crustaceans averaging only a millimeter in length, and impossible to tell apart with a simple lens. They are mostly creeping forms

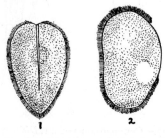

Fig. 128.—Common ostracod, *Cypris*, often found in green alga mats: 1, side, and 2, dorsal view.

which frequent the sunny protected areas of ponds, and intense light seems to quicken all their activities. They are omnivorous scavengers, especially upon decayed vegetation; few of them live in very clean water. They clamber about on submerged plants, laying their eggs upon stems and on the roots of duckweeds (*Lemna*); many live in the soft ooze of the bottom.

Subclass *Malacostraca*

Scuds, Shrimps, Crayfishes

The great majority of malacostracans live in salt water. Many of them are the jointed shell fish well known, at least, on the dinner plate—the prawns, shrimps, crabs, and lobsters. Those of the fresh water, the sow-bugs, scuds, and crayfishes, are but few compared with them. These are in general the larger fresh water crustaceans, and though some of them measure but a fraction of an inch, others are more than four inches long. Different species are very differently shaped, hardly recognizable as nearly related animals, yet the ground-plan of their bodies is strikingly similar. In *Asellus* (Fig. 131) as well as in a crayfish there are twenty body segments, joined in various ways along the back, each one bearing a pair of appendages. Five of these pairs are borne on the head, eight on the thorax, and seven on the abdomen and they function as feelers, eating tools, walking-legs, swimming paddles, and reproductive organs. The male crayfish transfers sperm cells to the female with the first pair of appendages on the abdomen; and the female carries her eggs on her swimmerets. Unlike as these appendages first appear, they prove to be strikingly similar when they are carefully compared.

Habitat.—Different orders of malacostracans live in different places and will be discussed separately. Most of them prefer small streams and quiet waters, but there are marked exceptions; they all hide away from the light, and are often quite unknown in places where they are abundant. Many of them take to underground life and all but one of the orders include species which live in caves, several being blind.

Food.—They are omnivorous, but prefer dead and decaying matter, and hence are very useful scavengers.

Enemies.—Amphipods are eaten by fishes, birds, and aquatic insects. The "Caledonia shrimp," *Gammarus limnæus*, is a favorite food of brook trout.

Scuds—*Amphipoda*

Amphipods are accomplished water acrobats and can climb, jump, swim, or glide with equal ease. They are shaped like fleas with arched backs and narrow bodies, with climbing legs on the thorax, and swimming and jumping appendages on the abdomen (Fig. 129).

Hyalella.—This is a very common amphipod in the ponds of all the eastern states (Fig. 129). In early spring it gathers in mats of the alga, *Spirogyra*, with another amphipod, *Gammarus* (Fig. 130), feeding on the dead filaments. Embody

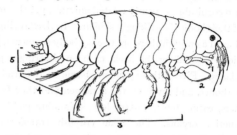

FIG. 129.—Amphipod, *Hyalella*, widely distributed through the eastern states: 1 and 2, grasping legs; 3, walking legs; 4, swimming legs; 5, jumping legs.

has seen them eating freshly killed snails, tadpoles, and crushed amphipods of their own species; and he once found a dead water-bird, the sora rail, "alive with *Hyalellas* which were feeding upon the decomposed flesh."

Hyalellas live well in aquaria so long as they are supplied with living plants—*Elodea*, *Nitella*, or *Myriophyllum*—and a few dead leaves. There, their mating and feeding habits can be watched very easily. In mating the male clasps the female with his gnathopods or grasping legs and swims about holding her beneath him for a period of several days until the female escapes by shedding her old shell, but she is usually captured again after a brief freedom. *Hyalellas* molt so slowly that the process can be easily observed especially through a hand-lens or reading glass. Females may carry their previous brood of young in their thoracic brood pouches even during the mating swim. One pair of *Hyalella knicker-bockeri* has been known to produce a clutch of about a dozen and a half eggs 15 times in 152 days.

Length of adult about one half inch.

Gammarus.—*Gammarus* (Fig. 130) and *Hyalella* (Fig. 129), two of the commonest genera of amphipods in the eastern states, have very similar habits. They can be found in ponds and streams the year round. They mate and lay eggs from

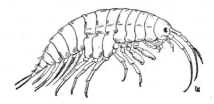

FIG. 130.—One of the commonest amphipods, *Gammarus*.

April to November, producing about 22 eggs every eleven days. Embody has reckoned that a single pair of *Gammarus fasciatus* might have 24,221 progeny in one year. This species is also easy to keep for observation in an aquarium.

Length one inch.

Isopods or Sow-bugs—*Isopoda*

These are broad backed, flattened crustaceans which live among the bottom trash of pools. They are commonly represented only by *Asellus*, which can be found in pools where there is hardly anything else living.

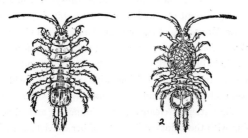

FIG. 131.—Isopod, *Asellus communis:* 1, dorsal; 2, ventral, showing egg pouch beneath the thorax.

Asellus crawl over muddy bottoms eating dead leaves and refuse in pools which appear very unpropitious for animal life, where they are often the only animals to be found in winter and very early spring. They are very light on their seven pairs of feet. From above an *Asellus* looks like a miniature armadillo, gray and heavy. Beginning in very early spring and continuing through the summer they have a new brood of young every 5 to 6 weeks and the females seem to be always carrying a brood pouch full of eggs or of young ones (Fig. 131). Length under one inch.

Crayfishes or Decapods—*Decapoda*

Except for the southern fresh water prawns, crayfishes are the only fresh water representatives of this group made widely known by the edible crabs and lobsters of the sea. Crayfishes with their five pairs of legs, the first pair armed with conspicuous nippers, look and behave like smaller editions of lobsters. They live in limy regions in quiet streams, sometimes in rivers, hiding under stones or burrowing into banksides. They lie in wait for fishes and water insects and clutch and tear them to pieces with their big pincers; they also eat all sorts of dead plant and animal matter. Some species, *Cambarus diogenes* and *limosus*, mate in the fall but do not lay their eggs till spring, but the more common crayfish, *Cambarus bartoni*, mates and spawns the year round. An interesting account of crayfish breeding habits is given in the *American Naturalist*, 1904, by E. A. Andrews, who kept them (*Cambarus limosus*) in aquaria the year round. Before laying, the female hid in a dark corner of the aquarium and assumed a peculiar tripod-like position with her body held high, propped up by her tail and outspread claws. Standing thus poised she patiently cleaned her swimmerets and abdomen, scraping with the points and combs of her other feet until the swimmerets and abdomen were as clean as if the shell had just been shed. Finally she turned over on her back, and lay

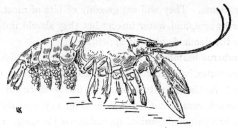

FIG. 132.—A female crayfish, showing the eggs attached to her swimmerets.

prone, while a milky glue gathering upon her abdomen was stirred and whipped up with her swimmerets (Fig. 132). Then she tipped her tail forward and her eggs gradually poured out from the openings in the bases of her third pair of walking legs on to the ventral side of her body which formed a glue-lined basket. At the same time she rolled slowly from side to side until all of the four or five hundred eggs were firmly stuck to her swimmerets (Fig. 132).

The young hatch in seven or eight weeks, usually about the middle of May, but instead of dropping off into the water each one takes firm hold of a maternal swimmeret with its nippers and rides about on it for six or seven days.

Aquarium study.—Crayfish can be kept for long periods in aquaria properly supplied with a little mud and plenty of

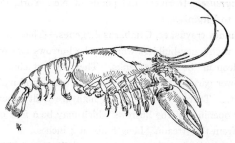

FIG. 133.—Common eastern crayfish, *Cambarus bartoni*, showing the smooth shell of the carapace.

water plants. They will eat greedily of bits of meat, pieces of earthworm, and water insects but they should not be fed up to the demands of their appetites.

Cambarus bartoni.—This is the commonest crayfish in the eastern states, being found in small quiet streams from Tennessee and the Carolinas to Maine. It can be distinguished by the smooth carapace of both sexes (Fig. 133) and the hooks on the first pair of abdominal appendages of the male. Length, 3 inches.

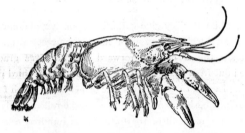

Fig. 134.—Spiny crayfish, *Cambarus limosus*, showing spines on the carapace.

Cambarus limosus (C. affinis).—The carapace is spiny in both sexes and the body is sparsely covered with hairs (Fig. 134). In the male the first pair of abdominal appendages are straight. Length about 4 inches.

Occurrence.—In rivers and ponds of New York, Pennsylvania to Virginia.

Chimney crayfishes, Cambarus diogenes.—These crayfishes are real chimney-builders which make burrows two or three feet deep in the stream banks. They dig out chambers in the lower parts of these, which fill with water and make safe retreats. Turrets several inches high are built around the upper openings of the burrows which may be a foot or more back from the stream. Length about 4 inches.

Occurrence.—Locally common especially in quiet streams, east of the Rocky Mountains to the Atlantic Coast.

CHAPTER XIV

WATER-MITES

Hydracarina

Form.—Water-mites are small, brightly colored relatives of the spiders. They have eight legs like them and at first glance their bodies seem to have the same form. However, those of water-mites are in a single piece (Fig. 135) while spiders have two distinct sections, a fused head and thorax and the abdomen. The group of *Acarina*, or mites, to which water-mites are related contains many parasites, some of them associated with such diseases as itch, mange, and spotted fever.

Most water-mites are brightly colored, dark red, scarlet, or sometimes orange (Pl. X). They are all small, rarely more than a quarter of an inch long. One of the largest of them, the bright red *Hydrachna* (Fig. 137), is about the size of a small pea. Others are only a little larger than the head of a pin.

Habits and habitat.—Although they breathe air and run about on the surface film and over the border plants they can stay under water for a long time. They live in the side waters of quiet streams and in still pools where there is water the year round. There they creep about on mud and sand bottoms and over the submerged plants and dart through the water with a peculiar sort of running glide. They are all carnivorous feeders, and like spiders clutch their prey and suck the juice from their bodies.

After mating the females lay their eggs in gluey masses on the undersides of leaves (Fig. 18), in fresh water sponges, on the gills and mantles of mussels (Fig. 261), and on the bodies of water insects, especially water striders, on which the bright red larvæ are familiar sights. Newly hatched mites have but six legs; they molt several times before they finally take on the shape of the adult.

Season.—Water-mites can be found at all seasons of the year, even under the ice in winter. Small but gaily conspicuous ones are abundant in early spring, but the greatest number appear in late summer and fall. During October and early November they can be found by dozens in beds of *Elodea*.

Aquarium study.—The largest water-mites are easily collected with a water-net or dipped up with a big nosed bottle as they hang motionless from water plants. They usually live but a short time in aquaria and will stay there only if it is enclosed by a fine wire screen. If they are to be kept for study, they should be preserved in small vials of formalin in the field (p. 41).

Identification.—Table of subfamilies of water-mites (modified from Pratt) with common representatives.

1. Large red mites with 4 eyes close together on a plate eye plate long and narrow. *Limnocharinæ* (p. 177)

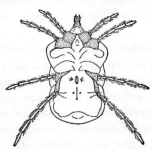

FIG. 135.—*Limnochares aquaticus*. (From Ward and Whipple.)

Limnochares aquaticus.—Body red, rectangular, about one-eighth of an inch long (Fig. 135); eyes near together on a long narrow plate. Common on the bottom of ponds where they walk over the mud and submerged plants; immature young known as larvæ attached to water skaters.

2. Eye plate short, broad and paired, eyes 4, near to-gether.   *Eylainæ* (p. 177)

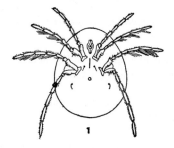

FIG. 136.—1, *Eylais extendens;* 2, eye plate. (From Ward and Whipple.)

Eylais extendens.—Body red, oval, about one-eighth of an inch long; eyes near together on a paired plate (Fig. 136). In ponds, where they glide rapidly through the water. Common.

3. Eyes not close together on a plate, but far apart, pedipalps pincer-like.   *Hydrachninæ* (p. 177)

Hydrachna geographica.—Body dark red with dark red spots on the back, oval, nearly one-third of an inch long; 4 eyes, 2 on

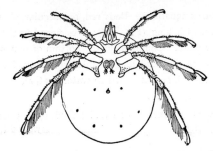

FIG. 137.—*Hydrachna geographica*. (From Ward and Whipple.)

each side, sometimes a fifth one in the middle (Fig. 137). In swamps and ponds, usually common.

4. Eyes not close together on a plate but far apart, pedipalps not pincer-like. *Hygrobatinæ*.

Several genera and species, members of which are parasitic in youth or permanently on water insects and on the gills of fresh water mussels.

CHAPTER XV

AQUATIC INSECTS

Insecta

Water insects and water plants have several points in common. Both groups are very limited when compared with the number of their terrestrial relatives and neither of them to any extent inhabits deep water nor lives far from shore. In most aquatic seed plants pollination occurs above the water; most aquatic insects mate in the air or upon the surface of the water. Aquatic insects live in the water mainly during their immature stages and even these show many marks of terrestrial origin. In aquatic insects, virtually all the adults breathe air and many of them fly away from the water, returning only to lay their eggs.

The insects commonly known as aquatic are the stoneflies or *Plecoptera;* the mayflies or *Ephemerida;* the dragonflies and damselflies or *Odonata;* the water-bugs or *Hemiptera;* the net-winged insects or *Neuroptera;* the caddis flies or *Trichoptera;* the moths or *Lepidoptera;* the beetles or *Coleoptera;* and the flies or *Diptera.* In addition to these there are the springtails, *Collembola,* which gather about the pond-margins, springing up from the surface film, and a few species of very small wasplike forms belonging to the order *Hymenoptera,* not included in this book. All of these aquatic forms have the typical insect structure and during their growth and life history they go through the same changes of form as their nearest land relatives.

The outside of an insect.—The skeleton of an insect entirely covers the outside of its body. It is chitinous or horny, thin and flexible at the joints, and even thinner over the tips of the

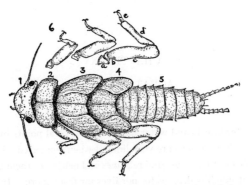

Fig. 138.—Diagram of stonefly nymph with legs of one side removed to show their segments: 1, head with simple and compound eyes; 2, prothorax; 3, mesothorax; and 4, metathorax with developing wingpads; 5, abdomen; 6, legs removed (*a*, coxa; *b*, trochanter; *c*, femur; *d*, tibia; *e*, tarsi and claws).

palpi and the antennæ or "feelers." It is made of the hardened fluid secretion of the skin cells beneath it and is molted or cast off at intervals, a new one being formed beneath it. Every hair and spine and claw is a part of it and is molted with it.

All insects are built upon the same plan. This plan can be easily traced in the stonefly already selected to show a simple type of insect structure (Needham, Bibliography, p. 416). The body of an insect is divided into three main parts, head, thorax, and abdomen (Fig. 138).

On the head are the simple and the compound eyes, the antennæ, and the mouth parts. The simple eyes are small and inconspicuous and it is only the compound eyes which are usually seen. Antennæ vary greatly in length even in different stages in the growth of the same insect, as in the nymph and adult stonefly (Fig. 144). The mouth parts are a labrum or upper lip, labium or lower lip, and two pairs of jaws, the mandibles and maxillæ, which open and close sidewise. In the stonefly nymph the labrum is a simple flap hanging forward over the upper jaws (Fig. 139).

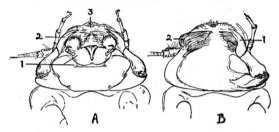

FIG. 139.—Mouth-parts of a stonefly nymph seen from beneath: A.—With labium (1) in place; 2, maxilla; 3, labrum. B.—With labium removed; 1, maxilla; 2, mandible.

The labium folds upward and covers the maxillæ or lower jaws; it is partly slit through the middle and bears a three-jointed feeler-like palp upon each side. The upper jaws or mandibles are single pieces of chitin, saw-toothed at the tips for biting and chewing. The maxillæ are also used in chewing but are more delicate and each is made up of several parts including a five-jointed palp. Insects test their food with their palps before they take it into their mouths, the hypopharynx or tongue being strongly coated with chitin and of little use as a sense organ.

Three pairs of legs on the thorax distinguish insects from all other arthropods, spiders and their kin and the crustaceans; one or two pairs of wings are also borne there. The thorax is divided into three parts, prothorax, mesothorax, and meta-thorax, on each of which is one pair of legs. The first pair of wings is on the mesothorax and the second pair on the metathorax. Developing wings or wing-pads of the stone-fly nymph can be seen on its thorax (Fig. 139). These are conspicuous on full-grown nymphs of dragonflies, damsel-flies and mayflies and usually look thick, often black, for a few days before the adults emerge (Pl. XV).

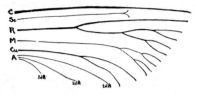

FIG. 140.—Diagram of the principal veins of an insect wing, showing their types of branching, cross-veins omitted: C, costa; Sc, sub-costa; R, radius; M, media; Cu, cubitus; A, anal. (After Needham.)

When the stonefly finally emerges from its nymphal skin it pulls the fully developed wings from the wing-pads and unfolds them to the air. They are thin membranous sails supported by rods of chitin, the veins. Toward the front edge of the wing the veins are stronger and set more closely together than they are further back. This strengthens the

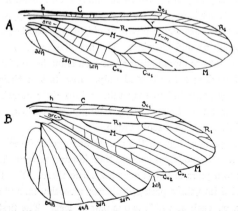

FIG. 141.—Front (A) and hind (B) wings of the stonefly, *Perla capitata*. The principal veins are marked by capitals; cross-veins, by small letters. (After Needham.)

edge which cuts the air during flight. There may be many small cross veins in the wings as there are in mayflies and their branching is often very complicated but the ground plan is simple (Fig. 140). There are five veins—costa (C), subcosta (Sc), radius (R), media (M), and cubitus (Cu), that strengthen the front and middle section, and three anal (A) veins stiffening the hindpart of it. Cross veins connect these main veins and their branches (Fig. 141).

An insect's legs are all built on the same plan. Beginning where it is attached to the body the leg has two short segments, the coxa and trochanter, followed by two long ones, the femur and tibia, which make the greater part of the length of the leg, and finally there are several (1–5) small segments which form the tarsus or foot, usually tipped by one or more claws (Fig. 138).

The insect abdomen is divided into segments, there being ten in the stonefly; it never bears any true legs though it may have short fleshy props or prolegs like those on caterpillars and the larvæ of midges (Fig. 228). Stoneflies and many other insects have tails or cerci which are many-jointed like antennæ; in adult mayflies these are a couple of times the length of the body and seem to help steer during flight (p. 205).

The inside of an insect.—The food tube or alimentary canal runs from one end of the body to the other; it includes a crop and a gizzard whose functions are similar to those of birds and behind which open the Malpighian tubules, the kidney-like organs of the insect (Pl. VIII). Beneath this tube is the nerve chain and above it is the long tubular heart whose pulsations can sometimes be seen along the midline of the backs of newly molted mayfly nymphs.

Insects do not breathe through their mouths as is so often supposed. All through their bodies there runs an intricate network of air tubes or tracheæ which carry air. In adult insects like the dragonfly the tracheæ open by spiracles along the sides of the body; in whirligig beetles their openings are

Pl. VIII.—Insect structures: 1, gill of mayfly, *Siphlurus*, showing the branching air-tubes; 2, underside of water penny showing its white, fringed gills; 3, subimago mayfly (*a*, œsophagus; *b*, gas-filled stomach; *c*, ovary; *d*, intestine; *e*, Malpighian tubules); 4, subimago mayfly with alimentary canal removed (*a*, muscles; *b*, nerve chain; *c*, ovary).

Photo. by A. H. Morgan

PLATE VIII

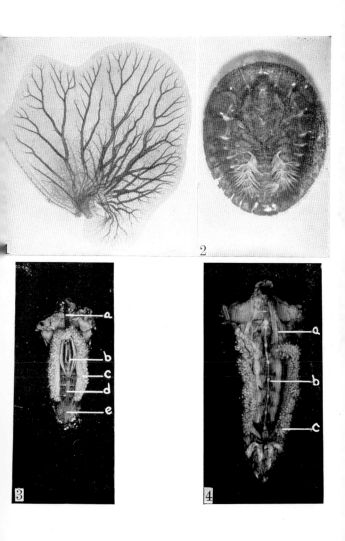

2

3
a
b
c
d
e

4
a
b
c

in chambers kept dry by the wings. Many aquatic nymphs, stoneflies, mayflies and others have no spiracles but the tracheæ branch out into delicate sac-like out-growths of the body-wall, forming the tracheal gills (Pl. VIII). These tracheal gills are so thin that oxygen can pass through their walls into the tracheæ and thence into the body. Many mayfly nymphs have leaflike gills in which the tracery of the tracheæ is clearly visible through a hand-lens, sometimes even to the naked eye (Pl. XV).

FIG. 142.—Gills of mayfly nymph, *Chirotenetes*, those of the right side turned with their under surfaces upward.

In dragonfly larvæ the lining of the hind intestine is infolded in delicate frills and flutings traversed with tracheæ, thus forming tracheal gills. These hang into the cavity of the intestine (rectal chamber) and the nymphs breathe by alternately taking water into it and forcing it out again (Pl. IX).

How insects grow.—The eggs of water insects have shells which are often beautifully sculptured and provided with safety devices. On the eggs of one mayfly, *Tricorythus* (Fig. 143), are threads by which they are suspended from plants out of the mud and where they secure abundant oxygen. On those of another, *Ephemerella rotunda*, there are floats which buoy them up out of the mud (Fig. 143.)

Mayfly nymphs and others go through only partial change of form as they increase in size. They shed their inelastic outside skeleton or skin soon after hatching and at intervals through their nymphal lives. After each molt the nymph grows for a period then sheds its skin again, and in mayflies this may go on for twenty times or more. When it molts for the last time in the water it comes forth with a shape

Pl. IX.—1. Wing-pad of mayfly nymph; dark lines are the tracheæ; soft gray lines represent the developing veins. 2. Air-tubes or tracheæ of a dragonfly nymph in dorsal view; the alimentary canal lies between the two large tracheæ but is hidden by masses of fat: *a*, large trachea (connected with spiracles in adult); *b*, fat; *c*, tracheæ in wall of intestine.

PLATE IX

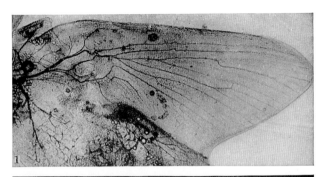

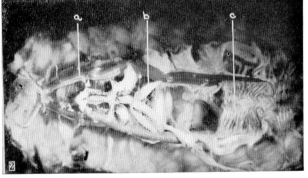

changed notably in those structures which have to do with reproduction. It has transformed from a nymph to a mature adult. After this (except in mayflies) it does not grow larger

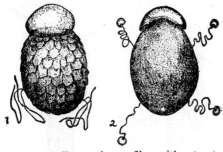

FIG. 143.—Eggs of mayflies with structures, threads and floats, by which they are suspended in the water: 1, *Tricorythus*; 2, *Ephemerella rotunda*.

or ever shed its skin again. In mayflies there is a second molt after the winged form has been attained, a change from the nearly adult sub-imago to the fully matured imago (Pl. XI) but this is an exception among all insects. The changes of form which the mayfly or stonefly undergoes during its life are known as incomplete metamorphosis (Fig. 144).

The change of form between the young insect and the adult may be far greater than this. A caterpillar hatches out of a moth egg; it shows no hint of wings, has a wormlike shape, a great appetite, and is known as a larva. After a period of eating and growing, it loses its appetite, stops moving about, moves into a secluded spot, and finally sheds its larval skin. This discloses a very differently shaped insect with wings and antennæ outlined on its skin which suggest the adult moth. The moth is now in the pupal stage during which it is made over, inside and outside. At the end of the pupal stage the fully formed adult moth comes forth from the pupal skin. The changes which it has gone through are called complete metamorphosis (Fig. 145). Incomplete and complete metamorphosis both occur in aquatic insects.

Incomplete metamorphosis.—Stages of the insect life—egg, nymph, and adult.

Stoneflies, mayflies, dragonflies and damselflies, water-bugs.

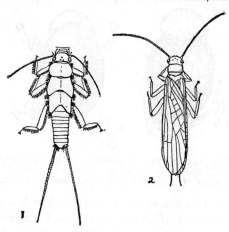

Fig. 144.—Change of form in incomplete metamorphosis: 1, stonefly nymph; 2, adult.

Complete metamorphosis.—Stages of the insect life—egg, larva, pupa, and adult.

Caddis flies, moths, beetles, flies.

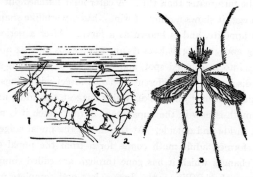

Fig. 145.—Change of form in complete metamorphosis: 1, mosquito larva; 2, pupa; 3, adult.

KEY TO THE ORDERS OF IMMATURE AQUATIC
INSECTS. NYMPHS AND LARVÆ. (AFTER
NEEDHAM)

(*Collembola* and *Hymenoptera* not included.)

1—Larvæ with wings developing externally (nymphs) and
no quiescent pupal stage.   2
—Larvæ proper, with wings developing internally, and
invisible till the assumption of a quiescent pupal
stage; form more wormlike.   5

2—With biting mouth parts.   3
—Mouth parts combined into a jointed sucking beak,
which is directed beneath the head backward beneath
the forelegs.   Water-bugs, p. 225.   *Hemiptera*

3—With long slender tails; labium not longer than the head,
and not folded on itself like a hinge.   4
—Tails represented by 3 broad, leaflike respiratory plates
traversed by tracheæ, or by small spinous appendages;
labium when extended much longer than the head; at
rest folded like a hinge, extending between the bases
of the forelegs.

     Damselflies and dragonflies, p. 213.   *Odonata*

4—Gills mainly under the thorax; tarsal claws two; tails
two.   Stoneflies, p. 193.   *Plecoptera*
—Gills mainly on the sides of the abdomen; tarsal
claws single; tails generally three.

     Mayflies, p. 198.   *Ephemerida*

5—With jointed thoracic legs.   6
—Without jointed thoracic legs; with abdominal prolegs,
or entirely legless.   Flies, p. 282.   *Diptera*

5—With slender, decurved, piercing mouth parts, half as
long as the body; small larvæ, living on fresh water
sponges.
     Families *Hemerobiidæ, Sisyridæ*, p. 245.   *Neuroptera*
—With biting mouth parts.   7

7—With a pair of prolegs on the last segment only (except
in *Sialis*, p. 241, which has a single long median tail-
like process at the end of the abdomen); these directed

backward, and armed each with one or two strong
hooks or claws.   8

—Prolegs, when present, on more than one abdominal
segment; if present on the last segment, then not
armed with single or double claws (except in gyrinid
beetle larvæ, which have paired lateral abdominal filaments), often entirely wanting.   9

8—Abdominal segments each with a pair of long, lateral
filaments.   Family *Sialidæ*, p. 241. *Neuroptera*

—Abdominal segments without long, muscular, lateral
filaments, often with minute gill filaments; cylindrical
larvæ, generally living in portable cases.

Caddis flies, p. 247. *Trichoptera*

9—With five pairs of prolegs, and no spiracles at the apex
of the abdomen.   Moths, p. 257. *Lepidoptera*

—Generally without prolegs; never with five pairs of them;
usually with terminal spiracles; long, lateral filaments
sometimes present on the abdominal segments.

Beetles, p. 261. *Coleoptera*

Springtails—*Collembola*

Wherever the shorelines make little bays of quiet water,
springtails gather in blackish patches on the surface film.
Thousands of them congregate there and if they are disturbed
the company will go up into the air like flying spray, coming
down again a foot or two away. They are so minute, that
they can jump upward like this and come down with all their
force without making more than a dent on the surface film.
Like water striders, though they live on the water surface,
they are thoroughly aerial insects.

All *Collembola* are minute and none of them has wings.
Many species dwell in damp, shady places on land; one of the
most familiar, the snow-flea, *Achorutes socialis*, appears on the
snow. Although springtails have six orthodox walking legs,
their unique locomotor apparatus is on the hind end of their
bodies. On the fourth abdominal segment there is a forked

tail-piece which the springtail can fold beneath its body and lock into two little appendages on the under side of the third abdominal segment (Fig. 146). When it forces its tail-piece suddenly downward, the springtail is lifted high in the air as a kangaroo might be if it sat on its tail and snapped it hard against the ground.

FIG. 146.—Water springtail, *Podura aquatica.*

Water springtail, Podura aquatica.—This common spring-tail of slow streams and pools is dull bluish black and although only one-fifth to one-fourth of an inch long the segments of its body show very distinctly through a simple lens (Fig. 146). These springtails are exceedingly gregarious and gather in enormous numbers, making a blue-black band along the margin of the water. The body surface is difficult to wet because of the hairs which hold a blanket of air around it. Springtails probably go to the bottom and hibernate there through the winter since they are among the earliest spring arrivals at the surface. They are said to live upon plant tissues, but their food habits need more study. In Miall's "Aquatic Insects" there is a quotation from an account by the entomologist De Geer, published in 1778. De Geer kept springtails for a long time in a dish of water and found that they crawled down to the bottom and lived there several days at a time. It has been suggested that springtails may climb down into the water and forage upon submerged plants.

Occurrence.—In still water, along the margins of ponds and streams. Common and generally distributed through eastern and central North America. Commonest October–November.

Pl. X.—Summer life in the quiet shallows: 1, broad-leaved arrowhead; 2, white water lily; 3, *Elodea;* 4, *Myriophyllum;* 5, 6, 7, dragonfly, *Libellula pulchella* (5, nymph; 6, cast skin of nymph; 7, adult); 8, 9, diving beetle, *Dytiscus* (8, larva; 9, adult); 10, adult backswimmer, *Notonecta;* 11, leaf-beetle, *Donacia;* and 12, holes through which *Donacia* lays her eggs; 13, whirligig beetle; 14, caddis worm, *Triænodes;* 15, water-mite; 16, fresh water sponge green with algæ; 17, nymph of mayfly, *Callibætis.*

PLATE X

Stoneflies—*Plecoptera*

Nymphs.—Stonefly nymphs hatch out in the water and live
there for a year or more before they shed their last nymphal
skins and take to the air. Fullgrown nymphs may be less
than half an inch long like the little black *Allocapnias* (*Capnias*) (Fig. 153) or they may even measure 2 inches like
Pteronarcys (Fig. 147). They have flattened bodies, two
segmented filamentous tails (cerci), and tufts of thread-like

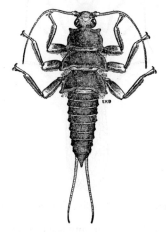

FIG. 147.—Nymph of the large stonefly, *Pteronarcys dorsata;* the thoracic gills and the paired
claws are characteristic of stoneflies.

gills. These gills are mainly on the thorax (Fig. 147), at the
bases of the legs, and sometimes on the neck, but they also
occur on the sides and tip of the abdomen. [A few small
species do not have any gills. Stonefly gills are always on
the underparts of the body, never on the back or sides as
they are in mayflies (Fig. 158). All stoneflies have two claws
on each foot; mayflies have but one claw.

Adults.—Like the fullgrown nymphs the adults vary from
one-half to two inches in length. Like the nymphs, too, they

have biting mouth parts and are dull-colored—dark brown, yellow, or pale green. Similarly they are squarely built but their tail filaments are very much shorter than those of the nymph. They hold their two pairs of wings closely to the body with the wide hind ones plaited and hidden beneath the front ones (Fig. 148). They do not fly about very much.

FIG. 148.—Adult stonefly, *Pteronarcys dorsata*.

Many species skulk about in any shady place which is near the water but in contrast to these shade-loving species are the little black *Allocapnias* (*Capnias*) and *Capnellas* which run over the dazzling sunlit snow from January to March.

Little is known of the egg-laying habits of stoneflies. When in captivity, *Perla immarginata* deposits her eggs loose in the water. This is probably true of many species since their eggs are not found in patches on stones and sticks as are those of caddis flies and some other water insects. Most adults live only a short time and probably eat little or nothing

Habits.—With few exceptions stonefly nymphs live in swift water, swirling brooks and waterfalls (Fig. 23). They clamber over the stones, keeping hold by their strong claws, always seeking the dark side of everything. They have a sidling gait and when the stones on which they live are overturned and exposed to the light they scatter like rats and drop off the edges into the water.

The adults hide on the under surfaces of the leaves of trees, falling to the ground if the tree is shaken. Dr. J. G. Needham writes that he "once found the stout-bodied *Acroneuria pacifica*, clinging in numbers to young pine-trees on the steep slopes of the Yellowstone Canyon, and obtained specimens very easily by shaking the trees, dashing the stoneflies to the ground, and picking them up before they had run to cover."

During their nymphal life of a year or more many species live on vegetable matter but a few such as *Perla* will devour other insects or even turn cannibal.

Associates.—Stonefly nymphs are commonly found on the same stones with mayflies, the net-building caddis worm, *Hydropsyche*, and water pennies (Fig. 23).

Aquarium study.—Stonefly nymphs cannot be kept alive more than a few hours, and usually not so long as that, without running water. They are dependent on rapid currents and as soon as they are put in pans of still water they begin to buck and pump their bodies up and down, thus creating a circulation over their gills.

Family Pteronarcidæ.—These are the largest known stone-flies (Fig. 148). They are vegetable feeders which are found emerging from streams during May and June. They are common in creeks and small rivers where they live among the decayed leaves brought together by the currents. Eastern states to Tennessee, west to Minnesota and Alaska.

Family Perlidæ.—This family includes many of the most familiar stoneflies. All of the genus *Perla* have a tuft of fine filamentous gills about the base of each leg (Fig. 149). Common in swift streams, the adults emerging through early spring. Length of nymph, one inch. Eastern states to Georgia.

FIG. 149.—Nymph of *Perla*, an early spring stone-fly.

Chloroperla or Alloperla.—Daintily beautiful, pale greenish nymphs about a quarter of an inch long, which have no gills (Fig. 150). The adults which emerge through late spring into midsummer are daylight fliers which like sunshine. Generally distributed through North America.

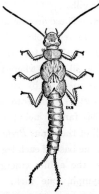

FIG. 150.—Nymph of green stonefly, *Chloroperla*.

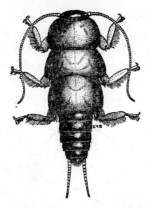

FIG. 151.—Nymph of *Peltoperla;* its gills are hidden beneath the flaring thorax.

Peltoperla.—In *Peltoperla* the clusters of thoracic gills are entirely concealed under the flaring margins of the thoracic segments (Fig. 151). Fullgrown nymphs are one half inch long. The genus is generally distributed over North America. Emerging in May–June.

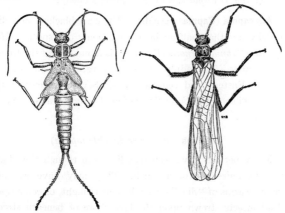

FIG. 152.—Nymph and adult of *Tæniopteryx nivalis,* a winter stonefly.

Tæniopteryx nivalis.—Both the nymphs and adults are slender, black or blackish-brown and the nymphs have no gills (Fig. 152). These are winter stoneflies (Pl. I), the adults first emerging from the water and crawling over the snow in February, but they are also commonly found through May. Length one-half inch. Eastern and central states south to North Carolina.

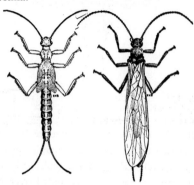

Fig. 153.—Nymph and adult of *Allocapnia* (*Capnia*) *vernalis*, an early spring stonefly.

Allocapnia (Capnia) vernalis.—These are blackish stoneflies usually less than half an inch long. Only one species, *Allocapnia* (*Capnia*) *vernalis* (Fig. 153), is found east of the Rocky Mountains. The adults usually emerge from January to April. Eastern and central states. Several species of the very similar genus *Capnella* are found in northeastern North America.

Mayflies—*Ephemerida* (*Plectoptera*)

Many persons have seen mayflies even though they have not recognized them as such. They may have watched great swarms of "flies" over a lake at twilight, or come upon dead insects strewn upon the lake shore or beneath street-lights, or have fished with the artificial bait-flies, many of which are modeled after mayflies.

Nymphs.—Mayfly nymphs are of many shapes and sizes; some have flattened heads and bodies and their sprawling legs are held akimbo as in *Heptagenia*. Active runners, like *Callibætis*, are set high on spindling legs, while the little creeper, *Leptophlebia*, almost drags its low slung body. But all mayfly nymphs agree in having seven pairs of gills on the abdomen, and with rare exceptions have no gills anywhere else. They have two or three long slender tail filaments, or setæ, and but a single claw on each foot. Stonefly nymphs, sometimes confused with mayflies, have two claws on each foot and nearly all their gills are on the thorax. Their differently shaped bodies reveal much about the places where they live and their way of getting a living. Many are well fitted for particular habitats but are helpless when they are out of them. *Epeorus* (Pl. XV) is so flat and its gills and claws such efficient hold-fasts that it can cling to a rock no matter how strong the current, yet it is quite helpless among slender plant stems where *Callibætis* is thoroughly at home (Fig. 158).

Adults.—Mayflies spend nearly all of their lives as nymphs in the water. During this time they eat a great deal and in a few weeks, or in the case of some species, in a year or more, they emerge into the air as subimagos or "duns" with pale gray wings (Pl. XI, 1). Subimagos soon shed their skins again and become fully matured imagos or "spinners" (Pl. XI, 2). As winged insects their lives last only a few hours or days at most, during which they do not eat at all. For a long time the fishermen have called them "duns" and "spinners." Fishermen of England have given them other picture names, like "the silver gray," "the evening spinner." Many of these fishermen have made their own "dry flies," wrought of silk and fur and feathers like those described in that most charming of guides, Ronald's "Fly-Fisher's Entomology."

Adult mayflies are delicately beautiful insects, soft gray,

Pl. XI.—Adult mayflies: 1, First winged stage (subimago) of *Callibætis;* it has just shed its nymphal skin and is resting on the surface film of water. 2, Second winged stage (imago) of *Blasturus;* it has shed its subimago skin which shows the dark wing-sacs.

PLATE XI

and brown, or pale and translucent, fragile and short-lived, as their name, *Ephemerida*, implies. They have large front wings and small hind ones except in some very small species such as *Cænis* in which hind wings are altogether absent. The adults have either two or three tail filaments, which are much longer than those of the corresponding nymphs. Their mouth parts are shrunken and useless; so that in the mayfly countenance the whole mouth region is like a receding chin. Their legs are weak and little used for walking; the front legs of the males are long and often held forward with a reception-line cordiality. Dr. J. G. Needham has aptly named one mayfly the "white-gloved howdy" (Fig. 159).

As soon as they emerge from the water the subimagos fly upward to overhanging trees or shrubbery. They molt but move about little until the mating flight which in some species occurs almost immediately, in others within a day or two.

The mating flight usually takes place in late afternoon or twilight. Then hundreds of spinners, mostly males, swing up and down through the air in a rhythmic dancing flight over streams or lakes. With their rudder-like tails stiffly extended they drop downward in swift descents of thirty feet and more and then bound upward with the lightness of springing thistledown. Hundreds or even thousands of them move up and down together. In half an hour they have disappeared into the trees as suddenly as they came, or they are strewn upon the water to become the food of eager fishes. During this flight a dozen or so from the hundreds of males mate with the few females which almost immediately lay their eggs in the water and then die upon its surface.

The little mayflies of the genus *Bætis* fly in a low compact mating swarm and the female literally climbs down into the water to lay her eggs (Pl. XII). The following description is taken from my notes on her habits.

Flying close to the surface of the water, the insect alighted on a stone projecting slightly from the water and well pro-

Pl. XII.—Eggs of mayfly, *Bætis:* 1, stone covered with egg-patches; 2, egg-patches enlarged showing straight edges where the mayfly stopped laying.   Egg patches, one quarter inch long.

PLATE XII

1

2

tected from the force of the current on its downstream side.
She at once walked to the protected side and downward to
the water. First, wrapping her wings about her abdomen,
she made several attempts to immerse her head and thorax.
This appears to be the critical stage in the performance, and
many mayflies are washed away while attempting it. Once
under the water she started on a tour of inspection. This
lasted for several minutes during which she continually
walked to and fro, pausing, feeling the stone with the tip of
her abdomen, and passing on unsatisfied. When she finally
found a suitable place she braced her legs firmly, bending the
end of her abdomen downward and her tail filaments upward.
She then began swinging her whole abdomen from side to
side with a slow pendulum-like motion, at each stroke leaving
an irregular row of minute white eggs adhering to the surface,
the first ones circular and somewhat longer than those which
came later. As the egg mass grew larger she moved forward
a little to allow the eggs to lie in succeeding rows. When her
supply was exhausted she jerked her abdomen upward and
abruptly clambered out of the water.

Habitat and season.—Mayfly nymphs live in clean fresh
waters, flowing rivulets or rivers, tumbling waterfalls or quiet
pools; they have become adapted to every aquatic situation
except foul water (Pl. III). In many ponds they far out-
number all other animals anywhere near their equal in size.

Spring is the mayfly season and the fullgrown nymphs with
their black wing-pads are abundant from March to late June
and adults are emerging and swarming at this time. Young
nymphs can be found in shallow brooks the year around.

Food.—These nymphs are confirmed vegetarians; their
staple food is the great crop of diatoms and desmids which
makes the golden-green color upon stones of the brook bottom
and covers almost every object in the water (Pl. IV). Besides this they eat the soft tissues of larger plants either living
or dead.

Associates.—Mayfly nymphs live upon food which is so abundant that the snails and entomostracans and the few herbivorous insects which share it with them in no way menace their supply. Mayfly populations are not kept in check by lack of food but by the animals which prey upon them, these being almost every carnivorous inhabitant of the water, including dragonfly nymphs, water beetles, and young fishes in enormous numbers. Mayflies are the most important food of these young fishes and if some method of breeding them in captivity could be discovered it would do much to solve the food problems of fish hatcheries.

Aquarium study and collecting.—Nymphs of quiet waters are easily kept in aquaria supplied with algæ and water plants. If they are fullgrown they will shed their skins and usually fly up to the nearest window-pane (Fig. 35). Either within doors or in the streams, nymphs can be kept in cages till they emerge as winged mayflies. These life history cages are elsewhere described.

Identification.—Mayflies are divided into three subfamilies which may be described, according to the nymphal habits of their members, as the *Ephemerinæ* or burrowers (Pl. XIII), *Bætinæ* or clamberers and runners (Pl. XIV), and *Heptageninæ* or flattened sprawlers (Pl. XV).

Burrowers or Ephemerinæ, Hexagenia.—*Hexagenias* bur-

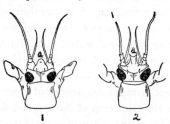

Fig. 154.—Heads of two burrowing mayflies distinguishable by the shape of the rostrum (a): 1, *Hexagenia;* 2, *Ephemera.* The nymphs are shown in Pl. XIII.

row in the muddy shallows of lakes and rivers, sometimes in the banks of upland bog-streams. They can be distinguished by the rounded, shelflike piece on the front of the head (Fig. 154). They are the largest of the mayflies, fullgrown nymphs being from one and one-half to two inches long (Pl. XIII). They eat the rich diatom ooze through which they plough their way. Sloping banks are sometimes mined by them, and the openings of the burrows with mayfly tails hanging from them can often be seen along stream margins (Pl. XIII). If such nymphs are pulled out and thrown down onto the mud they will burrow in again with the speed of ground-moles.

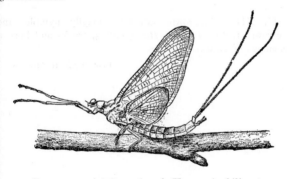

FIG. 155.—Adult male of *Hexagenia bilineata*, in its favorite position; one of the large mayflies which swarm over lakes.

These are the mayflies which fly in such great numbers beneath lights and on lake shores (Fig. 155). There are many stories and records of their abundance. According to Dr. F. H. Krecker's observations made at Cedar Point, Lake Erie, "when a brood is at its height it is a very common occurrence to find piles of the insects three or four feet square and six to eight inches deep under electric lights. At a neighboring amusement resort several carts were required each morning to haul away the dead insects."

Pl. XIII.—Fullgrown burrowing mayfly nymphs and burrows: 1, *Ephemera;* 2, *Hexagenia;* 3, tracks and burrow openings of *Hexagenia.*

Photo. by A. H. Morgan

PLATE XIII

Season: Emerging through late spring and midsummer.

Distribution: Widely distributed throughout North America.

Ephemera.—The rostrum of the nymph, the shelflike piece on the front of its head, is divided by a deep round notch into two spines (Fig. 154). The *Ephemeras* are smaller than the *Hexagenias* but very similar to them in appearance and habits (Pl. XIII).

Habitat.—They frequent smaller ponds, pools, and slow streams where *Hexagenias* are not apt to be found. Outside the large lake regions they are the commoner of the two genera and even in some large lakes this is the case.

Season.—Nymphs are emerging throughout the summer season but the maximum swarming of the adults occurs in the July twilights. Nymphs can be found at any time of the year; during a recent mild winter in New England they were collected each month from October to April. They were found in considerable numbers beneath muddy banks along with hibernating *Hemiptera* and spotted newts.

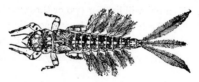

Fig. 156.—Nymph of *Potamanthus*, a mayfly which sprawls on the mud.

Potamanthus.—Nymphs of *Potamanthus* sprawl on the mud but they are not burrowers (Fig. 156). Their tusks (mandibles) are short, not extending beyond the head as they do in the burrowers, *Ephemera* and *Hexagenia* (Pl. XIII). They live in the side waters of streams, not far from the swift-water haunts of *Chirotenetes*. Length, nymph, three quarters of an inch. The conspicuous adults have broad, pure white wings, and at first glance appear more like moths than mayflies.

Occurrence.—Adults, July–August. Northern New York, Connecticut, Massachusetts.

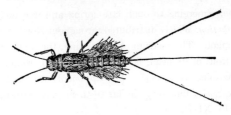

FIG. 157.—*Blasturus cupidus*, one of the commonest mayflies in early spring pools.

Family Bætinæ, Blasturus.— These are the commonest
nymphs in the ponds through March and late April. They
are chestnut brown with double leaflike gills which are similar
except for the last pair. They walk over the trash or swim
through the still water of the spring pools in which they constitute the major population. They do not try to hide from
the light and it is easy to see hundreds of them clambering
or swimming heavily about in the pools. Nymphs collected
in February are nearly fullgrown and adults begin to emerge
in March. Nymphs will live for two or three weeks in a dish
of water if kept fresh or supplied with aquatic plants; they
will shed their nymphal skins successfully and then fly to the
window-panes to rest on the glass till they cast their subimago
skins.

Occurrence.—The nymphs (Fig. 157) appear in great numbers during March to April but they soon emerge and disappear from the ponds, little ones appearing again in late fall
and winter. Length of fullgrown nymph half to three-quarters of an inch. Eastern states to North Carolina and Indiana.

Callibætis.—*Callibætis* nymphs have three tail filaments,
the outer ones being fringed on one side only (Fig. 158).

The pale green, brown-dappled *Callibætis* is one of the
daintiest of the dwellers in newly formed pools and ponds
where vegetation is plentiful and carnivores are few (Pl. X).
Unlike most mayflies it matures in less than six weeks, and
there are several generations in a summer. The nymphs will

live for several days in aquaria. If those with black wing-pads are captured they are almost sure to emerge within

FIG. 158.—Nymph of *Callibætis* among water weeds.

a few hours into subimagos whose spotted wings are margined with delicate hairs (Pl. XI, 1). Length, fullgrown nymph, half an inch.

Occurrence.—Generally distributed through North America.

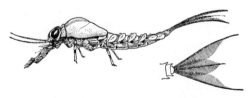

FIG. 159.—Nymph of *Chirotenetes*.

"White-gloved howdy," Chirotenetes.—The front legs of *Chirotenetes* are fringed with long hairs. In addition to its abdominal gills it has tufts of gills at the bases of its maxillæ and front legs (Fig. 159). This nymph lives in the tumbling waters of stony creeks, among which it leaps and dashes with amazing agility. There it braces itself, tail down and head up, and holds its front legs outward to catch its food from the current (Fig. 24).

Pl. XIV.—Clambering and running mayflies of Family *Bætinæ:* 1 and 2, two species of *Ephemerella* which clamber over trash in streams; 3, *Ameletus*, an active dweller in small ponds. Nymphs of *Ephemerinæ:* 4, *Tricorythus* and 5, *Cænis*, which live in bottom sand and ooze; 6, *Siphlurus*, a swift-moving dweller in small ponds.

PLATE XIV

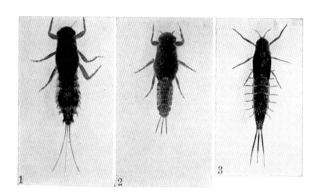

It is a rich chocolate brown color with a light median stripe extending from the mouth and running over the head onto the thorax; the front tarsi are white. *Chirotenetes* is a mayfly that has the habit, rare among mayflies, of taking a mixed diet of algæ and midge larvæ. Fullgrown nymphs are an inch long.

Occurrence.—May–July. Generally distributed through North America.

Family Heptageninæ, Heptagenia.—The *Heptageninæ* are flattened nymphs which live in rapid streams or on wave-beaten shores (Pl. XV).

In most regions the *Heptagenias* are the commonest mayflies of running water and they are by far the most generally distributed of the flattened, clinging nymphs. Their hardiness and their ability to endure changes in temperature and differences in current is probably responsible for their presence in so many varieties of streams. They avoid the light, staying on the under surfaces of the stones, and a brook which looks utterly deserted may shelter hundreds of them. They can be found all the year; in January the caddis worms, *Hydropsyche*, are with them by hundreds.

When fullgrown they migrate into quiet waters to emerge. Dr. W. A. Clemens calculated that *Heptagenias* take a year to complete their life cycle, spending all but four or five days of this time in the water. About two months after their mating and egg-laying season he began to find the small nymphs.

Occurrence.—Adults emerge through June and July.

Epeorus, Iron.—These nymphs have flattened bodies but only two tail filaments (Pl. XV). Nymphs of both these genera live in the most rapid currents, swift eddies, torrents and water-falls. The members of both groups are very beautiful insects, exceedingly delicate, susceptible to changes in temperature, and able to live only a very short time in still water.

Pl. XV.—Mayflies of the Family *Heptageninæ* which cling to the stones in running brooks: 1, *Heptagenia*, fullgrown, with black wingpads; 2, *Heptagenia*, another species. Mayfly nymphs of Family *Heptageninæ* which live in the swiftest currents: 3, *Iron*, fullgrown nymph; 4, *Epeorus*, showing its transparency just after molting. Note the white simple eyes.

PLATE XV

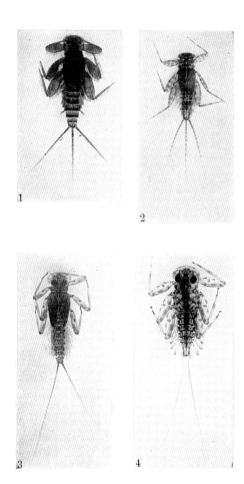

Their flattened bodies with thin, downcurved edges, their knife-blade legs, and grappling claws are all adjustments to life amid the constant pressure of moving water. Their gills are platelike and together form a suction disk which makes an efficient holdfast.

In *Iron* the first and last pairs of gills are incurved so that their tips come closely together; in *Epeorus* there is a space between these and the oval which the gills make is not complete. In *Epeorus* the body is wider, more flaring than in *Iron*.

Occurrence.—Adults emerge through May and July. Both genera are widely distributed.

Dragonflies and Damselflies—*Odonata*

Form and habits of adults.—The adults of this order are the swift-winged dragonflies or devil's darning needles which fly about the midsummer ponds on regular beats, round and round, stopping on the same reeds like watchmen at their time clocks. They are in pursuit of midges and such small insect game which they capture on the wing. The damselflies are leisurely, as they flit and loiter along the stream banks while the dragonflies cut through the air like arrows. Both groups of the *Odonata* have four wings with finely netted veins; when resting, dragonflies hold their wings straight out horizontally from the body (Fig. 162); most damselflies fold theirs close together vertically over their backs (Fig. 166). Both have strong biting mouth parts and long bodies, very slender, and often brilliantly colored in damselflies, stouter and usually more somber in dragonflies. In all of the damselflies and some of the dragonflies the female has an ovipositor with which the eggs are placed within the leaves and stems of water plants. Many dragonflies skim the surface, dipping repeatedly to drop the eggs into the water. Damselflies sometimes go below the surface of the water to find a good place for their eggs just as the little mayfly *Bætis* goes under

water to explore the stones before she lays her eggs (p. 201).
One of these, *Enallagma aspersum*, observed by W. C. Woods,
stayed under water for twenty-five minutes. She wound her
wings around the abdomen, enclosing a blanket of air about
her, then walked down the stem of a plant and explored the
stream bottom for fully two feet.

Nymphs.—Dragonfly nymphs usually require a long time to
mature; thus *Gomphus* needs more than a year. On the other
hand certain damselflies such as *Enallagma* and *Ischnura*
may produce more than one brood in a season. Both dragon-
and damselflies usually pass the winter as nymphs in the mud
bottoms or in trash caught here and there in flowing streams
and begin to emerge late in the spring, leaving their cast-
off nymphal skins clinging to stems several inches above water.
A newly emerged dragonfly is soft-bodied and weak, and for
a little while after molting it can fly only haltingly if at all.
Dragonflies and damselflies spend most of their lives in the
water as nymphs and during that time they are the dominant
insect carnivores of the ponds, preying upon any animal
smaller than themselves. Although they can lunge and dodge
with lightning quickness their gait is usually slow and they
have a "stop, look and listen" way of moving over the bottom

FIG. 160.—Dragonfly nymphs: 1, with labium in
place; 2, with labium thrust forward as when
catching prey.

and stealing up on their prey, which they seize with the extended lower lip (Fig. 160). Ordinarily this is folded back under the head; in some species it covers the face like a mask. When a nymph is capturing prey it thrusts its labium far forward (Fig. 21), ready to clutch at anything which moves and to jerk it back into its mouth and waiting jaws.

Damselfly nymphs are slender with three leaf-shaped gills extending from the hind end of the body (Fig. 167). Those of dragonflies are stout-bodied and without external gills (Fig. 162). They breathe by taking water into a chamber at the rear end of the alimentary canal whose walls are elaborately infolded and bespread with a lacework of airtubes. Water is drawn in and out of this tracheal chamber by way of the anus which is guarded by five pointed spines. In collecting-pans nymphs will often turn over on their backs and while they are thus "playing dead" with their legs bent double, they will be suddenly shot forward by the forcible expulsion of a stream of water from the tracheal chamber. Thus the chamber proves itself not only an efficient respiratory organ, concealed and out of the way, but a locomotor organ as well (Pl. IX.)

Occurrence.—Nymphs of some species of dragonflies or damselflies are almost certain to be abundant in mucky-bottomed ponds half filled with vegetation (Fig. 21). But some species of each group have settled into clear brooks and slow-moving marsh streams (Fig. 22). Adult dragon-flies and damselflies begin to emerge in late April and continue till September, but in New England active nymphs may be found in small ponds after the first of November.

Food.—These nymphs, especially the dragonflies, eat every kind of aquatic insect, beetle larvæ, midges, and small members of their own kind but they prefer mayflies, small crustaceans, and snails. Nymphs and adults as well are great enemies of mosquitoes.

Associates.—Dragonfly nymphs and young fishes are competitors for the same food, but dragonflies are themselves one of the most important foods for adult fishes—pickerel, perch, catfish, and small stream fishes (Fig. 21). An insight into the dangers which greet the nymphs from their earliest youth is given in an observation made by Dr. C. B. Wilson. "Two leaves of *Potamogeton illinoisensis*, which contained a large number of *Enallagma* eggs that were just hatching, were brought into the laboratory August 11, 1917, and placed in a small aquarium. On going over them with a hand-lens to remove the nymphs already hatched, a large brown hydra was found eating one of the tiny nymphs. It was attached to the under surface of the leaf, nearly in the center of a large cluster of *Enallagma* eggs, and could reach many of the nymphs with its tentacles as they emerged."

Aquarium study.—The nymphs of most pond dragonflies are very hardy and will live in an aquarium all winter. But they are thorough carnivores and must be supplied with small water insects or with worms like *Enchytræidæ*.

Dragonflies, Suborder Anisoptera, Family Libellulidæ, adults called skimmers.—Nymphs of this family have a mask-like labium which covers the whole front of the face up to the antennæ (Fig. 161).

FIG. 161.—Nymph of *Libellula:* face view showing the labium covering the face. (From Kellogg.)

Tenspots, Libellula.—Nymphs of *Libellula* distinguish-able by their squarish heads and flaring labia are common in vegetation-filled ponds and ditches. (Pl. X.) When fullgrown they are nearly two inches long.

Occurrence.—In New England the adults, called "ten-spots," emerge from the last of May to the middle of September (Pl. X).

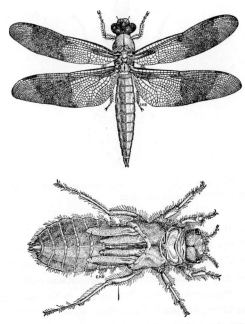

FIG. 162.—Nymph and adult of the whitetail, *Plathemis lydia.*

Whitetails, Plathemis.—The habits of these nymphs (Fig. 162) are essentially the same as those of *Libellula.* Fullgrown nymphs are about 1 inch long.

Occurrence.—Adults emerge from mid-May to late September.

Sympetrum.—These are the small, brilliant red dragonflies which fly about near ponds, alighting on low vegetation or sunning themselves in roadways (Fig. 163). Their striking colors make them well known in autumn when they are active

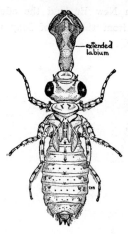

FIG. 163.—Nymph of *Sympetrum rubicundulum*, red dragonflies of autumn.

through the sunny days of September and even late November. Dr. Philip Calvert studied the autumn disappearance of species of *Sympetrum* and he writes, "Observations made over 20 years give the latest dates for the appearance of this species on the wing as ranging from October 17th to November 23rd."

Dragonflies, Subfamily Gomphinæ.—*Gomphus* (Fig. 164, 2) is a common representative of these stream-inhabiting burrowers. They have wedge shaped heads and stout 4-jointed antennæ. They sprawl or lie almost buried in the soft bottoms of slow streams and when they finally leave the water they usually crawl out on the flat shore to shed their skins. Length of nymph, one inch.

Dragonflies, Subfamily Æschininæ.—In this family the nymphs are smooth and slender, often green or marked with distinct color patterns (Fig. 164, 1). They have long thin legs and are active climbers among the vegetation of quiet waters.

The adults are among the largest dragonflies, those which

fly far from their native ponds and are often seen on roadways and about villages. They are great hunters for mosquitoes and swarming midges and mayflies.

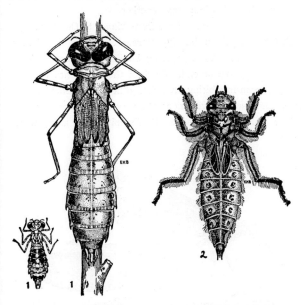

FIG. 164.—1, Young and mature nymphs of *Anax
junius*, one of the commonest dragonflies; 2,
nymph of *Gomphus*.

Anax.—The green darners (*Anax junius*) are probably the
commonest dragonflies in all parts of the country (Fig. 164).
The nymphs live in small ponds among water plants. Well
grown ones are grass green with a broken brown stripe through
the middle of the back but half grown ones are marked with
cross bands of black and white. Fullgrown nymphs are
plentiful all through October. They expel water from their
respiratory chambers with such force that when they are in a
shallow pan of water their spitting and squirting can be heard
several feet away (Pl. IX). Length of nymph, 1 to 2 inches.

Mating adults fly about together, seldom alighting except to deposit the eggs just below the water in the stems of pickerel weed or other shore plants. Even while the female lays her eggs the pair often stay together.

Occurrence.—Adults emerge from May 1 to October 20.

Damselflies, Suborder Zygoptera.—Damselfly nymphs are slender nymphs whose tapering bodies bear three leaf-like gills at the posterior end. Some of them are dark colored, often stream-inhabiting nymphs; others are delicate, pale green and usually live among the vegetation of quiet water.

The brilliantly colored adults fly loiteringly along water sides.

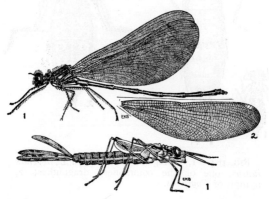

Fig. 165.—1, Nymph and adult male of blackwing, *Agrion* (*Calopteryx*) *maculatum;* 2, wing of female.

Blackwings, Agrion (Calopteryx).—These are the "black wings," the familiar damselflies with brilliant green or blue bodies and black wings (Fig. 165). They flutter along over the border shrubbery of shaded streams with all the uncertainty of butterflies. The commonest species is *Agrion* (*Calopteryx*) *maculatum.* The adult male is beautiful metallic green or blue with uniformly black or rusty black wings; the female is similar but each front wing has a white spot near the tip (Fig. 165). The female, unattended by the male, deposits her eggs in plant stems just below the surface of the water.

Occurrence.—Nymphs of various sizes may be found in shallows the year round. Length of fullgrown nymph, about 1 inch. The adults are on the wing from the middle of April to the last of August.

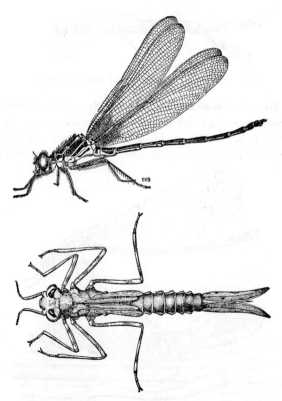

Fig. 166.—Nymph and adult of damselfly, *Hetærina americana.*

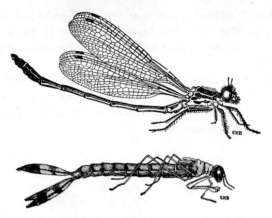

FIG. 167.—Nymph and adult of *Lestes inæqualis*.

Hetærina americana.—The adults (Fig. 166) have narrow transparent wings, very different from the dark spoon-shaped ones of the preceding genus, *Agrion* (*Calopteryx*) (Fig. 165), and the males can be distinguished from other damselflies by

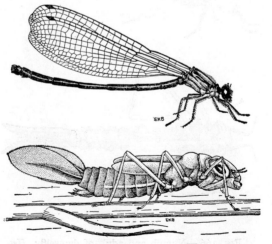

FIG. 168.—Nymph and adult of *Argia violacea*.

the carmine colored flush on the bases of their wings. They fly late in the summer (in Illinois they have been reported as late as October 22) when they are often seen gathered in little companies on streamside shrubs. The nymphs live in moving water—in rapids, sometimes in the lapping waters of lake shores. They are brown or green, without any color pattern (Fig. 166). Fullgrown nymphs are one and a quarter inches long.

Lestes.—Nymphs of *Lestes* all live in ponds and small lakes where they climb about among the plants of the shallow water. They are very long bodied and slender with green and brown bandings which camouflage them extremely well among their surrounding stems and leaves (Fig. 167). Length of nymph, three quarters of an inch.

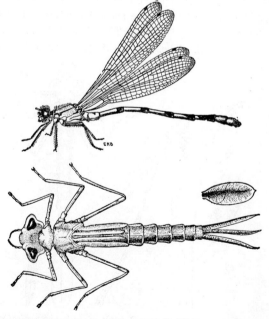

Fig. 169.—Adult and nymph, *Enallagma exsulans.*

Argia violacea.—This is the commonest species of this genus in the eastern states (Fig. 168). The nymphs live in almost every kind of aquatic situation but prefer slow streams and coves. The species is named from the violet colored abdomen of the adult male. The female commonly lays her eggs on mats of algæ which float in the shallow water. While she is ovipositing the male continues to clasp her body, holding his wings folded and his own body poised stiffly, sticking straight up into the air. Length of nymph, about one half inch.

Enallagma.—This is a large genus of damselflies whose nymphs live in the tangled vegetation of small weedy ponds, or slow-flowing streams, where they are among the most numerous of predatory insects. Nymphs of the different species are very much alike (Fig. 169). All are slender with the head nearly one-third wider than the rest of the body and the gills variable in size and color pattern but not so pointed as those of *Ischnura*. The labium is slender with a prominent median lobe. Length of nymph, one half inch.

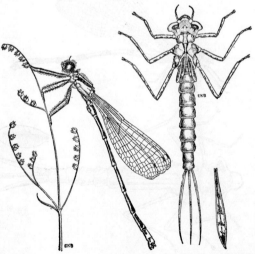

FIG. 170.—Nymph and adult of *Ischnura verticalis.*

Fork-tails, Ischnura verticalis.—This is one of the commonest damselflies in the United States. The nymphs resemble those of *Enallagma* but their gills have longer, more tapering points (Fig. 170). They occur almost anywhere in weed-grown water. The adults are among the earliest damselflies to emerge in the spring and the last to be seen in autumn. The males are green and black; segments 8 and 9 of the abdomen are blue with a black stripe on each side. They seldom fly out over the open water but flit about swamps and borders wherever there is vegetation. Length of nymph, one half inch.

Water-bugs— *Hemiptera*

Form and habits.—All water-bugs have jointed sucking beaks of needle-like sharpness. Some of them dive or swim in the water, coming to the surface for air (Pl. X); others prowl over submerged vegetation, a few live on the surface film. These are but a few species of the great order *Hemiptera* most of whose members belong to the forests and fields. Although these water-bugs live on the water or close to it throughout their days, in almost all cases, including all of the American species, they breathe air, for they have only partially committed themselves to aquatic life. They never have tracheal gills. The young nymphs look and act very much like the adults but they have shorter wings and there is no great change in their shape after the last nymphal molt as there is in mayflies and dragonflies (Fig. 183). While water-bugs are comparatively few in numbers of species there are apt to be large numbers of individuals. It is no unusual thing to be able to catch fifty or more water boatmen with one sweep of the net, or to see a hundred water striders in a small streamside pool.

Water-bugs live in protected waters, thickly grown with plants and littered with dead vegetation, or in gently flowing streams which have still pools and coves along their course (Pl. II). There they forage in the shallow waters where insects and snails and the young of many water animals are abundant (Fig. 22). They are active from very early spring, beginning to appear in the water as soon as the ice leaves the shore; some lay their eggs by the middle of April. Their activity goes on till late fall or early winter, depending upon the season. With a few exceptions they hibernate as adults. They gather for the winter in matted branches of *Chara*, and skulk in the trash beneath banks. They are long-lived, often surviving for a year or more.

Food.—Many water-bugs attack any animals which they can manage, large or small. Their larger prey includes young fish, snails, and dragonflies, but they devour also great numbers of small crustaceans, mosquito larvæ, midge larvæ, and insects which fall into the water from overhanging foliage. But the water boatmen are mainly herbivorous, gathering their food from the bottom ooze which consists largely of algæ and decaying plants. They not only maintain their own numbers but they furnish part of the food for their cannibalistic relatives.

Associates.—Water-bugs occupy the surface of the shallows with whirligig beetles, springtails, and pond-snails. Water-bugs and crayfishes are sometimes associated through a peculiar habit of the water boatman, *Ramphocorixa acuminata*, which lays its eggs upon crayfishes. The performance has been fully described in a paper by J. F. Abbot with photographs of crayfishes laden with eggs of the water-bugs. Many crayfishes have since been studied in eastern Kansas by Hungerford who believes that the eggs are placed on the regions of the crayfish (*Cambarus immunis*) where they have the best chances of aeration by currents of water from the gills. The female of another water-bug, *Belostoma*, places her eggs on the back of the male of her own species (Fig. 175), but the crayfish carries the boatman's eggs just as safely and takes the burden entirely off the family.

Aquarium study.—Water-bugs can be kept in aquaria for

long periods. The aquaria will need screen-covers, for they can fly out of their dishes just as they can from ponds. Only a few should be kept in a dish, for they need space, and a few water plants to make them feel at home. They will eat small water animals of almost any kind; the water boatmen need only some good bottom ooze full of plant tissues. Many water-bugs will lay their eggs and their young will hatch in captivity.

Identification.—Excellent accounts of all the families of aquatic *Hemiptera* have been given by H. B. Hungerford in his report "The Biology and Ecology of Aquatic and Semi-aquatic Hemiptera."

Key to families of aquatic *Hemiptera* here included, after Hungerford.

1. Antennæ shorter than head. 2
   Antennæ as long as or longer than head, exposed. 6

2. Hind tarsi with indistinct setiform claws (save in *Plea* which is less than 0.1 inch long). 3
   Hind tarsi with distinct claws. 4

3. Head overlapping thorax dorsally. Front tarsi 1-segmented, palæform. Water boatmen, *Corixidæ*, p. 239
   Head inserted in thorax. Front tarsi normal.
   Backswimmers, *Notonectidæ*, p. 237

4. Membrane of hemelytra (front wings) reticulately veined. 5
   Membrane of hemelytra without veins.
   Creeping water-bugs, *Naucoridæ*, p. 238

5. Apical appendages of the abdomen long and slender; tarsi 1-segmented. Water scorpions, *Nepidæ*, p. 235
   Apical appendages of the abdomen short and flat, retractile. Giant water-bugs, *Belostomatidæ*, p. 232

6. Head as long as entire thorax; both elongate.
   Water-measurers, *Hydrometridæ*, p. 228
   Head shorter than thorax including scutellum. 7

7. Claws of at least front tarsi distinctly ante-apical, with terminal tarsal segment more or less cleft.   8
   Claws all apical, last tarsal segment entire.   9

8. Hind femur extending beyond apex of abdomen; intermediate and hind pairs of legs approximated, very distant from front pair. Beak 4-segmented.
                          Water striders, *Gerridæ*, p. 230
   Hind femur not extending much beyond apex of abdomen; intermediate pair of legs about equidistant from front and hind pairs (except in *Rhagovelia*); beak 3-segmented.
             Broad-shouldered water striders, *Veliidæ*, p. 229

9. Antennæ 4-segmented. Membrane of wing without cells.   Mesoveliids, *Mesoveliidæ* (not included)

Water-measurers, Family Hydrometridæ.—These bugs are concrete examples of slenderness and deliberation. They have long thin bodies, spindly legs, and long, elbowed-antennæ and their heads are as long as the whole thorax, which is by no means short (Fig. 171). They walk over dead reeds at the margin of ponds, or on duckweed and lily leaves, and even on the surface film, always seeming to measure each step as they go. Sometimes they are found on sphagnum moss on the edges of bog ponds, one of the generic names in the group being *Limnobates*, which means "marsh-treader."

Water-measurer, Hydrometra martini.—These water-measurers (Fig. 171) are the most widely distributed of the

FIG. 171.—Water-measurer, *Hydrometra martini*.

family in our fauna, the other species being found in the south. They stay about shallow pools, shut in by cat-tails and overgrown with algal mats and duckweed where they can be sure of a quiet place to prowl for their food (Pl. II). In order to find out what these measurers do it is necessary to settle oneself comfortably in or near the pond since some time elapses between their doings. Hungerford used to keep watch on the pools, while seated on a three-legged stool well out in the water. He saw *Hydrometra* spearing its food in the water, capturing mosquito larvæ and pupæ, water boatmen, and small crustaceans.

Water-measurers lay their eggs from April through midsummer upon stems projecting just out of the water; they are brown and spindle-shaped, with beautifully sculptured shells, each one being fastened separately to the leaf. Hungerford watched water-measurers laying their eggs on cat-tail sprouts in April. Those which he kept in his aquaria placed their eggs on the sides of the glass just above the water line. Length of adult, about half an inch.

Broad-shouldered water striders, Family Veliidæ.—These stout bodied animals are similar to the common striders, *Gerridæ*, in general appearance and habits. Like them they are predatory and gregarious. The larger species belong to the genus *Rhagovelia* which inhabits rapidly moving water.

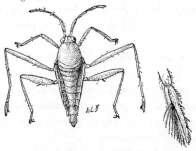

Fig. 172.—Broad-shouldered water strider, *Rhagovelia obesa*, showing split in tarsus of middle leg.

In one of the largest of these water striders, *Rhagovelia obesa*, the terminal tarsus of the middle leg has a split in it from which a tuft of hairs projects into the water (Fig. 172). These can be spread out like a fan and used as an oar-blade in travelling up the current of a stream. Length of adult, one eighth of an inch.

Water striders, Family Gerridæ.—Water striders or water skaters live on the surface of quiet or gently flowing water, skimming rapidly over the surface on their spider-like legs, drifting with the current or jerking themselves upstream (Fig. 22). The dimples which their feet make in the surface film cast shadows on the brook bed that are almost as often noticed as the water striders themselves. Water striders collect in schools along the quiet, shady, side waters of streams whence they scatter to shelter when alarmed but quickly congregate again.

Their bodies have pilose surfaces, like velvet, which hold a silvery film of air covering their undersides and completely enveloping them in their occasional plunges down into the water. Their legs are slender, often long and spindling; the middle and hind ones are close together, both pairs set far apart from the front legs; the long femora of the hind legs extend behind the tip of the body (Fig. 173). Very young nymphs are like frisky little spiders, but they soon begin to look like the adults except that they have short wings or none at all. In several species adults, too, may be wingless or short-winged.

Water striders are predacious on backswimmers, on emerging midges which come up from the water below them, and on leaf-hoppers which fall down from banks and overhanging shrubbery above them. The adults pass the winter beneath protecting mud-banks, often clustered among snarls of *Chara* and *Elodea* stems.

Like some other water-bugs they support many young water-mites. Scarlet patches of the latter can be seen almost as far as the striders themselves. Water-mites lay their eggs on aquatic plants and their six-legged larvæ hatch out, soon fastening themselves to water-insects by means of their hooked mouth parts. Their heads work deeper and deeper into an insect's body, their legs curl up and finally only the scarlet bag-like body shows on the outside (p. 176). Within this bag the six-legged larva transforms and finally emerges as a free-swimming eight-legged mite.

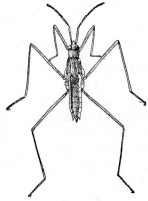

Fig. 173.—Large water strider, *Gerris remigis*, adult.

Large water strider, Gerris remigis.—Unlike the next species these water striders have dark under surfaces, and the adults (Fig. 173) are usually wingless. They seem to prefer clear running streams where they gather beside the tree trunks, and in quiet places near bends in the shore. They cannot migrate except by jumping and many of them are caught in isolated pools and die there when the water dries up in summer. Both adults and young are parasitized by water-mites. Adults, one half inch long.

Occurrence.—Common from Labrador to Mexico.

Gerris conformis.—The adults of *Gerris conformis* are always winged and slender and the underside of their bodies is yellowish. They frequent both lakes and streams and range south through all of the Atlantic states.

Fig. 174.—Small water strider, *Gerris marginatus.*

Gerris marginatus.—This small water strider (Fig. 174) is an abundant inhabitant of lakes and streams all over the United States. Adults, one half inch long.

Giant water-bugs, Family Belostomatidæ.—The members of this family are wide, flat-bodied insects which have front legs fitted for clutching and the others flattened and oar-like. They have a pair of short, strap-shaped breathing organs at the end of the abdomen.

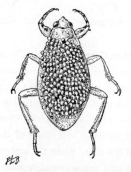

Fig. 175.—Male water-bug, *Belostoma flumineum,* carrying eggs fastened upon him by the female.

Water-bug, Belostoma flumineum.—This is one of the smaller members of the family, which has long been incorrectly known as *Zaitha fluminea*. It clings to stems and sticks in still waters which hold a congested population of water plants and insects—mayflies, damselflies, and the like. The eggs, a hundred more or less, are carried on the back of the male (Fig. 175) until they hatch, usually for ten days or more. Torre-Bueno has thus described the transfer of the parental burden. "The female places herself on top of the male, her thorax extending outward and her legs hooked under him; now starting somewhere near the middle and sidling along every little while, she works her way around him as she fastens her eggs on his back by means of the water-proof glue secreted for that purpose. The male all the while hangs from the surface, back up, with his legs curled up under him, bravely bearing up under his burden."

Occurrence.—Egg-laden males can be found commonly from May into early September. In the marsh waters at Ithaca, N. Y., they are very plentiful in August. Adults, one inch long.

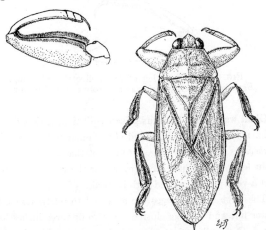

FIG. 176.—Electric-light bug, *Lethocerus americanus*, and front leg showing groove on the femur into which the tibia can be folded.

These water-bugs are predacious upon smaller insects Hungerford fed the nymphs with mosquito wrigglers. They winter as adults in the bottom trash and mud.

Electric-light bug, Lethocerus americanus.—In these giant water-bugs the femur of the front leg has a groove into which the tibia can be folded (Fig. 176). They are fiercely predacious, devouring dragonflies, and young fish whenever they are available, and Britton records the capture by *Lethocerus* of a young pickerel which was three and five-eighths inches long.

The brownish, oval eggs, about one-fifth of an inch long, have been found on reeds above the surface of the water. These bugs do not hesitate to leave the water, flying sometimes for a considerable distance, thus migrating from pond to pond. They have been captured around electric lights and so earned their popular name. Adults, one and one half inches long.

FIG. 177.—Front leg of giant electric-light bug, *Benacus griseus*, which has no groove in the femur.

Giant water-bug, Benacus griseus.—This electric-light bug (Fig. 177) is slightly larger and very similar to the preceding *Lethocerus americanus* (Fig. 176) except that the femur of its front leg does not have any groove for the tibia. It can inflict a very painful wound with its beak.

The large streaked eggs are attached to plants above the water line and the egg-clusters are two or three inches long. Dr. J. G. Needham has written a description of the hatching illustrated with a photograph that shows a young *Benacus* pushing back the loosened caps at the free ends of the eggs.

The line along which the cap will open is marked on the egg shell by a white crescent-shaped streak.

These bugs thrive in dishes of water if they are kept supplied with food, such as insects and pond snails, and are enclosed by a screen top. The eggs are so large that the young *Benacus* and its hatching can be clearly seen with the naked eye. The plant stalk bearing the cluster of eggs containing embryos should be set up in a natural position in an aquarium, when the whole process can be watched.

Water scorpions, Family Nepidæ.—The water scorpions have two long tail filaments which form a breathing tube, and they can rest on the bottom or some submerged support with the tube thrust up through the surface film for air. No other water-bugs have such a contrivance.

Fig. 178.—Water scorpion, *Nepa apiculata*, showing its clutching front legs and the tail-pieces held together to make a breathing tube.

Water scorpion, Nepa apiculata.—This dead-looking bug lurks among muddy leaves along the pond margin. Its apparent inactivity is a watchful waiting for mayfly nymphs, snails or crustaceans which it can clutch with its front legs (Fig. 178) and then suck till only their husks are left. Water scorpions do not lose their appetites easily and their fierce sallies upon their neighbors can often be witnessed even in the collecting pan.

The eggs are inserted into the decayed tissues of plants, but their little crowns of shell filaments are left waving from the surface and at hatching this end of the egg opens like the cap in *Benacus* eggs.

Length of adult, about one half inch.

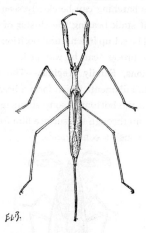

FIG. 179—Water scorpion, *Ranatra fusca*, showing the caudal tube which it thrusts up to the surface for air.

Water scorpion, Ranatra fusca.—*Ranatra* (Fig. 179) looks like a brown, water-logged stick which has taken to walking and when it is lying still it is hardly distinguishable from the twigs all about it. These water scorpions hang head downward on the rushes and sedges with their air tubes thrust up to the surface. They are common, too, among any dead leaves and shore trash. When they are lifted out of the water they sometimes squeak faintly, making this noise by rubbing a roughened patch on the outside of each front leg against the edge of the prothorax. Water scorpions are rapacious, wantonly clutching and sucking the life blood of pond-dwelling mayflies and tender young damselflies.

According to Enock, the eggs of *Ranatra* are laid on half

decayed stems of water-plantain, *Alisma*, and Hungerford has published photographs which show them beautifully defined upon cat-tail leaves. Each egg has a round cap at the top from which filaments extend out upon the surface of the leaf. Length of adult, one to one and a quarter inches.

Backswimmers, Family Notonectidæ.—The members of this family are unique in their ability to swim on their backs, which are shaped like the bottom of a boat (Pl. X). Their long hind legs are used like oars.

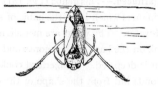

Fig. 180. — Backswimmer, *Notonecta undulata,* with hind tip of its body thrust through water surface for air.

Backswimmer, Notonecta undulata.—There are several species of backswimmers all of which hang head-downward from the surface with their long hind legs extended like oars and the ends of their bodies thrust up to the air (Fig. 180). When disturbed they dive to the bottom, carrying a silver film of air on the ventral side of the body, and remain submerged, anchored by their front feet to a plant stem. They are extremely active, with strong grasping fore-legs and a beak with which they can inflict a burning sting, the effect of which may last for some time in persons susceptible to poisons. Although they are themselves predacious, their young are preyed upon by nearly every other carnivorous insect including adults of their own kind. They produce many young; Hungerford found 252 mature eggs in *Notonecta irrorata*. In that species egg-laying goes on from March to June and the adults live at least a year. *Notonecta undulata* (Fig. 180) is the commonest backswimmer, and is generally distributed all over the United States. Length of adult, one half inch.

FIG. 181.—A slender backswimmer, *Buenoa margaritacea*, with front and middle legs folded.

Buenoa margaritacea.—This genus (Fig. 181) includes a few slender backswimmers which have the habit of swimming and hanging in mid-water. The wings are moonlight white; there is a flush of pink on the back of the thorax and the underside of the abdomen is deep red. Hungerford could not discover their eggs in ponds but from the shape of the ovipositor decided that they were laid in plants. When smart-weed stems were put in the aquarium with them the females promptly riddled them with eggs.

They live upon small crustaceans which they hold while they feed upon them in a sort of cage made by the bristles of their first four legs. Length of adult, one quarter of an inch.

Plea.—The pigmy water-bugs of this genus (Fig. 182, 2) are not more than a fifth of an inch long. They live in tangles of water plants feeding upon minute crustaceans.

Creeping water-bugs, Family Naucoridæ.—These are broad thick-set bugs of moderate size in which the hind legs are not flattened for swimming as they are in the backswimmers and water boatmen but the front femora are greatly thickened

FIG. 182.—1, Creeping water-bug, *Pelocoris femoratus*; 2, the pigmy water-bug, *Plea striola*.

(Fig. 182, 1). They creep about on the stems in quiet water which is densely grown with vegetation. They bite or "sting" on the slightest provocation.

Water boatmen, Family Corixidæ.—Water boatmen (Fig. 183) are dark grayish or thickly mottled gray and black. Their hind legs are flattened for swimming and extend out like those of the backswimmers, but water boatmen always swim with their backs up; their middle legs are long and end in very slender claws. The boatmen dive down with their bodies wrapped in a glistening blanket of air and being so much lighter than the water they have to anchor in order to stay below. They do this by almost imperceptibly catching one claw of the middle leg into some plant stem (Fig. 183) and hang there atilt in the water for long intervals. Indeed they spend a good part of their time on the bottom for they feed upon the soft vegetable ooze which gathers there, diatoms, desmids, filamentous algæ, and the like (Pl. IV). Hungerford discovered that water boatmen are vegetarians, thus disproving the old statement that all aquatic *Hemiptera* are wholly predacious. He found *Spirogyra* filaments with their cells sucked so empty by boatmen that only their walls remained. They are probably omnivorous since Hale in Australia observed them feeding on mosquito larvæ.

It is difficult to distinguish one species of water boatmen from another, and even the genera are hard to differentiate. One of the commonest species is here figured; many are similar to it.

Water boatman, Arctocorixa (Corixa) alternata.—Like others of the family this water boatman is active all winter. Large numbers of corixids have been taken every month of the year from a gently flowing stream near South Hadley, Massachusetts. In midwinter they hide under the banks in tangled masses of *Chara* where they are far from inactive (Fig. 183). In Ithaca, N. Y., on May 9 Hungerford found red water-mites (p. 175) on about eighty-five per cent of

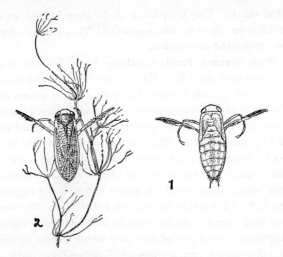

Fig. 183.—Water boatman, *Arctocorixa* (*Corixa*) *alternata*: 1, nymph; 2, adult grasping a submerged *Chara* stem, a characteristic pose.

this species and by May 15 the total population was infested with them. Length of adult, one quarter of an inch.

Alderflies, Dobsons, Fish-flies, Spongilla-flies—*Neuroptera*

Members of only two families of the *Neuroptera* in our fauna have aquatic larvæ, the *Sialidæ*, which contains the alderflies, dobsons, and fish-flies, and the *Sisyridæ* or Spongilla-flies.

Form and habits.—The adults have four wings and are named *Neuroptera* because of the many fine veins which run through the wings. There is a complete change of form from larva to adult, and the fullgrown larva always climbs out of the stream to pupate.

Occurrence.—The larvæ of the *Sialidæ* live in swift water, where they hide under stones and are frequently found in riffly shallows throughout the winter, but the Spongilla-flies have followed the sponges and are often found in them in quiet water (Fig. 187).

Food.—They are probably carnivorous but their food habits are not thoroughly known.

Aquarium study.—Neuropterans are secretive insects not easy to observe in their own homes, and the larvæ are difficult to keep in aquaria unless running water can be arranged for them. Something has been learned about them by field observation and by keeping them in cages.

Identification.—Key to genera of aquatic *Neuroptera* larvæ, from "Fresh Water Biology," Needham and Needham (Bibliography, p. 407).

1. Large forms with biting mouth parts.
   Alderflies, dobsons. *Sialidæ*, p. 241. 2
   Small forms with piercing mouth parts. Spongilla-flies, etc. *Hemerobiidæ (Sisyridæ)*, p. 245. 4

2. Body ending in a long median tail. *Sialis*, p. 241
   Body ending in a pair of stout hook-bearing prolegs. 3

3. Lateral abdominal filaments with a tuft of tracheal gills.
   Corydalis, p. 243
   Lateral abdominal filaments with no tracheal gills beneath. *Chauliodes*, p. 244

4. Bristles on back of thorax sessile. *Sisyra*, p. 246
   Bristles on back elevated on tubercles.

   Climacia, p. 246

Family *Sialidæ*

Alderflies, dobsons, fish-flies

Smoky alderfly, Sialis infumata.—Alderflies (Fig. 184) were so named by the English fishermen because they settle on the alder bushes which overhang the streamside; in Wales they are called "hump-backs." They are heavy, awkward fliers which are easily captured; when approached they will often run rather than take to their wings.

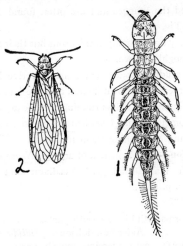

Fig. 184.—Smoky alderfly, *Sialis infumata:* 1, larva; 2, adult.

They are active in the day time, especially in bright sunshine, usually laying their eggs at midday. These are deposited in flat masses of 200–500 and there are usually several masses within an area of a few inches on some leaf, board or stone which overhangs rapid water, so that the larvæ fall into the current as soon as they hatch. The eggs are cylindrical, dark brown, and at the end of each there is a little club-shaped projection visible with a hand-lens. The eggs are placed slightly slantwise to the surface with the little projection pointing upward.

The larvæ (Fig. 184) live in the sandy or muddy bottoms of the streams or ponds, often buried several inches below the bottom surface where they are hidden from their relatives and greatest enemies, the *Corydalis* larvæ. They are brown, and heavy skinned; when fullgrown they are about an inch long. Each of the first seven segments of the abdomen bears a pair of five-jointed, tracheal gills which are fringed with hairs, and at the end of the abdomen there is a similar but unjointed gill.

The larvæ are predacious upon caddis worms and upon one another. They do not come out of their hiding places until they are ready to pupate, when they clamber out on land and seek another hiding place or burrow in the moist earth.

Dobson-fly, Corydalis cornuta.—The larvæ of *Corydalis cornuta* (Fig. 185, 1), commonly known as crawlers, hellgrammites, and bass bait, live under stones in the swiftest part of rapid streams (Pl. I). They are fiercely predacious insects, and will seize upon mayflies and stoneflies as soon as they are put in the same collecting dish with them.

When fullgrown they are 2 or 3 inches long with dark brown, rough looking skin, and large jaws which they extend lustily at the slightest irritation (Fig. 185). Their bodies are

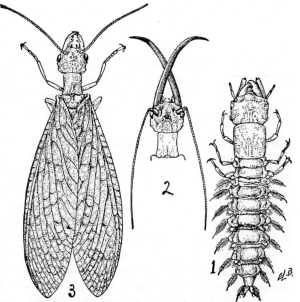

FIG. 185.—Dobson-fly, *Corydalis cornuta: 1*, larva; *2*, head of adult male; *3*, adult female.

flattened and sprawling and there is a tuft of white hairlike gills at the base of each of the lateral appendages on the first seven abdominal segments. *Corydalis* larvæ avoid the light and are seldom seen unless stones are suddenly pulled from the rapids; then they cling to the surface or hitch themselves rapidly backward by their posterior grappling hooks. In May and June when they are about three years old they crawl out on shore and under a stone or log to pupate. At first the pupa is pale-colored and soft but it gradually darkens during the pupal life which lasts about ten days.

The adults have cinnamon brown bodies, and gray-white spotted wings which measure four or five inches from tip to tip when fully expanded. The female (Fig. 185, 3) has short, stubby mandibles but those of the male (Fig. 185, 2) are tusklike, more than three times the length of the head, and used to hold the female during mating. As adults the dobson-flies are short-lived, and although they have strong jaws they probably eat nothing. They are often attracted to lights at night and sometimes fly high about street lamps, usually falling to the ground after a few circles. The eggs are laid on stones or sticks overhanging the water and there may be two thousand or more of them in a single chalky white mass but an inch wide.

Fish-flies, Chauliodes pectinicornis.—The larvæ of *Chauliodes* (Fig. 186, 1) are similar to *Corydalis* but do not have gill tufts at the bases of the lateral filaments and when full-grown they are only half as large. They are not confined to swift streams, but are often found clinging to submerged trash in quiet side waters. They are predacious, those kept in aquaria being successfully fed upon live backswimmers and house flies. The length of the larval life must be considerable, for Davis kept them in running water from September 1899 to June 1900 yet even at that date they had not completed their growth. Like *Sialis* and *Corydalis* they pupate beneath stones on the stream banks.

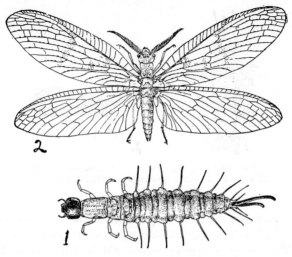

Fig. 186.—Fish-fly, *Chauliodes pectinicornis:* 1, larva; 2, adult.

The adult of the common species *Chauliodes pectinicornis* (Fig. 186) is cinnamon color, shaded and streaked with yellow, and the wings are gray-brown with an incomplete band and spots of white. The masses of reddish brown eggs, each mass containing from 1000–2000 eggs, are deposited on leaves or branches overhanging the water. Thirty or more of these egg masses have been found clustered together within a radius of two feet on a rock a couple of feet above the stream. The eggs are oval and lie with the long axis parallel to the surface, each egg bearing a little knob-like projection.

Family *Sisyridæ*

Spongilla-flies

Adult Spongilla-flies are small, smoky brown or variegated four-winged insects (Fig. 187, 2) that are little known except to the specialist.

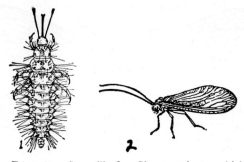

FIG. 187.—Spongilla-fly, *Sisyra umbrata*, which lives in fresh water sponges: 1, larva; 2, adult.

Their pale-colored larvæ (Fig. 187) live in the cavities of a fresh water sponge and feed upon its substance (p. 109). Their bodies are sparsely covered with bristles which catch torn fragments of the sponge and effectually camouflage them. Their long, slender jaws are grooved on the inner sides so that when they are held together they form a tube. This is thrust into the soft sponge and its tissues are sucked up through it. Either the food thus secured contains little waste or it is wholly absorbed in the stomach, for there is no posterior opening to the alimentary canal and it is unlikely that waste could pass out at the mouth as it does in *Hydra*. The fullgrown larva finally leaves the sponge, climbs out of water to some leaf or twig and spins its silken pupal cocoon. This silk is produced by its kidney-like Malpighian tubules which have taken on a silk-secreting function. It comes out of the hind end of the body through spinnerets similar to those of spiders.

There are two genera of Spongilla-flies which have similar life-histories and make such cocoons. Larvæ of *Climacia* weave a cocoon covered with a hexagonal meshed net while *Sisyra* makes one covered with a sheet of silk. Length of *Sisyra* larva, about one quarter inch.

Caddis Flies—*Trichoptera*

Adult caddis flies look like moths but their bodies are more slender and they are more delicately built. They are soft brown, or gray, sometimes black, very rarely bright colored. Their four wings are folded like a tent over their backs, and their thread-like antennæ, often longer than their bodies, are extended far out in front of them. As in the butterflies and moths their color lies mainly in the long, silky hairs and scales which cover their wings and soft bodies. Caddis flies do not go far from the watersides and they are seldom seen in the daytime. Some swarm at dusk over water and under trees but at night they gather around electric lights which are near streams or on lake shores, and they may then be seen by hundreds, creeping up on the lamp posts or fallen upon the ground below them.

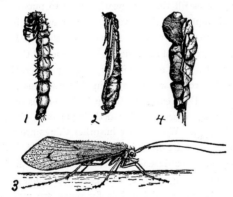

FIG. 188.—Caddis fly life-history: 1, larva; 2, pupa; 3, adult; 4, leaf-case.

Caddis flies are mostly known by their larvæ, the familiar caddis worms or stick-worms which live in every brook (Pl. I), often creeping over the bottom where they can be clearly seen from the banks. The best known are those which live in cases made of little pebbles, or sticks or leaves which they have cemented together with their own saliva (Fig. 198). When a caddis worm outgrows its case it occasionally squirms out and makes a new one, selecting the same materials and building by the same pattern, but it generally enlarges its case by simply building onto the front edge. It holds itself in the case by draghooks at the hind end of the body but its head and thorax are protruded during its continual clambering. Their gills are filamentous, in many being attached along the sides of the abdomen, completely protected by the case. Three tubercles (Fig. 188, 1) keep the body from pressing against the edge of the case and give the water a free entrance into it. It is kept circulating over the gills by undulating movements of the body which the larvæ will continue even after they are removed from the cases.

The pupæ (Fig. 188, 2) live in cases and some larvæ never have any cases till they are nearly ready to pupate. They are as truly aquatic as the larvæ, and they have gills like them. There are no other aquatic insects whose pupæ have gills except a few groups of flies, such as *Simulium* and *Chironomus*. The larvæ keep up a continuous foraging and eating until they are fullgrown, when they spin silken screens across the open ends of their cases, or fasten little pebbles over them, and within the cases they begin their pupation changing to the adult form. Water is let in, other things are shut out. Such pupal cases are often fastened to a stone and all through the early summer dozens of them belonging to little *Helicopsyche* pupæ (Fig. 199, 1) can be found glued fast to the edges of the rocks. All caddis fly pupæ are more or less active and many continue their undulating motions to keep the water flowing over their gills. By the end of the pupal period the heavy-jawed, hungry larvæ are changed into dainty adults which do not eat at all (Fig. 188, 3). In swift water species the pupæ after leaving their cases swim to the surface, shed their pupal skins, and instantly fly into the air; quiet water pupæ clamber out on the shore or upon projecting stones.

Some caddis flies, like the *Hydropsychidæ*, lay their eggs in beautifully regular layers upon submerged sticks, and the hundreds of little embryos can be seen through the transparent shells. The eggs of some of the *Phryganeidæ* are embedded in rings of gelatine, hung on aquatic plants.

Habitat and season.—For every kind of aquatic situation there is a caddis fly population, net-builders (Pl. XVI) in the rapids, clamberers and floating case-bearers in the gentle currents. Different species of caddis flies have very definite seasons when they emerge from the water as adults, and in many kinds these are brief periods. But some can be found all through the summer and a few, especially the net-builders, *Hydropsychidæ* (Pl. I, 12), can be found all winter.

Microcaddis flies, Family Hydroptilidæ.—The larvæ are all less than one-quarter of an inch long; abdomen wider than thorax; their cases (Fig. 189) shaped like spectacle cases and generally carried edge upward.

Fig. 189.—Larva and case of *Ithytrichia confusa*, a microcaddis worm. (After Lloyd.)

Ithytrichia confusa.—The case of at least one species, *Ithytrichia confusa* (Fig. 189), is fastened limpet-like to the stone. This is an oval parchment-like one, about a quarter of an inch long, with an opening at one end through which the larva feeds. They are common both in quiet water and flowing streams.

Family Rhyacophilidæ.—This family is divided into two subfamilies but the larvæ of both live in rapidly flowing streams.

Members of the subfamily *Rhyacophilinæ*, represented here by *Rhyacophila* (Fig. 190), do not make cases until they are fullgrown and ready to pupate when they wall themselves in loosely and spin a parchment-like cocoon. In the other subfamily, *Glossosomatinæ*, the larvæ make cases of which the turtle-shaped *Glossosoma* (Fig. 191) is a type.

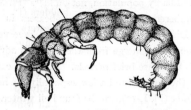

FIG. 190.—Caddis worm, *Rhyacophila*.

Rhyacophila.—This larva creeps about naked on the under surfaces of stones in riffles until it is fullgrown. It then enters a crevice between them and walls itself into a chamber much larger than itself, by fastening the pebbles together with its own saliva. Here it spins a brownish, parchment-like cocoon within which it transforms (Fig. 190). The adults emerge from late May to the middle of July, probably all summer. Length of fullgrown larva, one half inch.

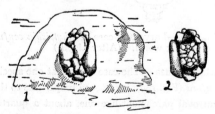

FIG. 191.—The turtle-shaped case of *Glossosoma americana*: 1, upper and 2, under side. (After Lloyd.)

Glossosoma americana.—These larvæ build turtle-shaped cases of pebbles and sand grains (Fig. 191). They live singly

on the brook bottom until they are fullgrown and ready to
pupate and then they congregate upon the sides of stones
with their cases placed edge to edge. Each larva cuts away
the old floor of its case and fastens the rim which is left to
the rock. Under this protecting canopy it spins its pupal
cocoon. Larvæ, pupæ, and adults are found all summer.
Length of case, little less than one half inch.

Net-spinning caddis worms, Family Hydropsychidæ.—This
family is represented in almost every shallow stony brook by
hundreds of *Hydropsyche* larvæ and their nets.

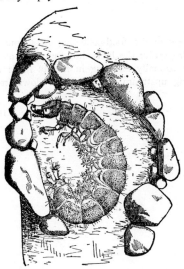

Fig. 192.—Caddis worm, *Macronema.*

Hydropsyche.—The cup-shaped nets of *Hydropsyche* are
built in crevices or on the edges of rocks in waterfalls and
riffles (Pl. XVI). The cup always opens upstream and
the larva lies in a loosely woven tube close at the side,
whence it can easily reach the food which the water brings
into the net. When fullgrown the larva makes a case of

Pl. XVI.—Cuplike food-collecting nets spun by caddis worm, *Hydropsyche;* the larva lies concealed at the side of the net, occasionally reaching in for its food: 1, inside of cups opening upstream; 2, bottom or downstream side of the cups.

Photo. by A. H. Morgan

PLATE XVI

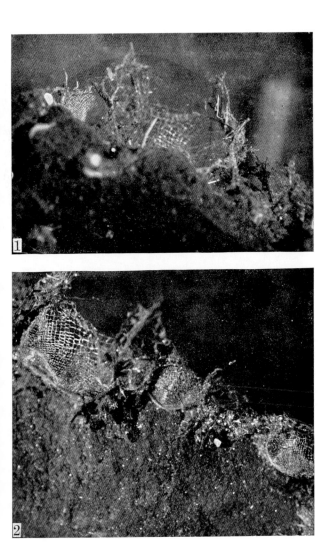

sand grains in which it pupates. It lives only in rapid streams and on wave-beaten shores. Length of fullgrown larva, one half inch.

Macronema.—The abdomen of this larva is dark green above and vivid green on the ventral side which bears conspicuous silvery gills. *Macronema*, Fig. 192, is locally common in rapid shallows. Length of fullgrown larva, three quarters of an inch.

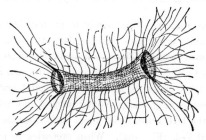

FIG. 193.—Net of *Polycentropus*. (After Noyes.)

Silken-tube spinners, Family Philopotamidæ. Polycentropus.—This genus makes delicate tubular nets (Fig. 193) 1 inch long. There are two openings, a large one facing upstream, at the end which is attached, and a smaller one at the end which floats free. Usually there are several, sometimes many, nets near together. The larva stays within the net and feeds on the food which is caught there.

Phryganeids, Family Phryganeidæ.—These caterpillar-like larvæ of ponds and gently flowing streams are the most conspicuous and the best known of the caddis fly larvæ. The black and yellow head and thorax and the habit of constantly "pumping" their bodies are characteristic of all of them They are plant feeders.

Neuronia.—Larvæ of *Neuronia* make cases, about one inch long, of bits of thin leaves cut almost square and arranged in

FIG. 194.—Cases of phryganeids: 1, *Neuronia postica*; 2, cases of larvæ of *Phryganea vestita*.

rings (Fig. 194, 1). When ready to pupate they creep into crevices and burrow into wood or beneath bark.

Phryganea vestita.—This caddis worm lives in ponds among submerged plants, rarely on the bottom. Its case is made of narrow strips of leaves arranged in a spiral and securely glued together (Fig. 194). Young larvæ do not trim off the ends of the leaf strips, which gives their cases an unkempt, unfinished look (Fig. 194). When preparing to pupate the larva burrows into submerged wood leaving the end of its case protruding. Adults emerge from the middle to the last of June.

Family Molannidæ.—Larvæ of the genus *Molanna* (Fig. 195) are often found in great abundance on the sandy bottoms of slow streams and ponds.

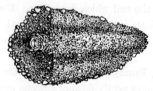

FIG. 195.—Case of *Molanna* made of sand grains.

Family Leptoceridæ.—These caddis worms all make portable cases but of diverse shapes (Fig. 196).

Leptocerus.—Larvæ of *Leptocerus* drag their cornucopia-shaped cases (Fig. 196) over the stones in riffles and in the side waters of rapid streams.

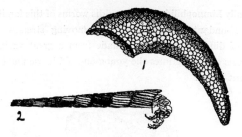

FIG. 196.—Cases of leptocerids: 1, *Leptocerus;*
2, *Triænodes.*

Triænodes.—The larva of *Triænodes* swims rapidly about carrying its case (Fig. 196) with it among submerged plants in quiet bays and ponds. The case resembles that of *Phryganea* (Fig. 194), but it is smaller and the leaf-fragments are finer and fitted together with more precision. The delicate spiral egg-masses are laid on the under surfaces of lily pads (Fig. 18 and Pl. XVII), sometimes containing about two hundred eggs though each is but one-fifth of an inch wide. The adults begin to emerge in the middle of June and the eggs are found from then on through early midsummer.

Family Odontoceridæ.—The larvæ of only a single species of this family have been described (Lloyd).

FIG. 197.—Case of *Psilotreta.*

Psilotreta.—Larvæ of *Psilotreta* are found in the riffles of stony brooks. During the winter they crawl over the bottom but in early spring when they are ready to pupate they gather on the sides of stones, fastening their cases (Fig. 197) there in piles. In these piles the cases are always placed parallel to one another with the head ends pointing toward the surface. Length of case, one half inch.

Family Limnophilidæ.—The caddis worms of this family are most abundant in ponds and slow-moving streams. The cases of different species are made from a great variety of materials and sometimes the young and old larvæ make very different cases.

Fig. 198.—Case of *Limnophilus rhombicus*.

Limnophilus rhombicus.—When they are young the larvæ make cases of the log cabin type, but when they mature they migrate away from the grassy shorelines and gather their building materials from the bottom, using bark and seeds. When little mollusks are available the case may be made almost entirely of *Planorbis* (Fig. 251), and *Sphærium* (Fig. 266) shells with their occupants often still alive; such cases are about three quarters of an inch long (Fig. 198).

Family Sericostomatidæ.—These are caterpillar-like larvæ which are found in both streams and lakes.

Helicopsyche.—The little *Helicopsyche* cases (Fig. 199) are good examples of objects which may be in abundance before our eyes yet altogether undiscovered. *Helicopsyche* larvæ are rarely seen when they are creeping over the sandy bottom, only becoming known when the fullgrown larvæ cluster by dozens upon the rocks and fasten their snail-shaped cases down tightly to them in preparation for the pupal change. They weave silken lids over the openings of the pupal cases; these can be seen with a hand-lens. The adults emerge in June and July.

Cases less than a quarter of an inch wide.

Goera.—The larvæ of *Goera* can be found on current-swept rocks from late summer till the end of March. Their cases

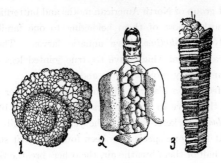

Fig. 199.—Cases of 1, *Helicopsyche*; 2, *Goera*; 3, *Brachycentrus*.

(Fig. 199, 2) are slightly flattened and like those of several other caddis larvæ they have ballast stones glued on each side which keep them from being carried away by the current. In March the cases are fastened down for pupation to exposed stones in the full current, and a pebble placed over the opening. The adults emerge through April and May.

Brachycentrus.—During its early life *Brachycentrus* (Fig. 199, 3) lives in the side waters of brooks actively foraging along the banks, then it moves into mid-channel and attaches one front edge of its case to a stone. It always chooses an exposed place and faces up-current, holding its legs extended upstream like the mayfly *Chirotenetes* (Fig. 24).

During its browsing days the larva first lives upon diatoms, and then upon other algæ, but when about six weeks old it adds to this a diet of mayflies, water-mites, midge larvæ, and small crustaceans. Case of fullgrown larva, one half inch long. The adults emerge late May–June.

Aquatic Moths—*Lepidoptera*

Water caterpillars.—Most caterpillars are like cats; they walk to the shore but they do not go into the water. Among the great group of North American moths and butterflies only a few moths, most of them belonging to one family, the Subfamily *Nymphulinæ*, have aquatic larvæ. They are typical caterpillars which have six true jointed legs on the thorax, and fleshy prolegs on the abdomen.

They feed upon diatoms and the tissues of higher plants. Most of them live in quiet waters overgrown with bladderworts, *Elodea*, pickerel-weed, or the yellow and white pondlilies. At least one species has been found in swift streams.

About half of them breathe air, the others breathe through thread-like gills which are arranged in rows along the sides of the body. Those of the genus *Nymphula* bite off pieces of leaf and make cases which they line with silk.

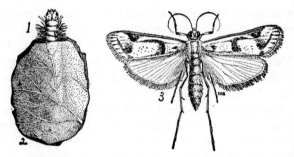

FIG. 200.—1, Lily-leaf caterpillar, *Nymphula maculalis*, and 2, its floating leaf-case; 3, the moth (one inch long).

Lily-leaf caterpillar, Nymphula maculalis.—The caterpillars of *Nymphula maculalis*, the lily-leaf caterpillar (Fig. 200), are common in quiet water among yellow and white water-lilies. They live in leaf-cases (Fig. 200) which they make by biting off two pieces of lily pad, each about an inch long, and fastening the edges together with strands of silk, or sometimes they bite off one section and attach it to the underside of the same lily pad. The pieces are arranged shiny side out and almost always appear newly cut. Sometimes they are separated from the lily pad, sometimes moored to it by a strand of the torn tissue. They are filled with water but the larvæ can breathe by means of bushy branched gills extending from the sides of the body. They feed upon the leafy walls of their cases, first upon the inner layer and when they are older, upon the shiny outside.

In this, as in other species, there appear to be two broods of caterpillars; the first one makes the full-sized cases common in June and July. These pupate within leaf-cases also usually beneath a lily pad, and the adults which fly about over the lily ponds have mouse-gray front wings and white hind ones (Fig. 200). Soon another generation arises, the caterpillars of which sink down through the water in autumn and hibernate among the water-sodden leaves of the lily plant. Common and generally distributed.

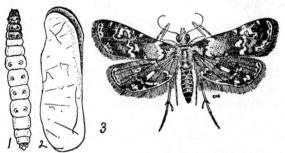

FIG. 201.—1, Lily-leaf caterpillar, *Nymphula obliteralis;* and 2, its floating leaf-case; 3, moth.

Lily-leaf caterpillar, Nymphula obliteralis.—In the southern states it is a pest upon water-lilies. These caterpillars (Fig. 201) make their cases, about one half inch long, of the leaves of water-lilies and pondweeds. They have no gills and are entirely dependent upon the bubble of air which surrounds them in their leaf-cases. The male moths are dull black with obscure markings of yellow and white; the females are browner and of larger size.

Occurrence.—Quebec and south; common southward, New York, Rhinebeck.

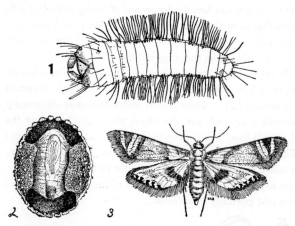

FIG. 202.—1, A caterpillar of rapid waters, *Elophila fulicalis* (after Lloyd); 2, pupal case, underside (after Lloyd); 3, the moth.

Although most aquatic caterpillars live in quiet waters, there is at least one, *Elophila fulicalis* (Fig. 202, 1), which is at home in the rapid streams where mayflies and stoneflies abound. There it lives on water-washed rocks, breathing by means of the unbranched tracheal gills which extend in double rows along each side of its body.

It weaves a silken canopy above itself, cementing the irregular edges to the rock except in two or three places. These openings allow the water to circulate freely beneath the curtain. Canopies made by young larvæ are only half an inch long but those of the fullgrown larvæ measure four or five inches long and are an inch wide. The caterpillars feed upon the algal ooze covering the rock beneath them, the abundant *Scenedesmus* and the beautiful green spheres of *Pediastrum*.

Shortly before it is ready to pupate the fullgrown larva

cuts its canopy away, leaving only a clean scar on the rock surface. Within the area of this scar it makes its pupal case. This has an inner case of loose-spun silk which encloses the pupa with radiating threads which suspend it from a canopy thicker than the larval one but perforated with a circle of six or more clean-cut holes which let in the water.

The moths (Fig. 202, 3) emerge in June and July and the vegetation near the stream sometimes swarms with them. Their front wings are gray-brown and their hind wings white marked with a curved blackish band. Common and general in distribution.

Beetles—*Coleoptera*

When they are fullgrown nearly all beetles have thick wing-covers or elytra which hide the thin hind wings beneath them. They change greatly in form from larva to pupa to adult (Fig. 203) and the young in no way resemble the mature beetles. As a group beetles are preeminently land insects. Of the 150,000 or so species of *Coleoptera* included in approximately eighty families only a few families are made up of water-loving beetles.

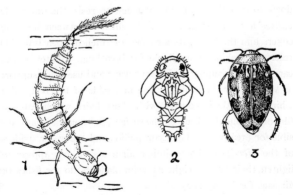

FIG. 203.—The change of form in a water-beetle:
1, larva; 2, pupa (after Wilson); 3, adult.

Adults and pupæ of water-beetles breathe air and most of their larvæ do likewise. Some of the most interesting habits and structures of these larvæ are those by which they remain in the water and still contrive to have access to air. Only a few of them have tracheal gills which enable them to breathe under water; the family *Gyrinidæ*, whirligigs (p. 271), and a few of the *Hydrophilidæ* (p. 273), have filamentous gills along the sides of the abdomen; *Dryopidæ* and the *Psephenidæ* or water pennies (Pl. VIII) have fringed gills beneath the body.

Some beetles are familiar to everybody although under names which disguise their identity, potato "bugs," rose "bugs," fire "flies," and maybeetles commonly called June "bugs."

If a diving beetle like *Dytiscus* be compared with any of them its adjustments to water life will be very apparent. An adult *Dytiscus* (Fig. 209, 1) has a compact, rigid, slippery body, its head forming the point of a wedge and the smooth sides of the body the rest of it. The underside is boat-shaped, and the hind legs bladed like oars. Between strokes it folds its legs close against the body, and pulls its antennæ down so that there are no outriggers to resist the water. It carries a reservoir of air tightly shut in between its wing covers and the body; its air-tubes or tracheæ open into this reservoir making it available for breathing. Water-beetles carry their air supply in different ways and use it for support as well as for breathing. The underside of the body of a whirligig beetle is covered with short hairs which catch a film of air, buoying it up on the surface, but none of it is accessible for breathing. The hydrophilids and the water striders of the *Hemiptera* have similar air-floats, which appear to lighten their body weight as swim-bladders do for fishes or air-sacs for honey-bees.

Habitat, season.—Nearly all aquatic beetles live in quiet water thickly grown with plants on which they hunt for their prey and on which they lay their eggs. They frequent still pools strewn with plant litter and overspread with algæ; shore waters populated with insects, and with young water animals of all kinds (Pl. X). The few larvæ such as the water pennies which live in rapid water are very unlike their relatives.

Among the mayflies and dragonflies the young are thoroughly aquatic while the adults are thoroughly aerial; the nymphs are the long-lived forms in which these insects winter over and get through the difficult crises of their lives.

On the other hand, most water beetles, except the water pennies, winter over as adults. Whirligig beetles hide in the mud and come out with the first spring days, sometimes on warm days in midwinter, and they abound in the open waters all summer as well and into the late fall. Water pennies, larvæ of *Psephenus*, forage through the winter on diatom-covered stones in swift riffles (Pl. I).

Food.—Diving beetles (*Dytiscidæ*) and whirligigs (*Gyrinidæ*) are predacious all their lives, the crawling water-beetles, *Haliplidæ*, and water pennies, *Psephenidæ*, are vegetarian, while the *Hydrophilidæ* are apt to be predacious as larvæ and vegetable eaters when they become adult. Larvæ of the dytiscids, gyrinids, and haliplids suck their food through mandibles which are grooved for the passage of juices; the others chew their food.

Associates.—Plants and animals which are the food supply of beetles will be mentioned in the discussions of the different families.

They have many enemies, counting themselves among the worst, for all of the predacious beetle larvæ are cannibals from the day they are hatched. Needham and Williamson worked with one beetle, *Hydroporus*, which was so blood-thirsty that they had to construct compartments in which each larva could be isolated during their study of its habits. The partitions projected well above the water but the larvæ climbed

over them and mingled; and there was soon but one sur-
vivor. Dragonfly nymphs devour many beetle larvæ; *Anax*
nymphs (p. 219) take a daily toll of them.

In the stomach of a painted turtle (Pl. XXIII), a little
over two inches long, Baker found that the wing covers of
beetles formed five per cent of the food mass, and in another
only about an inch long, the remains of beetles composed
forty per cent. Water birds harvest the beetle crop continually and ducks consume the adults by hundreds.

Aquarium study.—Both adults and larvæ thrive in aquaria
and many of their swimming and breathing habits can be
best observed there. Like other animals in captivity they
are apt to change their food habits; those which are herbivorous may become predacious. Larvæ will clamber out of
aquaria and adults will fly up from them as they do not do
from the ponds. If the water is well oxygenated and they
are given enough living prey they can be kept in aquaria the
year round.

Identification.—Keys to families of beetles here mentioned,
from Needham and Needham (Bibliography, p. 416), slightly
modified.

The Chrysomelidæ (except one genus, *Donacia*), a family
of terrestrial beetles later mentioned (p. 278), are not included in these keys.

Families of Adult Water Beetles

1. Hind leg shorter than the fore leg; eyes divided (whirli
   gigs).   Whirligigs, *Gyrinidæ*, p. 271
   Hind leg longer than the fore leg; eyes simple.   2

2. Base of hind legs covered by coxal plates (creeping
   water-beetles).
                  Crawling water-beetles, *Haliplidæ*, p. 265
   Base of hind leg exposed.   3

3. Antennæ shorter than the palpi (scavengers).
                  Water scavengers, *Hydrophilidæ*, p. 273
   Antennæ longer than the palpi.   4

4. Hind coxæ broadly fused with the metasternum.

                      Diving-beetles, *Dytiscidæ*, p. 266

    Hind coxæ free (riffle-beetles).

                      Riffle-beetles, *Psephenidæ*, p. 277

Families of Larvæ of Water Beetles

1. Tarsal claws two.   2
   Tarsal claws one.   3

2. Four hooks at each end of abdomen. *Gyrinidæ*, p. 271
   No hooks at each end of abdomen.   *Dytiscidæ*, p. 266

3. Carnivorous, with conspicuous rapacious mandibles.
                         Hydrophilidæ, p. 273
   Herbivorous, with short blunt mandibles.   4

4. Legs absent—larva attached to plant by a bristle tube.
           Donacia of *Chrysomelidæ*, p. 278
   Legs well developed.   5

5. Abdomen with numerous rows of dorsal spines.
                       Haliplidæ, p. 265
   Abdomen with 2 rows of low tubercles or none.
                       Psephenidæ, p. 277

Crawling water-beetles, Family Haliplidæ.—These are small beetles (Fig. 204), one-fifth of an inch or less, which crawl through the litter in every little pond; one can hardly sweep the net over bottom vegetation without getting two or three of them. They are oval, very convex, and their general color is brown irregularly spotted with yellow. On the wing-covers are rows of small punctures (Fig. 204). The coxæ of the hind legs are plate-like and so large that they conceal the basal part of the legs. According to Dr. R. Matheson who has published a study of the whole family, the adults feed almost exclusively on filamentous algæ, particularly *Nitella* and *Chara*. About forty species of *Haliplidæ* have been found in our fauna; the species most commonly seen belong to the two genera, *Haliplus* and *Peltodytes*, both of which are widely distributed.

Haliplids begin to mate in early spring and lay their eggs

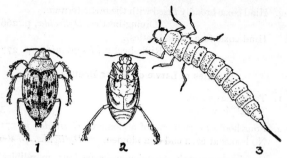

FIG. 204.—Crawling water-beetles, *Haliplus ruficollis:* 1, dorsal view of adult; 2, ventral view of adult showing the coxæ which cover the bases of the hind legs; 3, larva which breathes air.

in the latter part of April, May and June. Females of *Peltodytes* attach their eggs to aquatic plants, mainly *Chara* and *Nitella*, while *Haliplus ruficollis* places its eggs within the dead cells of *Nitella*.

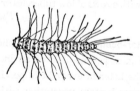

FIG. 205.—Larva of *Peltodytes*, showing the long spine-like gills through which it takes oxygen from the water. (From Matheson.)

The larvæ of both genera feed upon algæ and are abundant in the meshes of *Spirogyra* through which they creep very slowly or in which they more often lie inert. They are stiff, dead-looking objects very easily mistaken for frayed twigs. Larvæ of *Haliplus* (Fig. 204) breathe air through the spiracles or openings in the air-tubes; *Peltodytes* takes oxygen through long jointed spines (Fig. 205) which are supplied with tracheæ.

Predacious diving-beetles, Family Dytiscidæ.—The dytiscids are the dominant family of water-beetles. The adults hang head-downward from the surface of quiet waters, and although no insect looks more gentle and satisfied, none is more fierce and voracious.

They abound in ponds and pools and in the weed-grown side waters of streams. Some are only a few hundredths of an inch, others are an inch and a half long. Among them are some of the largest insects which live in the water, but, big and little, they constitute a population of blood-thirsty predatory animals.

They are black or brownish-black, often marked with dull yellow, and have slender thread-like antennæ (Fig. 209). By these they can be distinguished from the hydrophilids, another large family of beetles, whose antennæ are club-shaped and carried hidden in a pocket when they dive (Fig. 212). In some genera the males have clinging organs on the front feet; these are pressed down upon the smooth wing-covers of the female and act as clasping organs during mating (Fig. 208 and Fig. 209). Like many other water-beetles dytiscids have flattened hind legs which they use in swimming. Before diving they lift their wing-covers allowing air to enter the space beneath them into which their spiracles open. This is their diving supply and with it they can remain under water a long time.

Eggs.—The females puncture the surfaces of submerged leaves and lay their eggs singly in the plant tissues.

Larvæ.—The larvæ are the water tigers, a truly descriptive name for them and their habits (Fig. 209). When a water tiger catches sight of a promising young dragonfly it immediately rears up and stands at rigid attention with wide open mandibles. When the dragonfly comes near enough the beetle lunges forward and clutches its prey between its sickle-shaped jaws. These jaws are hollow and with its mouth still closed, the beetle can suck the body juices of the dragonfly while still keeping its firm clutch. It breathes air and has a pair of spiracles at the rear end of its body which it thrusts up above the surface whenever it comes to the top.

Collecting, aquarium study.—Diving beetles forage in the populous shallows near shore and are easily collected there by sweeping the plants with a net. Both larvæ and adults are interesting aquarium animals but they must be kept well supplied with live food. Harris kept an adult *Dytiscus* "three years and a half in perfect health in a glass vessel filled with water, supported by morsels of raw meat."

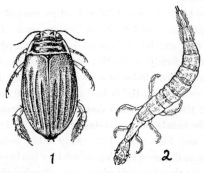

FIG. 206.—A common medium-sized diving beetle, *Acilius*: 1, adult; 2, larva (from Wilson).

Acilius.—This is the commonest of the medium-sized diving beetles. The adults (Fig. 206) are about one inch long, dull yellowish-brown with yellow margins on the thorax and wing-covers, each of which bears four furrows. The larvæ (Fig. 206) are easy, graceful swimmers. When they are resting below the surface the body is curved in a crescent, usually around a plant stem, and whenever they let go they are buoyed upward, tail foremost, by the air within their air tubes. Sooner or later they hang head down with tails thrust through the surface film.

In the larvæ of *Acilius* the prothorax is considerably longer than wide.

Coptotomus.—Unlike *Acilius* this larva (Fig. 207) is not dependent upon air and it is always found prowling on the bot-

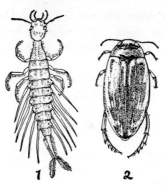

FIG. 207.—Diving beetle, *Coptotomus interrogatus:* 1, larva (from Wilson); 2, adult.

tom, breathing by means of its tracheal gills which trail off from the sides of the body. It is usually a half inch long.

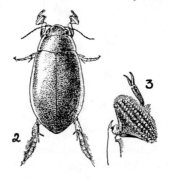

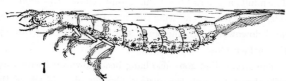

FIG. 208.—Diving beetle, *Cybister:* 1, larva (from Wilson); 2, adult male; 3, underside of his front tarsus, showing the roughened surface which is pressed against the back of the female in mating.

Cybister.—*Cybister* (Fig. 208) is a genus of large and very voracious water tigers. The fullgrown larva becomes 3 inches long and will attack tadpoles, other water-beetles, and small fish.

When larvæ come to the surface to breathe, they do not hang head downward like *Acilius* and *Dytiscus* but the head and thorax are both held near the surface. Their narrow necks are also good distinguishing marks.

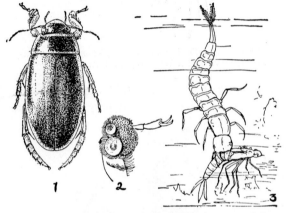

Fig. 209.—Large diving beetle, *Dytiscus:* 1, adult male; 2, underside of his front tarsus (cf. Fig. 208); 3, larva clutching damselfly nymph.

Adult dytiscid beetles (Fig. 209) are nearly an inch and a half long and the fullgrown larvæ may measure three inches. The adults are dark brown with a dull yellow stripe along the sides of the thorax and wing covers. When at rest they hang head downward with the tip of the body projecting through the surface film.

The larvæ (Fig. 209) also hang head downward with their tails thrust through the surface film for air. Much of the time they clamber about through the vegetation of the shallows and frequent the tadpole resorts; here they clutch the ~cft side of the tadpoles, sucking the body juices until only their puckered skins remain. The shallows where tadpoles sun themselves are almost sure to swarm with dytiscid larvæ whose appetite for tadpoles is a serious menace to the amphibian population. Neither adult nor larva of *Dytiscus* hesitates to attack an animal much larger than itself. There are records of an adult *Dytiscus* in an aquarium, which devoured seven snails, *Lymnæa stagnalis*, during one afternoon

Whirligig beetles, Family Gyrinidæ.—Whirligig beetles are one of the most easily recognized of all brook insects. With the first spring days they come to the surface in twos and threes, from their winter hibernation, and soon gather in companies on the surface of still or gently running water, resting motionless or circling round and round each other (Pl. X). They are blue-black or bronze, oval, and flattened; some are canoe-shaped on the ventral side and so smooth that they cut through the water with the greatest ease. Their hind legs, paddle-shaped and fringed with long hairs, are used oar-like in their rapid sculling (Fig. 210, 2). The compound eyes are divided by the sharp margin of the head so that in effect there is one eye for looking up from the water and one for looking down into it (Fig. 210).

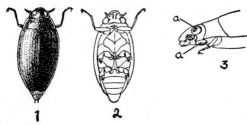

FIG. 210.—Smaller whirligig beetle, *Gyrinus:* 1, adult, dorsal side; 2, ventral side showing the middle and hind legs which fold tightly down to the surface; 3, side of head with divided eye *a*.

Gyrinids are more difficult to catch than would first appear. Though circling all about one they can evade a net with surprising agility and even after they are caught in it they frequently spring from it before they are landed. When handled they give off a milky fluid with a peculiar odor. In aquaria the males often make squeaking noises by rubbing the under-sides of the wing-covers against the body.

There are two common genera of *Gyrinidæ*, *Gyrinus* including the smaller whirligigs (Fig. 210) and *Dineutes*, the larger whirligigs (Fig. 211).

Adults of *Dineutes* which are kept in captivity will devour with avidity any freshly killed larvæ. Wilson fed these to whirligigs which he was observing and writes, "As many as could would seize the insect, crowd around it, grasping it, whirling around it in wild curves and sometimes diving beneath the surface, but always holding on to their prey and tearing out mouthfuls of insect tissues."

Their oval white eggs are laid on the under surfaces of lily pads (Fig. 18), or on *Potamogeton* leaves. Each egg is glued separately to the surface of the leaf.

Larvæ of whirligigs.—The larvæ of some insects, such as caddis worms, are very familiar, while adults are almost unknown, but this situation may be quite reversed. Thus among the whirligigs the adults are often seen, but the larvæ almost never. They are pale, slender creatures which crawl over the bottom trash or swim through the water with a sinuous motion of their bodies which is aided by eight heavily fringed gills which hang from each side of the abdomen. They are adepts at clambering backwards or forwards. On the tip of the abdomen there are four sickle-shaped hooks which they catch into anything convenient and pull themselves backward after the manner of caddis worms.

Whirligig larvæ capture young mayflies and dragonflies but they are less rapacious than some of their relatives. They can be kept in aquaria and will thrive on nymphs of the mayfly, *Callibætis* (p. 208). In *Gyrinus* larvæ (about one half inch long) the first two pairs of gills are fringed like the others, in the larger *Dineutes* (one inch) these two pairs are with-

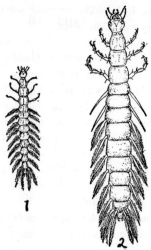

FIG. 211.—Larvæ of whirligig beetles: 1, *Gyrinus* (from Kellogg after Schiodte); 2, *Dineutes* (after Wilson).

out fringes; otherwise the larvæ of the two genera are similar.

Pupæ.—When fullgrown the whirligig larva crawls out on a moist bank and its gills shrivel up except for the last three pairs, which persist and seem to be used in locomotion. The pupating *Dineutes* observed by Wilson made pupal cases from pellets of earth stuck together with saliva. The full-grown larva selected a reed or grass blade near enough to the ground so that it could reach the earth, then hanging itself up by its posterior hooks it built a case round itself, repeatedly stretching downward to grasp a mouthful of dirt, sometimes taking a stick or leaf with it. When finished the pupal case is about half an inch long and the fullgrown larva is folded up in a C-shape within it.

Water scavenger beetles, Family Hydrophilidæ.—In the same protected water with the dytiscid beetles are other large black beetles—the hydrophilids or water scavengers—which look and act very much like them.

Adults.—But although they are similar there are several ways in which the adults of these two families can be distinguished. Hydrophilids hang at the surface with heads up (Fig. 212), dytiscids hang with heads down (Pl. X). Hydrophilids have very short club-shaped antennæ and long slender palpi which may easily be mistaken for antennæ (Fig. 212, 2), dytiscids have slender thread-like antennæ (Fig. 209). When adult hydrophilids come to the surface, they thrust their antennæ through the surface film and pull back a bubble of air which spreads over the ventral surface of the body like a silver blanket.

Eggs and larvæ.—They lay their eggs in beautiful silken cocoons, often fastened beneath floating leaves of water plants (Pl. XVII). Sometimes the cases are carried beneath the mother's body. They are all waterproof and contain about a hundred eggs but the young larvæ eat one another so lustily that the final crop is reduced.

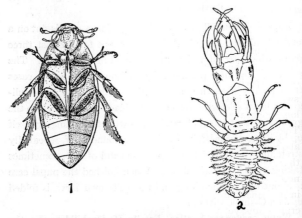

Fig. 212.—Water scavenger, *Hydrophilus:* 1, adult, ventral side; 2, larva, dorsal side.

Hydrophilus.—These are medium-sized black beetles on which there is a sharp spine in the middle of the thorax which projects backward between the legs (Fig. 212). The adults appear to feed entirely upon algæ. The young larvæ live on small entomostracans, later they eat tadpoles, insect larvæ and other beetles. They come to the surface to breathe. Projecting from the sides of the abdomen are seven pairs of filaments (Fig. 212), but these do not function as breathing organs. Fullgrown larva, a little more than half an inch long.

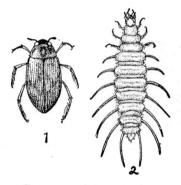

FIG. 213.—*Berosus:* 1, adult, and 2, larva showing long gills (after Wilson).

Berosus.—The adults are small, yellowish beetles (Fig. 213); both adults and larvæ feed upon green algæ. Wilson writes of one species, "These larvæ are very sluggish; they cannot swim at all but crawl about slowly over the vegetation, their long tracheal gills standing out rigidly on either side like rods. They cover themselves with green algæ and lie inert for hours at a time, only coming out after food." They breathe through their lateral gills, which contain tracheæ (Fig. 213), and do not need to come up for air like *Hydrophilus*. Wilson kept larvæ in an aquarium for a long time, supplying them with small crustaceans, yet they would take nothing but vegetable food, algæ, *Chara* and *Nitella*. He found them very hard to kill,

Pl. XVII.—Eggs of water insects: 1, mayfly, *Siphlurus*, eggs containing embryos, shells with slit through which insects have hatched; at the center note the head projecting from a shell; 2, mayfly, *Siphlurus*, with shell from which it has hatched; 3, eggs of horse-fly, *Chrysops*, on an iris leaf; 4, eggs of caddis fly, *Triænodes*, on underside of lily pad; 5, egg cocoon of hydrophilid beetle, on underside of lily pad.

Photo. by A. H. Morgan

PLATE XVII

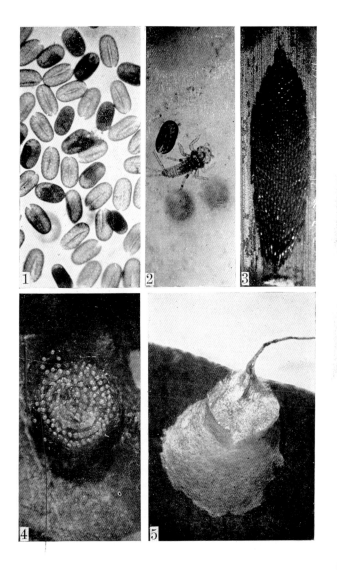

able to live from an hour to an hour and a half in ninety-five per cent alcohol. This larva is about three eighths of an inch long.

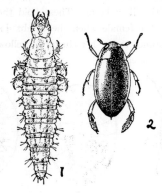

Fig. 214.—*Tropisternus lateralis:* 1, larva (after Wilson); 2, adult.

Tropisternus.—This medium-sized shiny black beetle (Fig. 214) abounds in nearly all beetle habitats, where it is often by far the commonest kind to be found. The adults are adepts at every kind of locomotion except jumping and are thus agile even on land. They are thorough vegetarians, living entirely upon algæ.

Wilson characterizes the larva of *Tropisternus lateralis* (Fig. 214) as follows: "Its exertions when eating demand a constant air supply, and it usually seizes its prey and swims to the nearest water plant. It then backs up the stem, dragging its prey after it until it can thrust its abdomen above the surface. It can thus eat and breathe at the same time, and it is engaged in doing both nearly all the time. . . . It is the very personification of voracity and gluttony and will eat any kind of an insect or larva that it can overpower." Usual length, one half inch.

Riffle-beetles, Family Psephenidæ.—The larvæ of riffle-beetles live in rapid currents, a habit which is rare among beetles. On hot days the adults (Fig. 215) settle on stones projecting from the midcurrents of rushing streams. They are small, about a quarter of an inch long, and their bodies are covered with silken hairs. These hold the film of air which blankets the female when she climbs down over the water-washed stones to lay her cluster of yellow eggs in the swiftest part of the current.

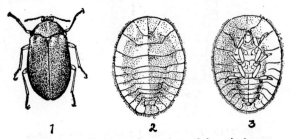

FIG. 215.—*Psephenus lecontei:* 1, adult; 2, its larva, the water penny, dorsal side; 3, ventral side.

The common eastern species, *Psephenus lecontei* (*Psephenidæ*), is known mostly by its larvæ, for which Comstock first suggested the fitting name of water penny (Fig. 215). These flat, copper-colored larvæ cling tightly to the dark under surfaces of water-washed rocks, and even when the rocks have been upturned and they are right under the eye they may not be seen at all. Only when they are turned over on their backs do water pennies display their legs and their five pairs of glistening white gills (Pl. VIII). Water pennies may be found in shallow riffles all the year round, where they feed upon the algal film on the stones (Pl. I).

The leaf-beetles, Family Chrysomelidæ.—In this large family of terrestrial leaf-eating beetles two subfamilies, the *Donaciinæ* and *Galerucinæ*, feed upon water plants. The commonest of these belong to the genus *Donacia*.

Donacia.—The larvæ of *Donacia* feed upon the underground stems of various water plants such as the yellow water-

278

lily, water-plantain, and *Potamogetons*, and all have a similar life-history. Only the adults and eggs are easily found. Their entire life cycle is still another example of the way in which insects though living several feet under water still contrive to breathe air.

FIG. 216.—Leaf-beetle, *Donacia palmata*, laying her eggs on the underside of a lily pad through a hole which she has cut. Length of adult, one half inch.

The long-horned leaf-beetles of the genus *Donacia* can be seen about ponds on any bright summer day, walking over the lily pads, flying up into the air and returning again to the lilies. They gleam in the sunshine with metallic green, or bronze, or purple against the dark lily leaves. The under sides of their bodies are pale brownish, and clothed with silky hairs which keep them from getting wet. They hold their long antennæ arched downward in front of them, busily feeling the leaf surfaces wherever they walk over them.

In ponds where these beetles are abundant the lily pads are riddled with holes where they have laid eggs (Fig. 216). When a female is ready to lay her eggs she stands on the upper surface of the leaf, bites a hole in it about one-quarter of an inch in diameter, inserts her abdomen through the hole and lays her eggs in a circle, often an incomplete one, on the under side, placing a double row of eggs in each circle and fastening them to the leaf by a gelatinous glue (Fig. 217). These

FIG. 217.—Eggs of *Donacia* glued to the underside of a lily pad around the hole which has been cut by the beetle.

conspicuous white egg-clusters are easy to find upon most lily pads all through the summer and early fall.

In about ten days the eggs hatch and the larvæ begin a remarkable existence in which, though living two feet or more below the surface, they constantly breathe air. Dropping down through the open water these larvæ seek the underground stems of the plant on which their own species of *Donacia* has lived for generations. When the stems of aquatic plants are broken beneath the water a flood of air bubbles comes pouring to the surface from the air spaces within them. The little *Donacia* larvæ rasp their spines against such stems, break through the walls of the air spaces, then push their heads into the holes they have made (Fig. 218). Thus, the larva taps the air supply of the plant and its head and thorax are surrounded by a layer of continually escaping air. MacGillivray and others found stems with dozens of little *Donacia* larvæ hanging to them feeding upon the plant tissues, and all breathing air, though they were three or four feet below the surface of the water.

When fullgrown the larva spins a water-tight cocoon provisioned with air from the air spaces of the plant. When the adult emerges from the cocoon at the end of pupation, some of this air catches in the silken hairs on the ventral side of

FIG. 218.—Larva of *Donacia palmata* with its head thrust into air space in a lily stem, breathing air though three feet under water (after MacGillivray).

its body, buoying it up, and at the same time furnishing it with a breathing supply sufficient for it until it reaches the surface of the water.

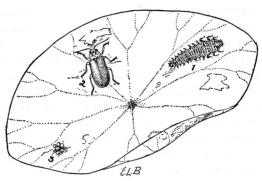

FIG. 219.—*Galerucella nymphæa:* 1, larva; 2, adult; 3, eggs.

Galerucella nymphæa.—This genus also lives mostly upon water-lilies but its whole life is spent above the surface of the water. The adults (Fig. 219) have indistinctly striped wing-covers; the females lay small clusters of shining yellow eggs on the upper surfaces of yellow pond-lily pads. The larvæ (Fig. 219), a little more than a quarter of an inch long, are black with fine whitish lines and spots. They feed on the leaf tissues until they are fullgrown and then pupate, often upon the same leaf.

Flies—*Diptera*

Flies have but one pair of wings, front ones, the second pair being represented only by little clublike projections called halteres. Flies include the familiar houseflies and mosquitoes. Dragonflies, mayflies, stoneflies, caddis flies and the like have four wings and are not flies. Flies undergo a complete change of form in larval, pupal, and adult stages. The *Diptera* form a vast group both in numbers of species and individuals, more than twelve thousand species having been found in North America.

Among them are many families whose larvæ are aquatic and a few whose pupæ are also aquatic. These include the gnats, punkies, midges, mosquitoes, horseflies, and craneflies. The worm-like larvæ are of diverse forms and sizes; thousands of midge larvæ are no longer than a quarter of an inch while some of the cranefly larvæ are more than two inches long. The pupæ may live in the water as do the midges and mosquitoes or in damp places near the water like many of the craneflies. Although the adults fly about in the region near water they are by no means confined to it. All adult flies suck their food through their tube-like lower lip or labium.

The habits of the aquatic flies are so various that they are best considered by separate groups.

Identification.—Key to families of *Diptera* larvæ from manuscript key by Dr. C. P. Alexander (slightly modified).

Key to *Diptera*

Larvæ

1. Caudal end of body prolonged into a long extensile breathing-tube: rat-tail maggot and similar types. 2
Caudal end of body not produced. 3
2. Head forming a complete non-retractile capsule.
Phantom craneflies, *Ptychopteridæ*, p. 287
Head reduced, capable of retraction within the body; true rat-tail maggots.
Syrphus-flies, *Syrphidæ*, p. 299

3. Head-capsule complete, not retractile into thorax,—i. e. encephalous.   4
   Head-capsule incomplete, capable of retraction within body.   7

4. Body depressed, subdivided into six primary divisions, each with a ventro-median sucking disk, with a tuft of gills on either side.

   Net-veined midges, *Blepharoceridæ*, p. 297

   Body not as above.   5

5. Thoracic segments fused into a complex mass, without prolegs; in most genera with an anal respiratory funnel.

   Mosquitoes, *Culicidæ*, p. 293

   Thoracic segments not so fused; if conspicuously dilated or extended, provided with a median prothoracic proleg.   6

6. Body with conspicuous anal gills, or else long, slender and snakelike (*Culicoides*); no mouth-fans or caudal sucking disk.   Midges, *Chironomidæ*, p. 289

   Body not as above, the abdominal spiracles small but distinct; body club-shaped; mouth with fans; a sucking disk on the club-shaped posterior end of body.

   Black-flies, *Simuliidæ*, p. 296

7. Head massive, incomplete behind; mandibles moving horizontally or obliquely across the mouth-opening; labial plate well developed.

   Craneflies (*Tipuloidea*), p. 283

   Head-capsule reduced, more or less retractile; mandibles moving vertically across the mouth-opening; labial plate not developed.   8

8. Body depressed, spindle-shaped, the surface finely shagreened; head little retractile; spiracular fissure transverse; pupates in last larval skin.

   Soldier-flies, *Stratiomyiidæ*, p. 299

   Body cylindrical, the abdominal segments with a girdle of pseudopods on each segment; body-surface usually longitudinally striated; head retractile; spiracular fissure vertical; pupa free, not in last larval skin.

   Horse-flies, *Tabanidæ*, p. 298

Craneflies, Superfamily Tipuloidea.—Craneflies are the large mosquito-like insects which rest on the streamside shrubbery, are caught in the spider webs of bridge railings, or dance in swarms over streams at twilight. They fly about lamps, and into houses, where they are familiar as long-legged flies which flutter into the corners of window panes and lose a leg with every new trouble that comes into their lives.

Adults.—Craneflies are long and slender,—body, wings and legs, especially the legs; they are the "daddy-long-legs" among flies. Just behind the wings are their clublike halteres or rudimentary hind wings. They seem to live mainly on the nectar of flowers but they take little food of any kind. In many species there are mating swarms, in most cases largely made up of males. The males of some species emerge before the females, seek out the female pupæ, and wait there, immediately mating with the adult females when they come out of the pupal covers. Craneflies usually fly about while mating, the females pulling the males after them. They lay their eggs in the water, flying over it and making sudden and frequent drops to dip the tip of the abdomen in the surface.

Certain craneflies like *Dicranomyia* can often be seen bobbing, a setting-up exercise widely practiced among craneflies. They stand firmly on the ground, springing on their legs and bobbing their bodies up and down. They may do this for a long time and some craneflies manage to eat during the performance.

Larvæ.—Cranefly larvæ are brown or white skinned, often so transparent that the coils of their air-tubes can be clearly seen from the outside.

In *Epiphragma* the smaller, pointed end is the head and when this is extended the brown biting mouth parts are conspicuous, but it is often kept withdrawn into the thorax so that they do not show at all. Larvæ of *Antocha* have anal gills (Fig. 223) and all of their oxygen supply is obtained from the water but with this single exception cranefly larvæ breathe air through two spiracles at the hind end of the body. These are surrounded by six to eight fleshy lobes, often lined with

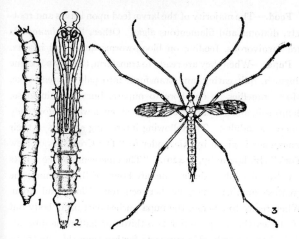

FIG. 220.—A typical cranefly, *Epiphragma:* 1,
larva which lives among water soaked leaves, head
down; 2, pupa, head up; 3, adult.

dark horny plates. This bizarre tail-piece, known as the
spiracular disk (Fig 221) is thrust up to the surface of the
water for air.

FIG. 221.—Spiracular disk, the tail-piece with
openings of air-tubes (black) which *Epiphragma*
thrusts up for air. (From Alexander.)

A favorite place for cranefly larvæ such as the common
Epiphragma (Fig. 220) is among the water-logged sticks and
leaves which catch here and there in riffly brooks; others like
Antocha (Fig. 223) live in very rapid water; still others like
Pedicia (Fig. 226) are found in springs. Very many of the
larvæ are only semi-aquatic, living in moist places in meadows,
in shady woodlands, in damp moss, and in decaying wood.

Food.—The majority of the larvæ feed upon leaves and rootlets, diatoms and filamentous algæ. Others like *Limnophila* are carnivorous, feeding on blood-worms and small insects.

Pupæ.—When they are ready to transform, the larvæ become sluggish, quit eating, and transform into pale colored pupæ. Most craneflies go on shore to pupate, burrowing in loose, damp soil, and remaining there for about a week before they emerge as adults. The following interesting account of their emergence is given by Alexander in "The Craneflies of New York" (Bibliography, p. 420). "The emergence of the adults usually takes place during the late hours of the morning, the greatest number emerging between ten o'clock and noon. When ready to emerge, the pupa pushes part of its body out of the earth, the posterior two-thirds or half remaining attached to the soil. If it projects farther than this, its transformation seems to be a very difficult operation. The pupa bends backward and forward constantly, flexing the body dorso-ventrally. This motion appears to exhaust it, since it frequently rests. The skin splits lengthwise up the mesonotum (middle section of back of the thorax) and the adult emerges. . . . The drawing out of the extreme tips of the antennæ is usually accomplished by the insect flexing its body backward. When the antennæ are freed, the insect walks a few steps from the cast skin, withdrawing its abdomen from the case."

Hibernation.—Cranefly larvæ can be found in brooks all through the winter (Pl. I). Alexander states that "it is probable that nearly all craneflies in the north temperate zone winter normally as larvæ."

Associates.—Craneflies have many enemies in every stage of their careers. The adults are poor fliers and are devoured by many birds from water-fowl to warblers, by amphibians, by spiders, and by other insects, especially dragonflies. Pupæ and recently emerged adults are seized by running spiders; larvæ are devoured by trout, by frogs and salamanders, and by birds,—the sandpipers, woodcocks and wading-birds.

Identification.—The Superfamily *Tipuloidea* contains four families, the primitive craneflies, *Tanyderidæ;* phantom craneflies, *Ptychopteridæ;* "false" craneflies, *Anisopidæ;* and the typical craneflies, *Tipulidæ.* Members of only two families are mentioned here.

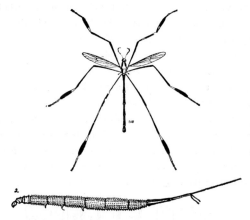

Fig. 222.—A cranefly with balloon feet, *Bitta-comorpha clavipes:* 1, adult; 2, larva.

Phantom craneflies, Family Ptychopteridæ.—One of the most striking members of this family is *Bittacomorpha clavipes*, a phantom cranefly with black-and-white-banded legs (Fig. 222). When these craneflies are mating the female flies ahead trailing the male after her. Their feet work like those of the winged Mercury but by a different device. The tarsi or feet of *Bittacomorpha* are pillowed out by sacs and tubes containing air, which buoy it up as it drifts in the wind relying upon wind currents as well as any modern glider. Alexander has quoted the following letter written to him by Dr. J. G. Needham: "A breeze was blowing up the gorge, and on the breeze a *Bittacomorpha* was drifting rapidly upward in the usual flight attitude with broadly outspread legs, the swollen metatarsi hanging vertically, all phantom-like in slenderness and in strongly contrasting black and white. It came from below the level of the rail, swept past within two feet of my face, and passed on upward with the breeze until lost to view, perhaps 100 feet higher than the bridge, and much farther upstream. Since the creature can fly only very slowly and here was moving several times faster (I could not see whether it was using its wings), it was obviously drifting in the wind. Perhaps this is a normal function of the expanded metatarsi."

The rusty red larvæ live in shallow water filled with decayed vegetation, among which they lie with the breathing tube pushed up through the surface film (Fig. 222). Like the larva, the pupa rests beneath the water with its air-tube at the surface. The larva becomes an inch and a quarter long.

Common and widely distributed in eastern North America.

Typical craneflies, Family Tipulidæ.—This is by far the largest family of craneflies, containing nearly 3000 species found in most parts of the world.

FIG. 223.—A swift-water cranefly, larva of *Antocha*.

Antocha.—The larva of *Antocha* (Fig. 223) is found upon stones in rushing torrents. There it lives in a crevice or among pebbles within a silken case one to two inches long and open at both ends, breathing through its four tracheal gills and the tracheæ of its caudal lobes. The pupa lives in the case previously used by the larva, its head always pointing downstream. Distributed over the northern hemisphere.

FIG. 224.—Larva of *Helius* (*Rhamphidia*).

Helius.—One species (Fig. 224) of the genus *Helius*, form‹ erly called *Rhamphidia*, is a common inhabitant of cat-tail marshes where it lives near the surface among floating leaves and refuse. Length of larva, about a half inch.

FIG. 225.—A carnivorous cranefly, *Limnophila*.

Limnophila.—The larvæ of *Limnophila* (Fig. 225), agile and snakelike in their movements, are among the most carnivo‑ rous of all cranefly larvæ. They live in water-soaked muck rather than in open water; some burrow in damp soil.

Length of larva, about half an inch.

FIG. 226.—Larva of *Pedicia*.

Pedicia.—The common eastern species, *Pedicia albivitta* (Fig. 226), is a dweller in cold springs throughout the north-eastern United States and Canada.

Length of larva, one inch and a half.

Giant cranefly, Tipula abdominalis.—This is a very large and very common cranefly. The larvæ, often more than two inches long, are abundant among the water-saturated, decaying leaves of little streams and are frequently turned up with such litter in midwinter collecting (Pl. I). They are her-bivorous, feeding chiefly upon diatoms and decayed plant tissue.

Midges, Family Chironomidæ.—On late afternoons in spring, swarms of little flies disport themselves in the sun-shine. They fly low, catching on clothing and gathering in the corners of window panes; in the evening they swarm around the lights. They are midges belonging to the family *Chironomidæ*, minute, delicate flies which are mosquito-like but of daintier build and of generally less offensive habits, though the family includes the punkies, abundant along mountain streams in the Adirondacks and White Mountains and sometimes at the seashore.

Adults.—Adult chironomids are seldom half an inch long (Fig. 228), sometimes confused with mosquitoes but a hand-lens will show that the wing-veins of mosquitoes are covered with opalescent scales (Fig. 227) while those of the chironomid

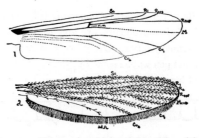

FIG. 227.—Wings of 1, chironomid midge with bare wing-veins; 2, mosquito with wing-veins covered by scales.

midges are bare or merely hairy (Fig. 227). When they are resting on a surface chironomids hold their front feet up, mosquitoes keep their front feet down and their hind feet up. In numbers and distribution the family *Chironomidæ* is a very successful group; like the related family, *Culicidæ*, the mosquitoes, they are known from Greenland to the tropics and there are more than twelve hundred species, most of them so similar that they can be distinguished only by specialists.

Eggs.—Some of them lay their eggs in strings of jelly coiled and snarled on stones in swift flowing water (Fig. 23); others deposit them near the surface of the water in quiet pools. The eggs themselves are white, usually oval, pointed at both ends, and though each egg is a mere dot to the eye they sometimes occur in such masses that their total bulk runs into quarts.

Larvæ.—Midge larvæ occur in vast numbers in all fresh waters. They are slender and wormlike, with fleshy prolegs at each end of the body, and they arch their backs like measuring worms (Fig. 228). Many of them cover themselves with soft dirt tubes (Fig. 19). Networks of these tubes cover the litter of dead leaves in the pools, and the sides of a collecting dish where the "catch" has stood for two or three hours. They are fragile and never portable like those of the caddis worms but new cases are made whenever the larvæ are forced out of the old ones.

Midge larvæ feed entirely upon algæ and decayed vegetation. On this plentiful food supply they thrive in vast numbers and constitute food for larger animals, the predacious insects, the young of fishes and other carnivores. They constitute a staple fish-food; it has been said (Garman) that no other one genus of insects constitutes so important an item in the food of so large a number of fishes.

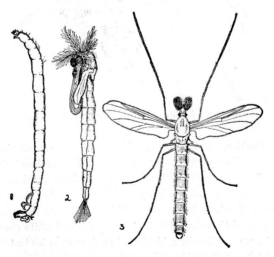

FIG. 228.—The midge *Chironomus:* 1, larva; 2, pupa; 3, adult.

Pupæ.—These live in the water and breathe air like mosquito pupæ. In all of them there is a large thorax from which the pair of air-tubes projects up like ears (Fig. 228).

Chironomus.—*Chironomus* larvæ live in tubes on the surface of the mud in pools. The best known ones are brilliant red, and are called blood-worms, their prolegs (Fig. 228) distinguishing them from the true worms, *Tubifex*, that are also called blood-worms. Larvæ of *Chironomus* have prolegs on the first and twelfth segments of the body, and on the eleventh there are two pairs of long "blood-gills," thin-walled sacs into which blood can flow freely (Fig. 228). Larvæ of various chironomids are from an eighth of an inch to an inch long.

The eggs are laid in strings of jelly, in which they are set in patterns characteristic of the species.

Fig. 229.—Midge, *Culicoides*, called "punkies":
1, larva; 2, adult.

'Punkies,' Culicoides.—In Maine the Indians call these midges "No-see-ums." There are great numbers of these biting flies in the northern forest country. A traveller's experience at a lodging house on the Kippewa River in Quebec is one of many. The lamp had been left lighted in his room for several hours, and the minute flies had gathered on all white covers and formed "literally a blanket of punkies upon his bed."

Adults of *Culicoides* (Fig. 229), *Ceratopogon*, and several other allied genera of the *Chironomidæ* share the same common names, "punkies," "sand-flies," or others according to the locality. They have very robust legs, and the thorax is low, not humping up above the head.

As in *Chironomus*, larvæ and pupæ are both aquatic. The larvæ swim with a snake-like motion, are whitish, slender and 12-segmented, with delicate, white blood-gills which can be retracted into the hind end of the body (Fig. 229).

Mosquitoes, Family Culicidæ.—Compared with related groups of flies this is a small family including only about a thousand species. However, it is an important one because of the trouble it makes. The habits of mosquitoes have made them familiar to everybody and much study has been devoted to them because of the association of certain species with malaria and yellow fever.

Some species of mosquitoes attack man and other mammals, a few attack birds only and many species do not suck blood at all. It is only the females which bite or suck blood; the males live on fruit and plant juices. The males can be recognized by their plumose antennæ. One of the most characteristic things about mosquitoes is the structure of their wings, which have a thick fringe of opalescent hairs and scales along their margins and on the veins (Fig. 227).

Larvæ.—Although they live in the water, all mosquito larvæ breathe air and are commonly known as wrigglers because of their swimming motions (Fig. 34). In all of them the head and thorax are large; the abdomen is slender with openings of air-tubes at the tail end. Mosquito larvæ are continually wriggling back and forth from surface to bottom where they feed on minute plant and animal cells and on submerged plants; a few are predacious (Fig. 230).

Pupæ.—A mosquito pupa is shaped like a question mark; the air-tubes open from its thorax, comparable in position to the top of the question mark. Mosquito larvæ lie parallel to the surface film or hang tails up but the pupæ hang with their backs up (Fig. 232).

Eggs.—The eggs are laid in almost any standing water, a lake, rain barrel, roadside puddle, or in marshes. In some species the eggs hatch very soon, in others not for a long time; probably many common mosquitoes pass the winter in the egg stage, hatching with the first spring warmth. Under favorable conditions our common mosquitoes go through their life cycle from egg to egg-laying adult in a short time. Mosquitoes can get along under difficult conditions of drought, cold, and starvation. They can live virtually anywhere, which accounts for their great numbers and for their wide distribution.

Fig. 230.—A carnivorous mosquito, the phantom larva, *Chaoborus* (*Corethra*).

Phantom larvæ, Chaoborus (formerly Corethra).—This is a group of mosquitoes not usually known as such because they do not suck blood. Their larvæ are the phantom larvæ of glass-like transparency, the only insects which are regularly found in the plankton or floating population of the open water. They are a half inch long, recognizable by the prominent, dark air-sacs, one pair at each end of the body, probably the regulators of their specific gravity (Fig. 230). Phantom larvæ are predacious, using their antennæ to grasp their prey, mainly entomostracans and rotifers.

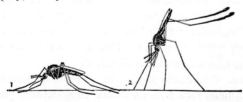

Fig. 231.—Adult mosquitoes: 1, common mosquito, *Culex*, with body held parallel to the surface; 2, malarial mosquito, *Anopheles*, with body tipped up behind.

Culex.—The genus *Culex*, common house mosquitoes, can be recognized by their hump-backs and their habit of standing with their bodies nearly parallel to the surface. Their wings are plain colored, never spotted like those of *Anopheles* (Fig. 231). None of this genus is known to carry either malarial or yellow fever organisms.

They lay their eggs on the surface of the water, each egg standing upright but glued to its neighbors so that the whole cluster makes a floating raft (Fig. 232, 1). The eggs hatch within about three days, depending on the temperature and the species.

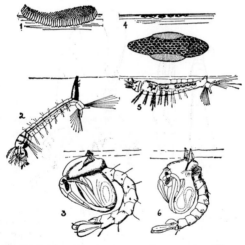

FIG. 232.—Water phases of mosquito life: 1, *Culex* eggs on water surface; 2. larva; 3, pupa; 4, *Anopheles* eggs at surface and one egg enlarged showing floats at sides; 5, larva; 6, pupa.

Anopheles.—*Anopheles* or "malarial mosquitoes" can be distinguished by their straight bodies which lack the "round-shouldered hump" of *Culex*, their black and white spotted wings, and their habit of resting with the hind end of the body tipped up (Fig. 231). *Anopheles* eggs float singly on the surface. When at rest *Anopheles* larvæ always lie parallel to the surface of the water, with the underside of the abdomen upward so that their two short air-tubes opening from the eighth segment can reach the air (Fig. 232).

Black-flies, Family Simuliidæ.—Thousands of these larvæ make up the swaying greenish "black moss" which covers the rocks in waterfalls and rapid streams from May to midsummer, where hundreds can be gathered at a stroke of one's hand. This family includes the Adirondack black-fly, *Prosimulium hirtipes*, which is a scourge along the northeastern mountain streams in spring and early summer.

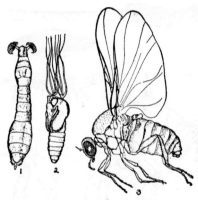

FIG. 233.—The black-fly *Simulium:* 1, larva which hangs to the rock by a caudal sucker and collects food with its fan-shaped brushes; 2, pupa showing tracheal gills; 3, adult. Length, larva, one quarter inch.

Simulium.—The larva holds fast to the rocks by a sucking disk at the hind end of its body. This frees the mouth to take in the diatoms gathered on the fan-shaped collecting brushes (Fig. 233, 1). The fleshy proleg just behind the head ends in a sucker like the rear one and on these two the larva walks over the stones. If it loses its footing or is brushed off the stone it hangs to its anchorage by a delicate silken thread spun from its salivary glands; by this means too it can travel downstream, swinging from rock to rock. *Simulium* larvæ breathe by the three retractile blood-gills at the hind end of the body.

The pupal cocoons form golden brown blankets on the rocks even more moss-like than those of the larvæ. They breathe through tracheal gills, the fringes which wave from the top of each case. Like all swift-water insects the adults fly as soon as they emerge, laying their eggs shortly afterward (Fig. 233). Black-fly larvæ are eaten in large numbers by fishes. Adult black-flies are pests both to human beings and animals, and black-fly cream and other repellents are sold all through the country where they abound. The Maine fishermen grease their hands and faces with kerosene oil and mutton tallow. Black-flies are active only during the daytime, leaving twilight to the mosquitoes and punkies.

Net-veined midges, Family Blepharoceridæ, larvæ.—The larvæ of *Blepharocera* cling to the stones in the rapids of mountain streams, in the waters of ravines, and in rushing brooklets. In their own special haunts they are abundant and no member of waterfall society is better equipped with holdfasts.

Clinging to its stone it looks like a row of six little black beads, less than half an inch long, the first bead consisting of the fused head and the thorax, the other five representing the abdomen (Fig. 234, 1). It has no feet, but down the mid-ventral line is a row of six sucking disks which it uses in walking and clinging (Fig. 234, 2). It breathes by means of the tufted tracheal gills on each segment.

Pupæ.—The pupæ are egg-shaped with a pair of ear-like gills at the large anterior end (Fig. 234).

Adults.—The adult females of some exotic tropical species are blood-sucking but the majority, including our North American forms, are not. Abundant in May.

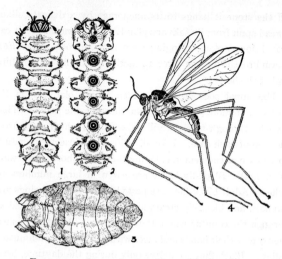

FIG. 234.—Net-veined midge, *Blepharocera:* 1, larva, dorsal side; 2, ventral side showing gills and the six suckers by which it clings to the stone; 3, pupa showing gills; 4, adult.

Horse-flies, Family Tabanidæ.—Tabanid larvæ (Fig. 235) live in stagnant, scummy water close to shore, sometimes in damp earth. They are half an inch long, whitish and worm-like, taper at both ends, and have roughened ridges running around the body. They breathe air usually through a pair

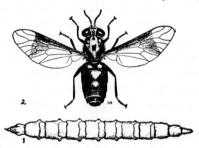

FIG. 235.—Horse-fly, *Chrysops niger:* 1, larva showing openings of air-tubes; 2, adult.

of openings at the hind end of the body, though there may be a pair at each end. They are predacious upon snails and insect larvæ.

Adults.—The adults are (Fig. 235) the once familiar horse-flies, now more frequently found on cows. Only the females are blood-sucking but both males and females can live on nectar if they can get nothing better. The larger horse-flies belong to the genus *Tabanus*, which includes the less common mourning horse-fly, *Tabanus atratus*. The smaller and more common banded horse-flies of the genus *Chrysops* attack man as well as animals. These have banded wings, brilliantly colored eyes, and black, or brown and yellow bodies (Fig. 235).

Eggs.—Masses of their shining black eggs are laid in beautiful symmetry upon the leaves of reeds a few inches above the water (Pl. XVII).

Soldier-flies, Family Stratiomyiidæ.—Adult stratiomyids are flower insects which get their name, soldier-fly, from their gay stripes. Many of the larvæ (Fig. 236) are not aquatic but live in decayed material and under bark. Although they are not abundant, the ones which do live in the water are noticeable because of their peculiar appearance. They are

FIG. 236.—Larva of a soldier-fly.

spindle-shaped, stiffened, and dead-looking, with a circlet of plume-like bristles surrounding the pair of spiracles opening at the small end of the body, usually thrust through the surface film for air. Above the surface film the bristles spread out like a flower whose upper surface is completely dry. They are carnivorous in their food habits. The pupa forms within the larval skin. Length of larva, 1-2 inches.

Syrphus-flies, Family Syrphidæ.—The adults (Fig. 237) are flower flies which love sunshine and among them are some

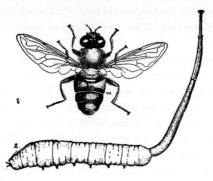

FIG. 237.—1, Drone-fly, *Eristalis tenax*; 2, its larva, the rat-tailed maggot, showing the tail-like air-tube.

of the largest and brightest colored of all the *Diptera*. In some species such as the drone-fly (Fig. 237) they look so much like honey-bees that they are easily mistaken for them.

Larvæ.—The larvæ are found in all sorts of materials and places,—water, decaying wood, in fungi, and in the nests of ants and bees. This larva of the drone-fly (Fig. 237) lives in foul water where it feeds on decaying organic matter. It was named "rat-tailed maggot" because of the long tail-like air-tube which can be extended to the surface when the larva is immersed in water or in decaying muck. This telescopic tube is composed of two segments, one of which can be slipped over the other; at its tip there is a rosette of hairs which keep water out of the air-tube. The body of the larva is about half an inch long. The larval skin contracts to form the dark horny pupal case.

CHAPTER XVI
SNAILS AND MUSSELS
Mollusca

Clams and mussels, oysters, snails and slugs are all mollusks; so are the less known chitons, the squids and the octopus tribe of sea story fame. All these have soft unsegmented bodies, and shells either covering them over the outside as in clams, mussels and snails or concealed in a mantle of flesh as in the squid and octopus. Counting those of land and water, approximately fifty thousand species of mollusks are known and one-fifth of them live in fresh water. All of these fresh water inhabitants are either snails, the class *Gastropoda* (stomach foot), or mussels and clams, the *Pelecypoda* ((hatchet foot).

Habits and dwelling-places.—Snails abound in shallow waters, one to six feet deep, where algæ and water plants, their main food supply, are also abundant. Snails and mussels together make up a very large part of pond and stream populations and are also plentiful in lakes and rivers (Figs. *21, 22*).

In general, large mussels (Fig. 265) live in large bodies of water but there are many exceptions. One known as the white heel-spitter, *Lasmigona complanata*, which is about four inches long, is equally abundant in large and small streams. Snails and the little mussels or "finger-nail" clams so plentiful in brooks and small ponds are also found in rivers and lakes sometimes at a relatively great depth.

Mussels live on the bottom, but snails migrate back and forth from top to bottom. Snails are great travelers and there is no level of the shore waters which is not accessible to them. They trail over the bottoms and along shore, climb the plant stems, glide over the underside of the surface film (Fig. 34) and swing down through the water on mucous threads. They carry a heavy load of shell and they can only move slowly, but they leave no crevice unvisited and have literally taken possession of every level of ponds and the shore waters of lakes.

In water deeper than six or eight feet the molluscan population begins to fall off, the number of species becomes smaller and where it is fifteen or twenty feet deep only a few kinds are found. In his study of the mollusks of Lake Oneida, N. Y., Baker found forty-six species in one to three foot shallows, forty species in water three to six feet deep, and only eleven species at a fifteen to eighteen foot depth. Shallows are the usual haunts of snails yet there are records of pioneers like *Lymnæa* (Fig. 245), *Planorbis* (Fig. 249), and *Valvata* (Fig. 257) which have been found in Lake Michigan at depths of eighty feet.

Associates and enemies of mollusks.—Companies of small snails and other animals seeking the same food can be found beneath nearly every lily pad. Such gatherings usually include a wheel-snail or two, *Planorbis*, a *Physa*, midge larvæ and bristleworms (Fig. 18).

In spite of their shells, snails and mussels are eaten by nearly all kinds of animals larger than themselves. Several leeches such as *Glossiphonia complanata* (Fig. 118) live exclusively on snails and worms. Other animals, certain dragonfly nymphs (*Epicordulia*), giant water-bugs, fishes, frogs, salamanders, turtles, and even muskrats, eat them along with other food. Piles of mussel shells are commonly seen near muskrat holes (Fig. 238). Muskrats carry the mussels out of the muddy shoal water onto land, piling them up near rocks or logs. There they soon die and their shells gape open, exposing their soft bodies to easy access.

FIG. 238.—A Japanese student's sketch of a musk-rat's pile of mussel shells. (Drawn by Fumiko Mitani.)

In his study of the food of fishes in Lake Oneida, N. Y., Baker found that forty-six out of fifty-four species of fish ate mollusks. The brook trout was one of only five kinds in which mollusks made as little as one per cent of the whole diet, on the other hand they made up twenty per cent of the bullhead diet and ninety per cent of that for sturgeons.

Collecting, aquarium study.—A good way to learn something about mollusk society is to take a census of a square foot or two of the pond or brook where they live. (Fig. 239.) If the other organisms which are present be included, leeches, dragonfly and mayfly nymphs, aquatic plants, a fair picture of the community will be secured. Plants provide food for mollusks, mayflies compete with them for the same food, leeches are rank enemies and eat them. Such inter-relations can be equally well studied in lily pad, algal mat and pondweed communities. Mollusks of each kind and sometimes other animals too should be preserved for identification and record (p. 40).

For aquarium study any pond snail is easy to keep, but *Physas* (Fig. 248) are the most active. They will live com-

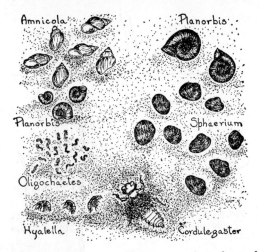

FIG. 239.—Diagram of one square foot of a pool bottom, showing snails and mussels and associated animals.

fortably with the simplest arrangements, a glass of water, with a little fresh supply occasionally added, some scrapings of algæ, and branches of water plants (Fig. 34). For more permanent living quarters the aquarium should contain four to six quarts of water and have a layer of sand and pebbles on the bottom in which a few branches of *Myriophyllum*, *Nitella*, *Elodea*, or other water weed have been planted. If some algal scrappings be thrown into the water algæ will grow on the glass sides if the snails do not keep it too well cleaned. Snails will live the year round in such an aquarium and will lay their eggs on the glass sides, and the embryo snails can be seen developing within their transparent jelly (Fig. 35).

Snails.—*Gastropoda*

Form and habits of water snails.—Snails are not only numerous but conspicuous and familiar. Unlike mussels they travel about in the upper levels of the water where they can be seen;

there their twisted shells attract attention and they are easily remembered. A snail's shell is a spiral cone and beneath its apex is the back or dorsal side of the animal. Most snail shells are right-handed, some are left-handed. When a right-handed shell is held with its opening toward the observer and its apex up, the opening will be at the observer's right. Held in the same position the shell of a left-handed snail will have its opening at the left (Fig. 240).

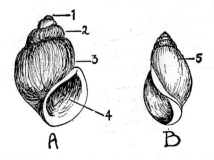

FIG. 240.—Diagrams of snail shells, showing regions and types of twisting. A.—Right-handed shell: 1, apex; 2, spire; 3, body whorl; 4, opening or aperture; 5, lines of growth. B.—Left-handed shell.

Shell is the hardened secretion of surface and border cells, of the fleshy mantle beneath it, and lines of growth show successive additions of new shell. The shell is twisted on an axis known as the columella (Fig. 240).

A snail's body is coiled and twisted like the shell and extends into its apex. A fresh water snail has a distinct head bearing two conspicuous tentacles with a small black eye at the base of each (Fig. 241). Land snails which occasionally wander down to the water margin can be distinguished by their four tentacles. Snails have one to three chitinous jaws in the upper part of the mouth and on the floor of it a ribbon-like tongue or radula whose outer surface is covered with rows of horny teeth (Fig. 241). This radula is their all-important eating tool, a flexible file by which they rasp off the cells of delicate plant stems and clean the algæ from stones and leaves. It is covered with small teeth and hooks, differently shaped and arranged in various species. The diversity of the teeth in different kinds of snails forms the basis for a large part of their classification.

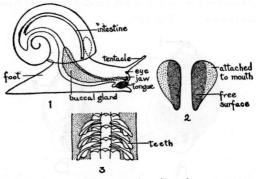

FIG. 241 —1, Diagram of snail; 2, jaws; 3, upper surface of tongue or radula.

Snails glide slowly about on their one large muscular foot over the bottom of which wave-like contractions of muscles constantly pass from front to rear. These quickly succeeding waves can be clearly seen on the feet of snails as they move over the sides of an aquarium or beneath the surface film of water (Fig. 242).

FIG. 242.—Pond snail, showing the under surface of the foot against a glass and (dark bands) the succeeding waves of contraction in the muscles.

Among the aquatic snails, one group, the *Streptoneura*, breathes by means of gills; another, the *Pulmonata*, by a lung-sac. The gills of the streptoneurans lie in the space between the body and the mantle through which water flows freely. They have an abundant circulation of blood to which oxygen is supplied by the water constantly flowing across the gill. Gill-bearing snails have a horny plate or operculum on the upper surface of the foot near the rear end (Fig. 243). When such a snail draws into its shell, pulling its foot after it, the operculum comes last and entirely fills the opening of the shell, thus completely protecting the body. The small, smooth opercula of marine snails, commonly known as "eye-stones," were once much used to remove irritating substances from the eyes. The "eyestone" was slipped under the eyelid in order to increase the flow of the lachrymal fluid and thus wash out the foreign particle. Different species of snails have distinctive opercula. They are often found in the stomachs of fishes and the kind of snail that was eaten can be determined by them.

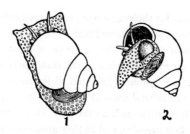

FIG. 243.—A gill-bearing snail showing the operculum: 1, snail extended, operculum on the upper surface of the foot; 2, snail drawing into its shell, pulling the operculum into the opening. (After Baker.)

The lung-sac of the pulmonate snail is an air chamber enclosed by a part of the mantle through which, as in the gill, there is an abundant circulation of blood. A pulmonate snail can take enough air into its lung to last it for a long time under water. An occasional bubble can often be seen escaping from lung-sacs of snails thus submerged.

In some snails the male and female sex organs are in different individuals; others are hermaphrodites with complicated male and female systems within the same animal. Usually two animals mate together, whether hermaphrodites or not. In the family *Lymnæidæ* (Fig. 245) there are some evidences of self fertilization. Many snails lay eggs, depositing them in masses of protecting jelly (Fig. 244), others, such as *Campeloma*, are viviparous, bearing their young alive.

Fig. 244.—Cluster of eggs of pond snail, *Physa*, showing the eggs within their capsules of jelly and these embedded within the general mass.

Eggs.—Snails lay their eggs on any submerged objects, especially upon plants and protected regions of stones. The little groups of them are embedded in drops of crystalline jelly. There are never many eggs in a clutch, each one is surrounded by its individual capsule of jelly and all the capsules are surrounded by the general mass (Fig. 244). Developing snails can be clearly seen through all the jelly; they turn over and over within their capsules, and as they grow older their black eyes and snail hump are clearly recognizable through a hand-lens.

Pond snails, Family Lymnæidæ.—These are air-breathing snails whose shells are thin, with a right-handed coil (Fig. 240), an acute spire and a large body aperture. The animal has a short, rounded foot and flattened, triangular tentacles. These snails live in lakes, ponds, swamps, and smaller streams

and are important in the diet of frogs, fishes, and wading
birds. The eggs are laid in an irregular slender oval mass of
jelly on stones and water plants.

Fig. 245.—Shell of pond snail, *Lymnæa palustris*,
with body aperture shorter than the spire.

Lymnæa palustris.—The shell (Fig. 245) usually has 6
whorls, sometimes more; it varies from pale brown to black
and has a white thickening (callus) on the side of the opening
next to the axis. Length of shell, one and one-fifth inches.

Occurrence.—Widely distributed and in many places the
most common snail.

Fig. 246.—Shell of great pond snail, *Lymnæa
stagnalis*, with long spire and flattened spire whorls.

Great pond snail, Lymnæa stagnalis.—The shell (Fig. 246)
has 6 or 7 whorls, the lower ones very gradually increasing in
diameter so that a long slender spire is formed. Those in the
spire are markedly flat-sided. Length of shell, two and one-
half inches. The animal is horn-colored with a bluish tinge
on its short foot.

The great pond snail lives in the quietest parts of ponds and
slow streams foraging on *Elodea*, *Myriophyllum*, and other
water plants or on rotting vegetation. It often travels on
the underside of the surface film. Some varieties live on the
wave-beaten shores of lakes. It lays one hundred or more
eggs in a single clutch.

Occurrence.—In the northern states throughout the country.

FIG. 247—Shell of *Lymnæa columella*, whose body whorl is three times as large as its spire.

Lymnæa columella (Pseudosuccinea).—The shell (Fig. 247) is greenish or yellowish, with 4 whorls the last of which forms nearly the whole shell; the lines of growth are very heavy. The body aperture is oval, expanded at the lower part. Length of shell, three-quarters of an inch.

Occurrence.—Like *L. stagnalis* this species lives in quiet water on lily pads, among cat-tails; it is rarely in running water. Generally distributed throughout the United States. Baker (Bibliography, p. 421) gives this species as *Pseudosuccinea columella*.

Pouch-snails, tadpole snails, Family Physidæ.—The shells of *Physidæ* are left-handed (Fig. 240), with a very large lower coil, and the spires are sharp-pointed but short. The animal has a narrow foot, pointed behind, and finger-like outgrowths along the edge of its mantle which are very characteristic. These are active snails which are extremely variable in color and shape and very difficult to identify.

Occurrence.—Most of them are found in the United States and Canada.

FIG. 248.—Tadpole snail, *Physa gyrina* (*Physella*): 1, animal showing the slender pointed foot (after Baker); 2, shell.

Tadpole snail, Physa gyrina (Physella gyrina of Baker).—The shell is thickened, heavy looking, with 5 or 6 coils. The body aperture is loop-shaped, the outer lip (Fig. 248) is apt to be flattened and to join the body at a sharp angle. Length one-half to three-quarters of an inch. Many references to *P. heterostropha* apply to this snail (Baker, Bibliography, p. 421).

Occurrence.—Common in eastern states.

Wheel-snails, Family Planorbidæ.—These are air-breathing snails without an operculum whose shells are twisted right or left in a flattened coil, with the spire sunken in the center.

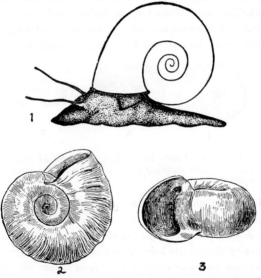

Fig. 249.—Three-coiled snail, *Planorbis trivolvis:* 1, animal expanded (after Baker); 2, shell coils; 3, shell showing body aperture.

Three-coiled snail, Planorbis trivolvis (Helisoma trivolvis of Baker).—The shells are transversely lined and thin lipped. Width of shell, about five-sixths of an inch. Typical *trivolvis* lives in protected places, bays, pools, marshes, and swamps, where the water is shallow. It is one of the larger wheel-snails; this and its expanded body aperture (Fig. 249) help to identify it.

FIG. 250.—*Trivolvis parvus:* 1, shell coils; 2, shell showing body aperture.

Trivolvis parvus (Graulus parvus of Baker).—Its shell (Fig. 250) is small, only one-fifth of an inch wide, with 3 or 4 rapidly enlarging coils. These very small wheel-snails are common in mats of filamentous algæ (p. 50), on pondweeds and *Myriophyllum*, on most thick submerged vegetation.

FIG. 251.—Hairy wheel-snail, *Planorbis hirsutus:* 1 and 2, shell showing coils; 3, shell showing body aperture.

Hairy wheel-snail, Planorbis hirsutus (Graulus hirsutus of Baker).—These snails (Fig. 251) are found in still water of ditches and swamps. They are sometimes distinctly recognizable by the delicate hair-like projections of the outer shell layer; these disappear when the outer layer is worn off. Shell small, about one-fifth of an inch. Found in the eastern and northern United States.

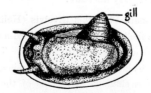

FIG. 252.—Limpet, *Ancylus (Ferrissia* of Baker); underside of the animal showing its gill.

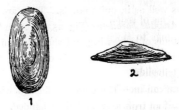

FIG. 253.—Fresh water limpet, *Ancylus parallelus* (*Ferrissia parallela* of Baker): 1, shell from above showing the parallel sides; 2, the low cone in side view.

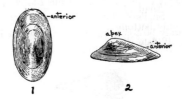

FIG. 254.—Fresh water limpet, *Ancylus rivularis* (*Ferrissia rivularia* of Baker): 1, shell from above showing the slight flare of the front end; 2, side view.

Fresh water limpets, Family Ancylidæ.—The shells are small, about one-fifth of an inch long, shaped like a low cone. The animal has short blunt tentacles and a very large oval foot. It has a lung-sac like other air-breathing snails but also has a cone-shaped gill or pseudobranch extending out beyond the shell on the left side (Fig. 252). These snails live

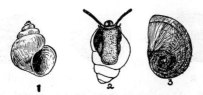

FIG. 255.—1, Shell of *Amnicola limosa*; 2, animal of *Amnicola limosa porata*, showing the truncated foot and slender tentacles; 3, operculum of the last variety, greatly enlarged (2, 3 after Baker).

in streams as well as in quiet ponds. They are common on vegetation; *Ancylus parallelus* (Fig. 253) is often found on the submerged stems of sedges in pond shallows, but *A. rivularis* (Fig. 254) clings to stones in lively currents. Limpets are generally distributed.

Family Amnicolidæ.—These are small snails with shells not more than half an inch long, and right-handed. The animal has an oblong foot truncated in front and rounded behind (Fig. 255); its right gill is the only one developed. These snails lay eggs, sometimes deposited on the shells of other snails in clusters of eight or ten, as in the genus *Bulimus*, or singly as in *Amnicola*. Snails of this family are common in shallow water, on sandy bottoms, but also on pondweeds and other vegetation. Widely distributed and common.

FIG. 256.—Shell of *Goniobasis*.

FIG. 257.—*Valvata tricarinata:* 1, animal (after Baker); 2 shell, showing keeled edge of whorls; 3, shell, showing operculum in the body aperture and cavity in the base of the spire; 4, shell from the side, showing the blunt apex of the spire.

Family Pleuroceridæ, Goniobasis.—These are gill-bearing snails with an operculum. The shells have a long, conical, right-handed spiral with 7 or more whorls (Fig. 256); full grown ones are one and one quarter inches long. The animals live in rapid currents, among water plants on lake shores, in varied habitats.

Family Valvatidæ.—These snails (Fig. 257) are small, with shells not more than a quarter of an inch wide, with prominent keels or ridges on the outer surface. The animals have a short siphon which is two-lobed in front. The gills are extended out of the shell when the snail is moving; the left one is carried like a plume; the right is only a degenerate finger-like process. Found in lakes in both shallow and deep water. Widely distributed.

Fig. 258.—*Vivipara contectoides*, which has the top-shaped shell characteristic of the family; shell aperture filled by the concave operculum.

Family Viviparidæ.—The shells of these gill-bearing snails (Fig. 258) are globular or top-shaped, moderately large but not more than two inches long. The young snails are born alive. The species *Vivipara contectoides* has four brown bands on the body whorl. Found in lakes and rivers on muddy bottoms.

Mussels—*Pelecypoda*

Mussels are the only other fresh water mollusks besides the snails. They are familiar either as rather large, dark-shelled mussels which burrow in muddy bottoms or as "finger-nail clams" lying upon the bottoms of clear pools and brooks. **All of** them have two shells made by the hardened secretion of the

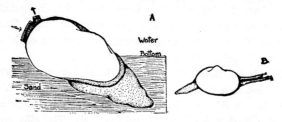

FIG. 259.—A.—A large mussel with its fleshy foot pushed out into the mud. Arrows indicate water passing in and out of the "neck" or siphon (after Baker). B.—A "finger-nail clam" (*Sphæridæ*), showing its delicate two-parted siphon (modified after Baker).

fleshy mantle (Fig. 261) beneath, and all have a soft more or less hatchet-shaped foot which has given them the name *Pelecypoda* or hatchet-footed. At the rear end of the body is the tube-like siphon (Fig. 259) through which water passes in and out of the cavity within the folds of the mantle. In salt water clams the siphon is called the "neck," as in "little neck clams". Neither clams nor mussels have heads but their mouths are located at the end opposite the siphon, recognizable from the outside by the greater width of the shell.

Form and movements of the shell.—The two shells or valves are joined by a spring-hinge at the back near the umbo (Fig. 260) and the closure is strengthened by hinge teeth. The spring-hinge automatically opens the shells when they are not pulled together by the animal. They are closed together by means of two large adductor muscles whose opposite ends are attached to opposing shells. Their attachment places can be seen on the shell of any bivalve (Fig. 260). The familiar "fried scallops" are the adductor muscles of the scallop (Pecten). When a mussel relaxes its adductor muscles they stretch and let the shells open automatically. This occurs when a mussel extends its foot out between its shells

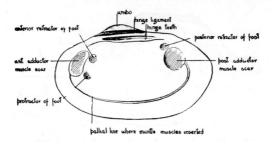

FIG. 260.—Mussel shell: the inner surface, with scars made by the attachment of muscle.

(Fig. 259) or lies at rest on the bottom with its shells partly open. When they gape wide apart, the mussel is usually dead.

Growth of the shell.—The shell is produced by the outer surface and border of the mantle. Additions are built on at the edge and there the shell is newest and thinnest. In the larger muscles there is a dark horny covering or periostracum on the outside, then a thick limy layer, and finally the pearly lining. The outer surface of the shell is marked by lines or rings, usually more conspicuous than the similar ones on snail shells. These heavy lines or ridges seem to indicate periods when cold or lack of food or some other cause lowered the activity of the animal and kept it from secreting very much new shell. They signify slow shell growth and the spaces between them mark periods of rapid shell growth. Both hard and easy times in the mussel's life are recorded by these lines of growth.

Form of the body.—These headless mussels rely entirely upon currents of water to bring them food and oxygen. Such currents are created by the movements of microscopic cilia borne upon the mantle and body surfaces. By their motion water is brought into the incurrent siphon, and distributed through the gills and toward the mouth, carrying minute food

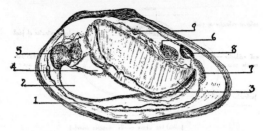

FIG. 261.—A mussel, with the shell and mantle of its left side removed to show the body lying within the mantle cavity: 1, mantle flap of right side; 2, foot; 3, gills of left side; 4, triangular lip hiding the mouth; 5, anterior and 6, posterior adductor muscles; 7, incurrent and 8, excurrent siphons which have been cut open; 9, cut edge of mantle of left side.

particles with it. The foot is the fleshy process by which mussels plough their way through the mud. Mussels are often said to "lie on the bottom with their tongues out". These "tongues" are their feet. The mussel's whole body, gills, foot, and other organs lie within the mantle cavity.

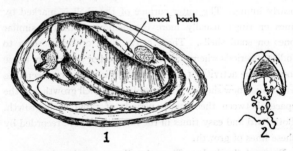

FIG. 262.—1, A female mussel, with the left valve of shell and mantle removed to show the brood pouch; 2, a larval mussel or glochidium much enlarged.

Eggs and young.—The small mussels (*Sphæridæ*) are hermaphrodites but in the large ones eggs are produced by one in-

dividual and the sperm cells by another. Eggs pass from the
ovary into the mantle cavity and thence into the gills of the
parent mussel. Each gill is a flattened sac, partitioned off
into water tubes, and currents of water carry the eggs into
their open tops. Sperm cells are discharged into the water
by a male which is usually nearby. They are carried through
the incurrent siphon of the female and finally into her gill
where fertilization of the eggs takes place. Thus the thin
curtain-like gill becomes the brood pouch (Fig. 262) and each
water tube is filled with eggs like peas packed in a pod.
There the developing embryos remain until they have become glochidia, larval mussels with their first juvenile shells.

A brood pouch is brown or whitish according to the color
of the eggs or embryos contained in it and so full that the
slightest tear in it will bring them streaming out like sand.
The number of embryos in the pouches varies with the species;
according to counts and computations there may be from
seventy-five thousand to three million of them to a parent.
In the little glochidia the shells gape wide open, but are
snapped together intermittently by the single adductor
muscle. If a few glochidia are put in a drop of water on a
piece of glass their convulsive snapping can be seen easily
with a hand-lens. The least jar in the water will start them
clapping almost in unison and if a drop of fish blood or a little
salt is dropped into the water there will be the wildest excitement.

Their persistent snapping stands the glochidia in good stead
when they are thrown out of the brood pouch. Then their

Fig. 263.—Minnow with larval mussels or glochidia clinging to its fins and body, taken from a brook
in midwinter.

only chance for life is in clamping their shells into the bodies, gills, and fins of fishes (Fig. 263). They become imbedded in the flesh, the skin grows over them, and they are protected and nourished by the fish, being carried as actual parasites for several weeks.

The glochidia of one species of mussel will usually stay only on certain species of fish and if they get onto the wrong one they will drop off. This seems to be a proof of their extreme sensitivity like that shown in their behavior toward fish blood.

Pearly mussels, Family Unionidæ.—These are large mussels usually three or four inches long. Their shells are covered with a dark colored horny periostracum and the inside is pearly. The outer gill is used as a brood pouch. They are abundant in the larger lakes and streams but are by no means confined to them.

This family includes all of the large mussels except a few now grouped in the *Margaritanidæ*. The family *Unionidæ* has been split up into subfamilies containing many genera. Representatives of only two genera are mentioned here. A detailed treatment of the mussels will be found in Ward and Whipple's "Fresh-Water Biology" and Baker's "Fresh Water Mollusca of Wisconsin."

FIG. 264.—Right side of *Elliptio complanatus*.

Elliptio complanatus (formerly Unio complanatus).—The shells (Fig. 264) are thick, and oval or elongate, with smooth or slightly corrugated surfaces. Their linings are nearly always purplish and coppery. The breeding season is from the last of April to the middle of May; the shells of the glochidia are without hooks.

Found in creeks and small rivers on muddy bottoms in shallow water, sometimes in sand. A common mussel on the Atlantic slope to Georgia.

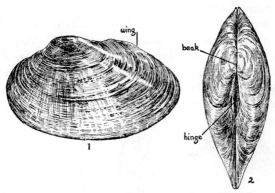

FIG. 265.—Paper-shell mussel, *Anodonta cataracta*
1, left valve; 2, shell, showing beaks and hinge.

Paper-shells, Anodonta.—The shells are thin, generally smooth and shining, often winged posteriorly (Fig. 265). The outer surface is greenish or brown and is often marked by light and dark concentric bands indicating rest periods in growth (p. 317); the lining is dull white or pinkish. The breeding season is in late summer. When full the brood pouch of the outer gill looks like a thick brown pad. The glochidia can be found in the pouches through October and often into mid-winter; each shell bears a hook. Length of adult about 4 inches.

Found in clear running streams, also in lakes. Common on the Atlantic slope, south to South Carolina.

Finger-nail clams, Family Sphæridæ.—Few of these small white mussels or "finger-nail clams" are more than half an inch long; *Sphærium sulcatum* (Fig. 266), one of the largest of the family, measures three-quarters. The shells are thin, usually white, or yellowish, and the lining is dull white. The form of the animals is similar to that of the larger mussels but the brood pouch is formed by the inner gill and the number of young is comparatively small, from two to twenty varying with the species. The breeding season seems to continue more or less through the year.

Members of this family live in lakes and rivers as well as in ponds and pools and small streams (Fig. 22). They live on bottoms of sand and mud or clay and often creep up over plant stems. They are widely distributed, almost sure to be found in any kind of fresh water. Species are numerous and difficult to distinguish.

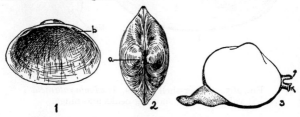

Fig. 266.—Sphere-shells, *Sphærium*: 1, *S. sulcatum*, left valve, showing small hinge teeth (*b*); 2, same shell with centrally placed beaks (*a*); 3, animal of *S. striatum*, showing divided siphon (after Baker).

Sphere-shells, Sphærium.—Mussels of this genus have oval shells and centrally placed beaks (Fig. 266); the hinge teeth are very small. The incurrent and excurrent siphons are separate except at the base. The unusually large species *S. sulcatum* is often found in moderately swift streams. East of the Rocky Mountains.

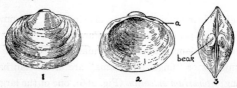

Fig. 267.—Shell of *Musculium* showing the cap-like beaks: 1, left valve; 2, inner surface of right valve, hinge teeth hardly developed (*a*); 3, shell with cap-like beak.

Musculium.—The shells of *Musculium* are thinner than those of *Sphærium;* the hinge teeth are small, almost missing, and in nearly all of the species the beaks are cap-like (Fig. 267). The siphons are longer than those of *Sphærium* and are attached to each other throughout their length. Length of the shells, three-eighths of an inch. *Musculium* and *Sphærium* live in the same kind of haunts.

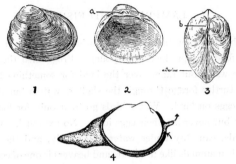

Fig. 268.—Pill clam, *Pisidium:* 1, *P. virginicum,* right valve, note the long anterior end; 2, same, left valve from within, showing cardinal teeth (*a*); 3, same, shell showing beaks (*b*) located posterior to the center; 4, animal of *P. politum decorum,* showing the single siphon (after Baker).

Pill-clams, Pisidium.—The valves of the shell are slightly unequal in size; there is one cardinal tooth in the right and two in the left valve (Fig. 268). The foot is tongue-shaped and large for the size of the animal. The siphon is short and only the excurrent part is present; water enters the mantle cavity through a cleft in the mantle. Like the other small mussels the members of this genus live in varied habitats. They not only burrow in mud but they crawl up on plants; *Elodea, Potamogetons,* and floating algæ frequently hold many of them. *Pisidium virginicum* is recognizable by its size, unusually large for *Pisidium,* its oblique shell and peculiar cardinal teeth. Length of shells, one-quarter to three-eighths of an inch.

CHAPTER XVII

LAMPREYS AND FISHES

Fishes belong in the water and nowhere else; there they find their food and produce their young. Frogs shed their eggs in the water but range over the land for something to eat; pond turtles forage through the shallow waters but deposit their eggs on land. Water birds go to it only for food and safety but never lay their eggs in it. No mammal, not even a whale, can stay under water indefinitely, and the life of aquatic mammals like muskrats and beavers is one of constant come and go from water to land. But fishes are ever-present in water society—the only group of vertebrates which can survive a constant water environment.

Fishes have taken possession of the streams and lakes as well as the sea. They are surface skimmers and bottom feeders, dwellers in rapids and in still coves; they are big and little, long and slender or short and thick, drab gray or silver and gold colored, metallic blue and green.

Structure of fishes.—All are vertebrates. They breathe by means of gills; they all have fins, and they are usually covered with scales. Most of them lay eggs which are fertilized in the open water as soon as they are laid, but some give birth to living young. The eggs of most marine fishes float upon the surface, but those of fresh water fishes lie loosely on the bottom or are stuck fast to stones. All fish eggs are well stocked with yolk, and the young fish carry a yolk-sac about with them for several days after they hatch and are thus well provided with food wherever they go.

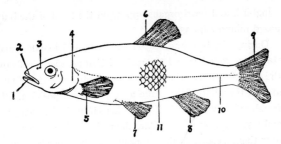

FIG. 269.—Diagram of a fish: 1, mandible; 2, premaxillary; 3, nostrils; 4, operculum or gill cover; 5, pectoral fin; 6, dorsal fin; 7, ventral or pelvic fin; 8, anal fin; 9, caudal fin; 10, lateral line of sense organs; 11, scales.

The fins of fishes are thin membranes supported by stiff spines or by finely segmented rods, the fin rays, which are often branched (Fig. 269). Fins are very constant in number and position. Behind the head are the paired pectoral fins, and further backward, low down on the sides of the body, are the paired pelvic or ventral fins; others—the dorsal, anal, and caudal fins—are single.

The operculum forms part of a fish's cheek and covers the four blood-filled gills, that are often visible when it is lifted in breathing. The jawbones, mandible and movable premaxillary, usually bear sharp teeth, and besides these, fishes have several patches of short teeth on the roof of the mouth.

Breeding habits.—As the spawning season approaches, fishes move toward the shores of ponds and lakes or upstream in the creeks. Some of them, such as perch and sunfish, only swim in among nearby weeds or protecting stones. The journeys vary from such short ones to the famous migrations of river salmon, extending over hundreds of miles; but they all end at spawning grounds or nesting sites. During this time color differences between male and female appear or become more marked. Fins of the male darters redden, the colors of male sunfish (Pl. XVIII) take on the brilliance of a hummingbird, and pearl organs appear on the head of the blunt-nosed minnow (p. 336).

During the breeding season the male and female usually stay close together and the male discharges sperm cells over the eggs the instant they are scattered into the water. Often at this time both fishes take a very definite position. The female rainbow darter half buries herself in the bottom gravel and lays a few eggs at a time, the male shedding sperm cells over them as soon as they appear. Many fishes build nests, sometimes elaborate and constructed by both parents, sometimes only by the male, as in the brook stickleback (p. 339), which fashions its nest and then swims forth to coerce a mate into it.

The eggs may be guarded and cared for, the male often taking the greater if not the sole responsibility for them. Among the yellow catfishes both parents keep the eggs clean by stirring and fanning them with their fins; occasionally they take a few into their mouths, then spit them out again, repeating the performance over and over. After hatching, they tend the young fry even more thoroughly and turn them over and about, using their barbels (Fig. 278) for stirring rods.

Aquarium study.—Several of the fishes later mentioned live well in aquaria, but whatever their kind, they must be small, unless the aquarium is a very large one. A fish about one inch long should be given a gallon of water, and water should always be allowed in proportion to the size and number of fishes. They should have plenty of water plants (p. 39) about them and a small supply of food. Natural food is the best for them, is healthier and far more interesting than prepared fish foods. The best natural fish foods are small crustaceans like *Daphnia* and *Cyclops*, midge larvæ, and other small insects, especially the nymphs of quiet water mayflies.

In selecting the fishes it is important to choose those which will live peaceably together. Different kinds of minnows will do this, but sunfishes, catfishes, and sticklebacks will not.

LAMPREYS AND FISHES

A pair of the hardier sticklebacks (p. 339) will sometimes nest and carry on all their egglaying activities in a comfortable aquarium supplied with their building materials.

Fall is the best time to collect fishes for aquaria. They are in good condition then and during the cool weather it is easier for them to get used to the close aquarium. When they are newly captured they are liable to jump out of the water; they are safer if the aquarium is kept covered with a screen. If an aquarium is properly balanced the water will not need changing (p. 39); and if cleaning becomes necessary, it is better to pour the old water out, strain it, aërate it by pouring it through the air, and then use it again. Fishes get on best in the old water to which they have grown accustomed.

There are several good books on aquarium making; some of these are listed in the Bibliography (p. 409).

Common brook and pond fishes.—A few families of pond and small-stream fishes are briefly discussed here. These are selected because they are common, or easy to observe, or both. Keys and more particular descriptions can be found in Jordan's "Manual of the Vertebrates" and other books named in the Bibliography (p. 421).

Fig. 270.—Lake lamprey, *Petromyzon marinus*, attached to a fish. Above the pectoral and ventral fins are scars showing where other lampreys made ragged openings with their rasping tongues. (Pen drawing by S. H. Gage.)

Lampreys.—*Petromyzonidæ*

Lake lamprey, Petromyzon marinus.—Lampreys are neither eels nor true fishes although they resemble both. Almost every feature of a lamprey is peculiar. Its most striking one is the large suction disk which surrounds the mouth, bearing circlets of horny teeth upon its surface. The adult lamprey fastens this armored oral disk to the side of a fish, rasps its teeth into the flesh and sucks out the blood, and the fish carries it about as long as it is able to swim (Fig. 270).

Most species of lampreys pass part of their lives in salt water but several kinds live entirely in fresh water and all of them lay their eggs there. The lake lamprey or lamprey eel, *Petromyzon marinus*, is one of those which lives in fresh water. It is a land-locked form, generally considered the same species as the great sea lamprey. Lampreys are abundant in the Finger Lakes and tributary streams and in Oneida Lake alone it is estimated that tons of fish are killed by them every year.

In spring these lampreys leave the lakes and migrate up the creeks. They rest by day but travel by night until they finally reach the riffly shallows where they make their nests. There the male lamprey or a pair working together clears a sort of shallow basin on the bottom, moving pebbles away from a middle space and piling them in a low circular wall surrounding it. They pick up the stones with their oral disks, sometimes actually carrying them a foot or more.

After the nest is completed the lampreys mate. They cling to its upstream wall as if resting, but their rest is brief. Using his oral sucker the male grasps the female behind her head, twines his tail tightly against her sides, and for a short period, generally only a few seconds, the two lampreys shake and twist their bodies in great excitement. During this time the eggs are laid and almost immediately buried beneath the sand which is whirled over them by the struggling lampreys. By the time the mating excitement is over the eggs are mostly covered but as soon as they separate the two lampreys move more sand and pebbles over them. They fan the sand with their tails, the females having an extra growth of fin (anal) at this time of year. They work at this for a few minutes.

and then mate again. At each mating the female lays 20 to 40 eggs, and matings are kept up at intervals for 2 to 4 days until 25,000 or 35,000 eggs are laid. In streams which flow into Cayuga Lake the lamprey spawning season lasts through April, May and June. The worm-like eyeless and toothless larvæ stay in the nest for a few weeks after hatching, and then burrow into the sand, living like worms in the stream banks until they are about five inches long, when they transform to the adult shape. Adult lampreys live wholly upon fish blood except during their actual breeding season. They are ravenous for a long time before this and kill hundreds of fish, which appear floating upon the surface with large holes bored through their sides. The upturned body of a dead fish with its quota of lamprey holes is a familiar sight in more than one of the New York Finger Lakes.

Size.—Length of adults 2 to 3 feet.

Distribution.—Lampreys which live entirely in fresh water are found in the Great Lakes and their tributaries and in some streams in New England and the middle Atlantic states. Along the Atlantic coast large sea lampreys go up the streams to spawn. They are found in the Merrimac River, the Connecticut, the Delaware, and some of the streams of Long Island.

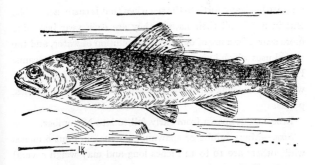

FIG. 271.—Brook trout, *Salvelinus fontinalis.*

Trout—*Salmonidæ*

Brook trout, Salvelinus fontinalis.—Brook trout are the choicest of the famous salmon family, the symbol of high spirited gaminess in fish life. In America several kinds of fishes are called trout and the word does not connote the wild grace and delicacy which especially belong to real trout. But the English keep the special name "charr" for this branch of the salmon family. Other members of this genus are the Rangeley Lake trout (*Salvelinus oquassa*), and the "Dolly Varden" trout or salmon (*Salvelinus malma*) which lives in streams west of the Rocky Mountains. These and other trout in the genus *Salvelinus* are brown or olive colored, spotted with gray or scarlet, and their fins are tinged with bright colors. Their scales are small and well hidden in the skin.

The brook trout, *Salvelinus fontinalis* (Fig. 271), is covered with red spots on a mottled black and olive background which fades almost to white upon the ventral side. It is heavier headed than other "charrs," rather large mouthed, and though it varies in size with its living place, it seldom weighs more than seven pounds and is usually smaller. Brook trout can live only in clear cold water, but it does not matter whether they are in ponds or brooks, or rivers, and they will even migrate back and forth to the sea when that is easily accessible. But in nearly all their haunts they are each year becoming more scarce because of overfishing, pollution of water, and the varied uses which humanity has made of their native streams. For most persons, even many sportsmen, the place of the wild trout is being filled by fattened trout reared in private ponds.

Brook trout spawn from early fall to late November.

Size.—Many adults of spawning age measure but 6 inches while others are 10 to 12 inches long and may weigh several pounds.

Distribution.—Only east of the Mississippi and Saskatchewan Rivers; from northern Georgia to Labrador and Hudson Bay.

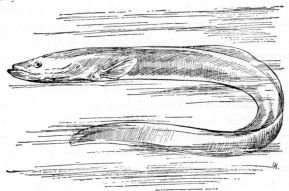

Fɪɢ. 272.—American eel, *Anguilla bostoniensis.*

Eels—*Anguillidæ*

American eel, Anguilla bostoniensis.—Fresh water eels (Fig. 272) are snake-like fishes which live in fresh water from their early youth to breeding time and then migrate into salt water, probably never to return again. The eels which come up the streams are the young ones of another generation which have traveled the long and unknown way from the sea.

Fullgrown eels are about three feet long, plain colored, greenish brown above and pale greenish gray beneath. Every inch of their bodies is sinuous and flexible, well earning the phrase "squirms like an eel."

During their fresh water sojourn eels usually live on the muddy bottoms of streams or in stream-fed ponds. Although they generally seek deep streams they often work their way up brooks along the coast. It is a surprising but not a unique experience to catch an eel on the hook which is meant for a brook trout. Sometimes eels come out of the water and hide under stones in swampy ground a few feet from the shores and they have been seen foraging on the sand along stream sides.

Eels eat almost any animals dead or alive—insects, fishes, frogs, water-rats—as well as aquatic plants.

The life history of eels was not completely known until 1925 when Schmidt published his studies of both American and European species. The breeding place of American eels appears to be north of the West Indies, west and south of regions where European eels breed. Eels spawn in these deep waters and the eggs hatch into transparent floating larvæ. American eels keep their larval form for about a year during which they drift near the surface. Then they are caught in the current of the Gulf Stream and carried toward the American coasts. Only when they near the coastal waters, at a depth of 3000 feet or less, do they begin to take on the shape of adult eels. Finally small eels but 2 or 3 inches long begin to come up the rivers in great numbers. In Rhode Island young eels go up the Taunton River through April and May; in some other rivers they appear later; in many of them, thousands can be seen on the mud flats at river mouths when the tide is out. Like lampreys they rest by day and travel by night, with unbroken persistence working their way up toward the regions forsaken by their parents. Only the females persevere to the head waters; the males stay in the lower parts of the stream. They live in these places for 6 or 8 years and then another change comes over them. They cease eating, their skins turn white and shimmering and they begin their long journey to the sea. These are the "silver eels" which are caught in traps, as they journey downstream, resting by day and moving by night as they did when they traveled upstream 6 or 8 years before.

Size.—Fullgrown, 3 to 4 feet long.

Suckers—*Catostomidæ*

Common sucker, mullet, Catostomus commersonii.—Common or white suckers are easily recognized by the rounded

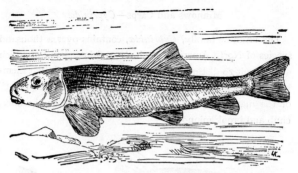

FIG. 273.—Common sucker, *Catostomus commersonii*.

sucking mouths (Fig. 273) located well under the head, not at the end of it as in most fishes, and by their thick fleshy lips. Fullgrown suckers may be a foot long, but in small streams they tend to be much shorter.

In early spring soon after the ice breaks, suckers usually swim upstream into the shallows to lay their eggs, but this does not appear to be a universal habit, for some spawn in ponds. By late July the younger fish are nearly an inch long, and at this stage they have terminal mouths instead of sucking ones like their parents. Although suckers are usually a nondescript olive, during the breeding season the fins of the male become tinged with rose color. One female spawns with two males, one of them crowding against each side of her, discharging their milky sperm fluid (milt) as soon as any eggs leave her body.

Suckers are bottom feeders on mud rich in diatoms, midges, worms, and mollusks. They are used, to some extent, for food, and those of Lake Erie are of considerable commercial importance.

Size.—Up to 18 inches, or more, but this is unusually large especially for small streams.

Distribution.—Abundant in almost every small stream and pond east of the Rocky Mountains.

Minnows and Carps—*Cyprinidæ*

The minnow family, *Cyprinidæ*, contains over a thousand species of North American fresh water fishes, many of which are difficult to distinguish from one another. Familiar members of the family are the large German carp or lake "trout" of the markets, gold fish, or such small fishes as the dace, chub and brook minnows.

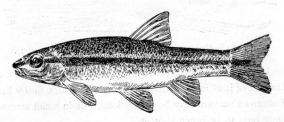

FIG. 274.—Black-nosed dace, *Rhinichthys atronasus.*

Black-nosed dace, Rhinichthys atronasus.—This is a little minnow (Fig. 274) usually less than three inches long, which can be caught by shuffling the stones and gravel of brook beds, at the same time holding the net on the downstream side of them (p. 34). During the fall and winter months they are almost sure to be carrying young mussels on their fins (p. 319).

The "black-nose" is marked by a broad black band which runs along each side of its body from the tip of the nose back to the tail, separating the olive green of the back from the silvery white of the underside. The short underjaw makes its head look blunt.

Black-nosed dace avoid the wide creeks and live in little streams where there are rapids and clear pools. They are nearly always found in trout streams and brook trout are known to eat the young ones. They breed in spring and early summer. Then the male's fins are tinged with red and the long black stripe is bordered with bronze. Although they are common fishes very little has been written about their spawning habits.

Size.—3 inches.

Distribution.—New England to Minnesota, southward to Oklahoma; very common.

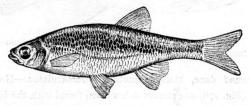

Fig. 275.—Common shiner, *Notropis cornutus.*

Common shiner, redfin, Notropis cornutus.—Shiners (Fig. 275) are abundant in most brooks and creeks whether they are warm ones or cold. Several of the silvery hued minnows are called shiners but the true one is the common shiner or redfin, known as the shiner to fishermen, who use it for black bass bait. It is about five inches long and has a deep, compressed body whose sides are covered by diamond-shaped scales. Its back is olive green, the rest of the body silvery white. In the breeding season the fins of the male are bordered with red, its back is iridescent blue, and its sides are rainbow hued. At this time little horny cones appear on its head, giving it the names "horny head" and buck fish.

Redfins spawn during May and June. A single pair or often a small school of a single male and several females assemble in a riffle 6 to 8 inches deep. The nest is a basin-shaped clearing in the gravelly bottom, about a foot in diameter and a couple of inches deep. According to one observation of Dr. G. C. Embody, just as soon as the eggs were dropped to the bottom they were sought as food by other dace, which wedged their bodies in between stones in pursuit of them.

Size.—Up to 8 inches.

Distribution.—East of the Rockies except Texas; very common.

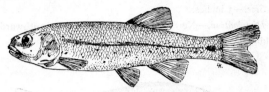

Fig. 276.—Horned dace, *Semotilus atromaculatus.*

Horned dace, chub, Semotilus atromaculatus.—Horned dace (Fig. 276) are stream fishes often found with the black-nosed dace. They are dusky bluish in color with a conspicuous black spot at the base of the dorsal fin, which is bordered with red in the male. During the breeding season through May and July the heads of the males are orange colored and are covered with little hornlike growths or "pearl organs," which have given them the name of horned dace.

The male builds the nest in the riffles. It is a shallow pit walled with small stones which he pushes into position with his head. Females enter the nesting basin, lay a few eggs and leave it, but the male remains to guard them.

Size.—10 inches.

Distribution.—Maine to Wyoming, south to Alabama; common.

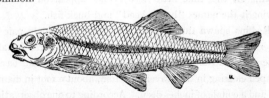

Fig. 277.—Blunt-nosed minnow, *Hyborhynchus notatus.*

Blunt-nosed minnow, Hyborhynchus notatus.—The blunt-nosed minnows (Fig. 277) are never more than four inches long, olive colored, bluish on the sides lighted with dull silver, and have a black spot at the base of the dorsal fin and another at the base of the caudal fin. They frequent small streams, either muddy shoals or gravelly bottoms, and they breed in quiet water, two feet or so deep. The eggs have been found glued on to the undersides of stones or boards and closely guarded by the males. The breeding season extends through late May to mid-July.

Other names for this minnow are spotted minnow, flathead, and chub.

Size.—4 inches.

Distribution.—Quebec to Dakota, southward to Alabama; very common in small streams of the Alleghanies.

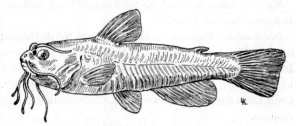

FIG. 278.—Common bullhead, *Ameirus nebulosus.*

Catfishes—*Ameiuridæ*

Bullheads and Catfishes.—The barbels or "whiskers" of the many species of bullheads and catfishes easily distinguish them from all other fresh water fishes. They are smooth skinned, flat headed, large mouthed, and dull colored fishes which have a knoblike, fleshy fin behind the dorsal fin. The common names, bullheads and catfishes, are used interchangeably. The name stonecat is used for the members of this family which can sting by means of the spine on the front edge of the pectoral fin and its associated poison gland.

There are few ponds and creeks without bullheads or catfishes in them. The common bullhead or horned pout, living in ponds and sluggish streams, is the commonest of the smaller catfishes (Fig. 278). It is dark yellowish brown above, varying to black, mottled on its sides and lighter beneath. The black bullhead (*A. melos*) is very similar but small—not more than 6 inches long—and almost black.

Most of the stonecats, *Schilbeodes*, live among the stones in the riffles of rapid streams, skulking under the stones and feeding upon insects, entomostracans, minnows, sometimes crayfish. Their opaque yellow eggs are fastened to the under sides of stones, in masses about two inches across and an inch thick; they spawn in June and July. Names for various fishes of this family are common bullhead, horned pout, stonecat, mongrel bullhead, deepwater bullhead.

Size.—Common bullhead, up to 18 inches; black bullhead, 10 inches; stonecat, 12 inches.

Distribution.—Common bullhead, Maine to North Dakota; south to Florida; introduced into California; very common. Black bullhead, northern New York to Nebraska; southward to Kentucky; common, especially westward. Stonecats, Great Lakes region and westward to Montana; south to Texas; common.

FIG. 279.—Common pickerel, *Esox niger*.

Pickerels—*Esocidæ*

Common or chain pickerel, Esox niger.—Pickerel live in sluggish streams and in large ponds and lakes, where they lurk among the weeds and beneath the lily pads. They have slender bodies, long flat heads, and projecting underjaws which contribute to their sullen watchful expression (Fig. 279).

Like their relatives, the common pickerels hang stately and quiet in the shadows of floating leaves, painted into the background by the olive brown and olive green network which covers all but the pale undersides of their bodies. Now and then they dart forth as swift as arrows, and clutching a hapless fish or a frog, take it down at a gulp and resume their motionless watch.

Size.—Up to 24 inches.

Distribution.—Maine to Florida, west to Arkansas; common.

Sticklebacks—*Gasterosteidæ*

The stickleback family is a tribe of fishes between two and three inches long which have a row of sharp upstanding spines on their backs. They live among the weeds of small streams and are famous both for their pugnacity, and their industry in nest-building. The sticklebacks are generally greedy and quarrelsome; they will attack others, eat their eggs, and keep themselves generally busy with other fishes' affairs.

Brook stickleback, Eucalia inconstans.—The brook stickleback has four free spines and a fifth spine which is attached to the dorsal fin and is marked with indistinct dark bars across its back (Pl. XVIII). In spring the male's back is almost black, lightening to yellow beneath; at the same time the female is olive colored, mottled and dotted with brown.

The nests of sticklebacks look like birds' nests and like them are made of plant stems, but these nests are stuck together by a fluid from the kidneys of the male; the females take no responsibility in its building.

Each nest is a delicate sphere about three-quarters of an inch in diameter, with a hole on one side. It is made of fine fibres, plant stems, and filaments of algæ and attached to a plant stem or a submerged twig. Against a background of leaves and plant stems these little nests are well nigh undiscoverable except by a chance happening. The male stickle-

Pl. XVIII.—1, Brook stickleback, *Eucalia inconstans;* its nest is made of algæ and plant stems; 2, common sunfish, *Eupomotis gibbosus;* its nest is a basin-like clearing on the pond bottom.

PLATE XVIII

back selects the nest site, bites off the plant stems, smears them over with his mucous cement, smooths the walls by repeatedly pushing his head and body against them and finally swims outside for a mate and drives her into the finished nest. She stays inside the nest a little time, laying the eggs, and he keeps guard, swimming round and round it. She swims out as soon as she has laid the eggs, and he immediately enters the nest to pour the sperm cells over them. This performance may be repeated several times in quick succession by the same male and different females.

Sticklebacks can be kept in a balanced aquarium and if they are supplied with proper material the males of breeding pairs will build their nests just as in the open.

Size.—Length up to 2½ inches.

Distribution.—New York to Kansas and northward; common.

Sunfishes and Bass—*Centrachidæ*

Sunfish, "pumpkin seed," Eupomotis gibbosus.—The sunfishes and their relatives, the rock bass and the black bass, are all food fishes, beautiful and gamey, too. Probably best known of all of them is the common sunfish or pumpkin seed, of less economic importance because of its small size, but greatly treasured as countless strings of "pumpkin seeds" could testify.

"Pumpkin seeds" are shaped like their namesakes. When they are seen from above or in the pond bank shadows they are drab olive colored, but as soon as they move into the sunshine their sides are rich iridescent blue and green flecked with orange and dimly barred with olive. Near the edge of the gill cover is one bright scarlet spot (Pl. XVIII). The males are brighter colored than the females and they have black ventral fins while those of the females are yellowish. In the males the dorsal and caudal fins are more brilliant blue.

Sunfish nests are basin-like clearings on the pond bottom

over which the male keeps close guard. In late May and June he cleans a space on the bottom, about a foot across and several inches deep, fanning gravel away with his tail and pulling heavier stones with his mouth. Then he brings a female to the nest and the two swim round and round with their ventral sides close together while eggs and clouds of sperm cells are discharged into the water. Soon after this she departs, leaving him to guard the eggs, which become attached to the small stones and gravel of the nest bed.

Size.—8 inches.

Distribution.—Very common, especially in ponds; Maine to Minnesota, southward to Florida, but less abundant there.

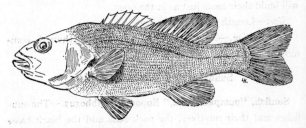

Fig. 280.—Small-mouthed black bass, *Micropterus dolomieu.*

Small-mouthed black bass, Micropterus dolomieu.—Famous as sportsmen's fish, both the small- and large-mouthed black bass are well known and widely distributed in clear, cool waters, streams and stream-fed ponds with rocky bottoms They thrive where crayfishes are abundant, these being the favorite food of the adults.

Neither of the black basses is black. The small-mouthed species is silvery to golden green with indistinct darker cross bands; the large-mouthed black bass is green, darkly mottled on the back and along a line on each side. But both vary greatly in color and can only be distinguished by structure. The small-mouthed bass has only a moderate sized mouth (Fig. 280) and its angles do not extend backward behind the eyes, which is the case in the large-mouthed species. Bass move into the shallow waters to breed, usually selecting regions where there are rocks or stumps around which the nests may be hidden. In May or June, sometimes much earlier, the male makes a basin on the bottom by fanning away the sand with his tail until he reaches the mud three or four inches below. Two or three females gather near and when the nest is finished the male seeks out one of them, biting her cheeks and cajoling her until she enters the nest area. When the eggs and sperm are being shed the female lies on her side and the male is upright beside her. This process lasts but a few seconds at a time but a female may stay within the nest for an hour or two. The male may mate with two or three females but he continually guards the nest and the eggs until they are hatched. He not only tends the nest but guards the small fry as long as they stay in it and swims about with them afterward.

Size.—Up to 12 or 15 inches.

Distribution.—The small-mouthed bass is found widely distributed from the St. Lawrence River region to Arkansas, and southward, living in cool streams not cold enough for brook trout.

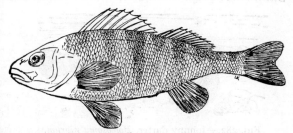

FIG. 281.—Common perch, *Perca flavescens.*

Perches and Darters—*Percidæ*

In the perch family are the yellow perch, the wall-eyed pike, and a large number of dwarf perches or darters which live in

clear rapid streams. Darters and perches have two dorsal fins
—a spiny one followed by a soft-rayed one (Fig. 282). Their
scales are toothed on the free edges, making the body of the
fish feel rough to one's fingers.

Common or yellow perch, Perca flavescens.—The yellow
perch (Fig. 281) is one of the commonest fishes in ponds and
lakes, and one of the easiest to recognize. Its back is olive,
blending into brilliant yellow on the sides and under part of
its body, and the yellow of the sides is crossed by dark bars;
the lower fins are bright orange, especially during the breeding
season in April. Through the winter, perch stay in the deeper
water, ten feet or more, and large numbers of them are caught
by hook and line through holes in the ice.

Perch do not make nests of any kind but lay their eggs in
strings of jelly from two to seven feet long, twined about the
water weeds of the shallows. With its surrounding jelly each
egg is about one-eighth of an inch across and there may be
many thousands of them in a string. They are laid in March
and April or May, depending on the temperature, and hatch
in from ten to twenty days.

Size.—Reaches a foot in length but is usually 6 to 10 inches

Distribution.—Great Lakes region; eastern states.

Fig. 282.—Johnny darter, *Boleosoma nigrum.*

Darters.—Darters are so small and swift and brightly
colored that they take the same place among fishes that the
wood warblers do among birds. There are many kinds, re-
sembling one another so much that species are difficult to

separate. They all live in swift streams, lying on the bottom, hidden among the stones, often supporting themselves by their expanded ventral and anal fins, frequently resting with their heads turned to one side. They make lightning-quick darts and short stops like rabbits. They feed upon the insects of the riffles, especially upon midge larvæ.

Johnny darter, Boleosoma nigrum.—The "Johnny" or tessellated darter is common in both swift and sluggish streams and ponds, in New England and New York. It is about three inches long, pale olive brown with black W-shaped markings on its sides (Fig. 282). Its name "tessellated" refers to the fine black flecking on its tail fin. In spring the males are almost all black. The Johnny darter often swims about over a mud bottom, an unconventional place for darters.

Size.—Up to 2½ inches.

Distribution.—Eastern states, and westward to Pennsylvania, Great Lakes, Dakota.

FIG. 283.—Miller's thumb, *Cottus bairdii.*

Sculpins—*Cottidæ*

Miller's thumb, mufflejaw, muddler, Cottus.—These are grotesque little fishes with heads too large for their bodies and flattened like the proverbial miller's thumb. Fullgrown ones are not usually more than five inches long. Their general color is olive green or brownish, speckled and mottled with darker brown, the whole pattern matching the bottom of the clear streams and ponds where they hide. They are smooth-skinned except for fine prickles behind the front fins and the warty roughness on the head.

Two similar species of miller's thumbs, *Cottus bairdii* (Fig. 283), and *Cottus cognatus*, are common in clear, rocky brook, and lakes. Although they most commonly hide on the stony bottom they are also frequently found in tangles of stonewort and pondweed. They feed upon insects, small crustaceans and algæ; occasionally they eat the eggs of other fishes.

They spawn through April to July. The eggs are salmon-colored, about one-eighth of an inch in diameter, and laid in a grape-like cluster of a hundred or two, glued to the under sides of stones in shallow water, where there is more or less current. The male seems to select the site, while the females tarry about. Later one of them joins the male and then deposits her eggs. He loiters near the eggs protecting them until they hatch.

Size.—Small, up to 5 to 6 inches.

Distribution.—Canada to Georgia and westward to Missouri.

CHAPTER XVIII

AMPHIBIANS

Salamanders, Frogs, and Toads Found In or Near Water

Toads forage through city parks and gardens, and frogs raise their spring choruses from every roadside swamp. Anybody who is acquainted with amphibian life knows the heavy wet plash of the bullfrog, the translucent daintiness of the red newt half hidden beneath wet leaves, and the industry of the common toad, collecting insects near the rose bushes at evening, intimate and friendly, yet aloof.

General form and habits.—Amphibians generally spend their youth in the water, leaving it only to return again. But there are notable exceptions. Red-backed salamanders never go into water even to lay their eggs, while a few others like the mud-puppy and the hellbender do not go out of it. With rare exceptions, our native frogs and toads leave the water but return to it. Like fishes and reptiles, amphibians are cold-blooded, back-boned animals, but amphibians seldom have scales or bony plates while fishes and reptiles are usually covered with them. Almost all breathe by gills during their larval period and later they have lungs or other devices; but all their lives most of them take oxygen through their thin moist skins. The salamanders have tails and are shaped so much like lizards that they are continually mistaken for them, in spite of their soft, scaleless skins. The frogs and the toads are tailless after they have grown beyond the tadpole stage.

Amphibians are timid animals and their chief defense is in flight or concealment. They do not bite and they neither scratch nor sting. None of our native species is poisonous or harmful. It is true that the skin of a maltreated toad gives off a milky fluid which is peppery and irritating; any dog which picks up a toad usually drops it quickly, but is rarely badly poisoned by it.

Habitat.—Frogs and toads live in very different places during different seasons and stages of their lives. So long as they are tadpoles or larvæ they all live in the water, but the air-breathing adults take to the land, the frogs generally keeping to marshes and meadows and damp woods, and the toads going to shaded spots in gardens and roadsides. They vary in their choice of winter hibernation places; some hide beneath stones, others dig into the bottoms of streams and ponds. But in spring, they are sooner or later to be found in the water; there they lay their eggs, and there the fishlike tadpoles hatch and grow to adult form. American salamanders are more apt to spend their lives either entirely in the water or entirely upon land, but some of them, like the spotted salamander, *Ambystoma maculatum*, live in the water until they become adults, then clamber out and live on land hidden beneath stones and logs, but return to the water to lay their eggs.

Food.—Frog and toad tadpoles are mainly vegetable feeders, preferring filamentous algæ like *Spirogyra* or desmids and diatoms. After transforming they become carnivorous, eating insects, snails, worms, and the like. In their new form even the shape of the food canal is changed, from the long intestine coiled like a watch-spring such as can be seen through the body wall of a big bullfrog tadpole to the short one characteristic of carnivorous animals (Fig. 284). Salamanders are carnivorous in both larval and adult stages, thriving upon worms and water insects, mollusks, and small tadpoles of their own species.

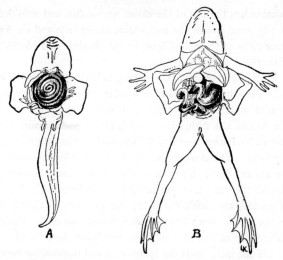

FIG. 284.—Tadpole (A) and young frog (B) with their body walls spread open, showing the long watch-spring intestine of the herbivorous tadpole and the short food canal of the frog, which has become carnivorous.

Breeding habits.—The sexes are easily distinguished, especially during the breeding season. Male frogs have swollen thumbs (Fig. 285) or thumb-pads while the females

FIG. 285.—Right front foot of frog showing shape of the thumb in different sexes: 1, male with swollen thumb, in the breeding season; 2, male with thumb of smaller size as it is out of the breeding season; 3, female.

have more slender ones; in male toads the upper surfaces of the thumb and first finger are rough and horny. In male

salamanders the lips of the cloaca are swollen and wrinkled
and in some species the males have keeled tails and on the
inner sides of their hind legs the skin is thick and blackish
(Fig. 288).

In spring, frogs and toads congregate in the ponds and their
voices, chiefly male, join in the familiar choruses. They mate
soon after they reach the water. Climbing upon the back of
the female the male clasps her behind her forearms, and
presses his horny thumb and finger pads against the sides of
her body. The two continue in this position for hours, often
for several days. They do not eat and, although usually
shy, at this time they can easily be picked up in the hand.
When they are caught the male generally keeps his tight hold
on the female even when the pair is roughly handled. Under
natural conditions, as soon as the eggs leave the body of the
female the male sheds the sperm cells and fertilization takes
place in the open water; then the pair separate.

Many male salamanders deposit gelatinous capsules of
sperm cells, the spermatophores (Fig. 289), upon twigs and
leaves in the pond. While this is going on the female follows
the male about and clasping the sperm-filled top of one of
these between the lips of her cloaca, pulls it inside where the
sperm cells are stored in special sacs (spermathecæ) until the
eggs are fertilized. Among the spotted newts and other salamanders an elaborate courtship precedes the depositing of
the spermatophores.

Life history.—Although different species have their own
peculiarities, amphibian life histories are in general very much
alike. The young forms or larvæ are fish-shaped, with tail-
fins and gills. Very young toad and frog tadpoles have
suckers by which they can suspend themselves well up in the
water where there is plenty of oxygen and no mud; most
young salamander larvæ have "balancers" and their gills are
large and bushy (Fig. 286). Transformation to the adult
form progresses slowly, the time required differing greatly in

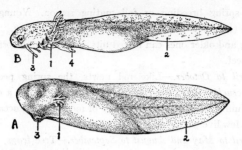

FIG. 286.—A.—Young frog tadpole showing 1, gills; 2, fin; and 3, suckers. B.—Larva of salamander (*Ambystoma*) with 1, gills; 2, fin; 3, balancers; and 4, front legs.

different species. This involves great changes in any amphibian, the development of legs and lungs, absorption of gills and shifts in the circulation, and in toads and frogs, a different shaping of the mouth and a new kind of teeth, the absorption of the tail and a making over of the food canal (Fig. 284). The insect-catching toad has a digestive system which is very different from that of its alga-eating tadpole.

Suggestions for aquarium and vivarium study.—In the following table the months named are those in which these frogs and salamanders are most easily captured but they can be found at other times, too.

March to April.—Eggs and larvæ, spotted salamander, *Ambystoma maculatum* (Pl. XIX). With a lens the blood can be seen circulating in their gills even before they hatch out of the jelly. In an aquarium larvæ at first need only plenty of water and a few plants to oxygenate it (p. 39). When they are older they can be fed on small crustaceans and worms (*Enchytræidæ*).

April to May and September to October.—Adult spotted newts, *Triturus viridescens* (Pl. XIX), will live the year round in shallow water with a stone or two placed in it so that they can climb out. They mate readily in the aquarium either in

their spring breeding or fall mating season. Young red
newts (Pl. XIX) are most at home in a damp fernery. Both
young and older ones can be fed bits of meat, earthworms or
raw beef.

April to October.—Like red newts, the spring peepers,
Hyla crucifer (Fig. 302), will live the year round in a damp
vivarium. They only need plenty of moisture and occasionally a few live worms and insects.

April to May and August to September.—Tree frogs, *Hyla
versicolor* (Fig. 301), also live well in a damp shaded vivarium
(p. 40).

March to November.—Bullfrog and green frog tadpoles will
live on algæ for months but a medium sized aquarium holding
about a gallon or more of water should have only two or three
in it.

Salamanders—*Caudata*
Giant Salamanders—*Cryptobranchidæ*

Hellbender, Cryptobranchus alleganiensis.—The hellbender is an animal which is rarely discovered but once seen
it is warranted to hold one's attention. It is commonly a foot
and a half long, the largest salamander in North America.
Its body is olive colored or reddish brown with darker patches
and is so broad and flat that it almost completely overshadows
the short, bowed-out legs (Fig. 287). Its small eyes are nearly
hidden in an expanse of slimy forehead. The thick oozy skin
fits loosely, gathered into fleshy folds along each side of the
body, and when lying quietly on the bottom a hellbender
looks like an old, wrinkled, and defunct cucumber.

Habits, habitat.—Hellbenders stay in the water all their
lives. Although they have lungs they do not use them, but
rely chiefly on their skins for respiration; their gill-slits which
open into the sides of the throat do not seem to have any
function. Hellbenders live in crevices among rocks or in
woody débris in creeks and rivers.

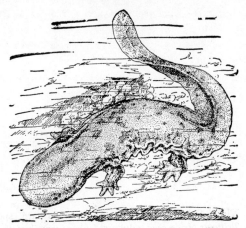

Fig. 287.—Hellbender and eggs, *Cryptobranchus alleganiensis.*

Food.—They eat all kinds of small water animals, foraging only at night.

Breeding habits.—In breeding habits hellbenders are more like fishes than salamanders. Like the sunfish and other fishes, the male hellbender clears a basin-shaped cavity or nest on the bottom, usually in September. There he awaits the female, which enters it, and as she lays her strings of eggs he sheds the spermatozoa over them, afterward chasing her from the nest and standing guard above them, but occasionally eating a few himself (Fig. 287).

Size.—Length of adult 12 to 18 inches.

Range.—Western New York and central Pennsylvania to Louisiana, and westward to Iowa.

Newts—*Pleurodelidæ*

Red newt, spotted newt, Triturus viridescens.—The "red eft" or "red lizard" of the woods, and the "spotted newt" of the ponds are different color phases of the same animal,

Pl. XIX.—Salamanders: from above downward, spotted newt, *Triturus viridescens*, adult; red phase usually found on land; larva; two-lined salamander, *Eurycea bislineata;* dusky salamander, *Desmognathus fuscus;* spotted salamander, *Ambystoma maculatum.*

PLATE XIX

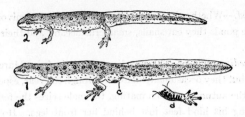

FIGS. 288.—Spotted newt, *Triturus viridescens*, in breeding season: 1, male showing tail-fin, swollen cloaca (*c*), and black ridges on inner surface of the hind legs (*d*); 2, female which has a generally slender form.

Triturus viridescens, one of the commonest salamanders in the eastern states. (Pl. XIX.)

Adult *Triturus*, the "spotted newts" or "vermilion spotted newts," live in ponds, and in quiet stretches of meandering streams. The upper surfaces of their bodies are reddish or olive or dark green and the underparts are lemon yellow covered with fine black dots, and along each side of the back there is a row of scarlet dots ringed with black. The male has a swollen cloaca, stocky hind legs, much stouter than the front ones, with their inner surfaces covered with thick black ridges of skin during the breeding and mating seasons (Fig. 288, 1). The cloaca and tail fin become especially conspicuous during these times. The females have delicately molded legs, the hind ones nearly the same as the front ones and without the blackened skin folds (Fig. 288).

Habits, habitat.—Young "red newts" wander about the woodland near their home waters, moving hesitantly in and out among the dead leaves. A red newt peering from the curve of a dried oak leaf is the picture of alert shyness. On foggy or rainy days they come out of their hiding places to forage for insects or whatever small animals they can find. Some of them are brick red, others are orange colored, but, like the adults, all have a single row of scarlet black-bordered dots on each side of their backs.

355

Food.—Whether in the water or out newts are carnivorous. In the ponds they eat snails, small crustaceans, and their own larvæ.

Breeding habits.—The breeding season is from March to April but they occasionally mate all through the year, especially in the autumn. When mating, the male seizes the female, clasping his hind feet just behind her front legs. Holding her firmly he bends his own body in an S-shaped curve and begins rubbing the side of his head against hers, and at the same time steadily tapping his tail against her body. Occasionally he yanks and shakes her and together they shift and twist their bodies. This performance may go on for hours and as readily in aquaria as in the pond. Soon after the pair separates, the male deposits the white vase-shaped spermatophores (p. 357). Dozens of these can often be seen scattered here and there on submerged leaves. As the male moves away from the spermatophore which he has deposited, the female follows him and crawls over it, taking its mass of sperm cells into her cloaca (Fig. 288). She lays her eggs singly, each in a capsule of jelly, placing them on leaves or in the axils of leaves and stems of *Chara* and *Elodea*. These are brown at one end, creamy or light green at the other, and 80 to 100 of them may be laid by one female.

Life history.—The newly hatched larvæ have branching gills, "balancers," the buds of their front legs, and fish-like tails (Fig. 286). Toward fall they gradually lose their gills and acquire lungs, and their color changes from green to red. Their further migrations and color changes vary; in many places they climb out of the ponds and spend at least one winter on land, while in some regions they do not appear to leave the water at all. Sizes and ages at which the young, usually brick red sub-adult finally matures seem to depend upon differences in food, temperature of the water, character of the ponds, and perhaps upon other still unknown factors.

Vivarium.—Both young "red newts" and adults are most

at home in a vivarium with a "pool" and a damp mossy floor
(p. 40) although the adults can get along almost anywhere so
long as they are given a little water and kept cool. They
eat fresh meat, showing little preference between pieces of
beefsteak and earthworm except when the worm wriggles.

Size.—Length of adults 4 inches or less.

Range.—Common, eastern United States and Canada.

Mole Salamanders—*Ambystomidæ*

Spotted salamander, Ambystoma maculatum.—The eggs
of this and other species of *Ambystoma* are far more familiar
than the secretive, nocturnal animals which lay them. Spotted salamanders have large, stout bodies, and broad, flat
heads. Their upper surfaces are shining black scattered over
with a few large, round yellow spots; underneath they are
slaty-gray, sprinkled with bluish-white flecking (Pl. XIX).

Habits, habitat.—Through most of the year the adults
skulk beneath logs and stones, in any dark, damp place in
pastures and light woodland; they have also been found in
lawns and gardens, even in cellars of houses. During the
nights of early March and April they come out of their hiding
places and migrate into ponds. The larvæ live in spring-
fed ponds and streams.

Breeding habits.—Adults congregate often in great num-

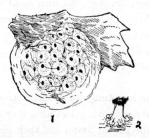

Fig. 289.—Eggs and spermatophore of the
spotted salamander: 1, small cluster of eggs attached
to leaf, showing coverings of jelly; 2, spermatophore.

bers in certain small ponds and slow streams. Not one can be seen during the day though each morning may show dozens of new egg clusters, but at night they can be easily found with a spotlight. The males deposit spermatophores about half an inch high which look like glass push-pins and hold hundreds of spermatozoa. The females crawl over these, taking the spermatozoa into the cloacal chamber (Fig. 288), where they are held ready to fertilize the eggs that are always laid during the night or very early in the morning. Each egg is enclosed in an envelope of jelly and the whole cluster is covered by a thick layer of it (Fig. 289). The eggs are larger and further apart than frogs' eggs (Pl. XX).

Life history.—The greenish brown larvæ hatch in two or three weeks according to the temperature. They are about half an inch long and have noticeably flattened heads, "balancers," the stubs of front legs, and a lusty growth of gills (Fig. 286). During their transformation in late fall and summer the gills stop growing and gradually become absorbed.

Aquarium and vivarium study.—*Ambystoma* eggs are so large that they show early stages of development very clearly, much better than frogs' eggs, but like them they grow very rapidly, and in the warm water of an aquarium these early stages are passed through in a few hours. The larvæ can be reared in dishes of water stocked with filamentous algæ, and later (as their legs develop), fed with small worms (p. 351). Adults can be kept the year round in a damp vivarium and fed on bits of beef or pieces of earthworms.

Size.—Adults 6 inches long or more.

Range.—Locally common in eastern and central North America.

Tiger salamander, Ambystoma tigrinum.—Although tiger salamanders are rare in many localities, they are very widely distributed in the United States and their life history is one of the most interesting among salamanders. They are heavily built and their rusty black bodies are covered with blotches of yellow running together in irregular marbling and cross-

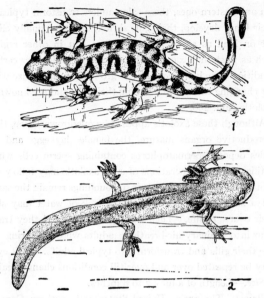

Fig. 290.—1, Adult tiger salamander, *Ambystoma tigrinum;* 2, axolotl or larva which matures without transforming (axolotl found only in southwestern United States).

bars, except on the under surfaces, which are plain gray (Fig. 290, 1). These yellow spots and their yellow chins distinguish them from the marbled salamander, *Ambystoma opacum.*

Habits, habitat, food.—The fully transformed adults hide beneath stones and logs near ponds or in moist places where they forage for worms and ground insects during the night or in rainy weather. The larvæ live in cold, spring-fed ponds.

Breeding habits.—Their breeding habits are much like those of the spotted salamander, *Ambystoma maculatum,* and the egg masses are very similar (Fig. 289).

Life history.—All tiger salamanders start life as typical salamander larvæ, breathing by gills and growing like other aquatic salamanders. In many regions, especially our northern and eastern ones, these salamanders transform typically, their lungs develop, their gills shrink, and they finally climb out on land as air-breathing adults. But in other regions such as western Texas and the southwest, and under certain conditions, the larvæ continue to grow to full adult size without changing their form or losing their gills and are known as axolotls (Fig. 290, 2).

Although these axolotls appear like overgrown larvæ, their reproductive organs mature, the females lay eggs and the males deposit spermatophores containing sperm cells which fertilize them. Generations of such axolotls may follow one another for a long time if their surroundings remain the same, but a sudden change of climate or lack of water may shift their course of life. Then their gills shrink and they transform into ordinary air-breathing adults whose offspring will lose their gills and transform into typical adults. This cycle may be repeated over and over till conditions change again.

Size.—Length of adults 7 to 8 inches.

Range.—The entire United States and southern Canada; rare in the eastern states, especially in New England; abundant in the western and southwestern United States where the axolotl form is often treated as a separate species.

Fig. 291.—Adult marbled salamander, *Ambystoma opacum.*

Marbled salamander, Ambystoma opacum.—The general color of the marbled salamander is slaty-gray turning to bluish beneath the body. Its large spots and blotches form about fourteen irregular grayish-white bars (Fig. 291), never yellow like those of the spotted and the tiger salamanders nor in small flecks like those on Jefferson's salamander.

Habits, habitat.—Although they go to the ponds to breed they are likely to hide under stones on dry hillsides or to burrow into earth, often in sandy places.

Breeding habits.—Dr. A. H. Wright found clusters of *A. opacum* eggs in autumn under logs and driftwood, in moist soil but not in the water. Their outer coats were tough and very unlike other *Ambystoma* eggs.

Size.—Length of adult about 5 inches.

Range.—Only occasionally common; eastern and central regions of North America; coastal Massachusetts to Texas; up Mississippi Valley to Illinois.

FIG. 292.—Adult Jefferson's salamander. *Ambystoma jeffersonianum.*

Jefferson's salamander, Ambystoma jeffersonianum.— Jefferson's salamanders are uniformly dark brown all over but they may have small blue white flecks along their sides

(Fig. 292). On the ground the old adults appear plain brown, the flecks of pale blue on their undersides being hardly apparent, but on the younger ones the blue is conspicuous and the spots are scattered over the body and the back of the head as well.

Habits, habitat.—The adults live beneath logs, in rotting stumps, beneath the litter of sawdust piles, and under stones. They migrate to the ponds even earlier than the spotted salamanders. The larvæ live in sphagnum ponds, cold quiet streams and woodland ponds.

Breeding habits.—They deposit their eggs in small firm masses of jelly attached to submerged twigs, sometimes in the same pond with those of the spotted salamander with which they are confused even by experts. But these eggs are generally laid earlier and in smaller masses, under two dozen eggs in a clump.

Size.—Length of adult about 6 inches.

Range.—Hudson Bay to Arkansas, Nova Scotia to Virginia or even further south.

Lungless Salamanders—*Plethodontidæ*

Dusky salamander, Desmognathus fuscus.—Dusky salamanders stay in crevices and under stones in moist earth near shady streams. The adult dusky has a stout body with a reddish brown back and gray under parts (Pl. XIX). On its back there are two irregular rows of black spots and upon its sides a mottling of black; a white line extends from the eye to the angle of the jaw.

The larva is uniformly brown on the back except for two rows of small light spots which extend along it upon each side. Its gills are more or less prominent unless the change to adult form has already begun. Both larvæ and adults have a peculiar rigidity in their lower jaws, and they use them as entering wedges when they are pushing their way under stones. Whenever a dusky salamander opens its mouth it holds the lower jaw straight as a rod and lifts the upper jaw away from it.

Habits, habitat.—The adults hide under stones near shallow streams, and the larvæ live in running water. Neither larvæ nor adults seem comfortable unless they are hidden beneath something. In the swift shallows of certain streams one young dusky will flash out from almost every stone which is up-turned.

Food.—Adults and larvæ are carnivorous; their diet is chiefly of insects, earthworms, and snails.

Breeding habits.—They lay their 15 to 20 creamy white eggs in moist cavities or beneath stones, very near the edge of a stream. There are one or two clusters, closely guarded by the female, which usually lies with nearly all of them in contact with her body. They hatch in about eight weeks. In western Massachusetts eggs have been found from mid-June to September.

Life history.—The larvæ live on land until they are 15 to 16 days old and about three-quarters of an inch long. Then they enter the water and remain there 8 to 9 months, transforming to adults the following spring, when they go out on land to breed. A female will continue to guard her eggs even in captivity.

Vivarium.—An adult dusky will burrow down, completely hiding itself in the dirt unless stones are provided for it. Dr. I. W. Wilder once found two adults entirely covered in the dry earth of a terrarium where they had been living for two years.

Size.—Length of adult male $5\frac{1}{2}$ inches; female smaller.

Range.—Common. Canada to Mississippi, westward to Illinois.

Red salamander, Pseudotriton ruber.—This bright coral-red salamander is locally common in and near streams in the eastern states except New England. The older animals are purplish brown but the young adults are coral-red with small,

FIG. 293.—Young adult red salamander, *Pseudo-triton ruber.*

irregular black spots scattered over their backs (Fig. 293). Their sides and under parts are lighter, unmarked and so transparent that the pulsations of the heart can easily be seen through the body wall.

Habits, habitat.—Like the two-lined salamander, it crawls under flat stones, sometimes in swampy places, but more often in small streams; in winter it lies beneath stones in shallow rapids. This is a lungless salamander which takes oxygen through its throat membrane and moist skin. It takes little risk of drying, keeping to water or damp places, moving about only at night.

Food.—Its diet of worms and insects is similar to that of other salamanders.

Breeding habits.—The red salamander lays its fifty or more eggs in the fall, gluing them to the underside of a stone where they are in the constant wash of the current. The eggs are clustered in small patches of a dozen or two but each one is attached separately by a jelly-like stalk.

Life history.—Although the eggs hatch in October or November, the larvæ remain relatively inactive through the winter months, but in spring they begin feasting upon little crustaceans or anything else which is lively and within their capacity; by mid-spring they are about an inch long. When they are about four inches long and two years and a half old their gills begin to shrink and their brownish color turns to the bright coral-red of the young adult.

Vivarium.—Red salamanders live well in the ordinary damp shaded vivarium (p. 40); they thrive upon bits of earthworm and fresh meat.

Size.—Average length of adult 4 to 5 inches.

Range.—Locally abundant in the eastern states except New England; Albany County, New York, to Ohio, Kentucky, New Jersey, North Carolina, westward to the Mississippi River.

Two-lined salamander, Eurycea bislineata.—The two-lined salamander is small, slender, and very active and hides beneath stones along brook borders (Pl. XIX). Its ground color varies from brown to yellowish. On each side of the back a dark line, gray or brown or black, extends from the eye backward along the tail; below the dark lines the sides of the body are finely speckled with black and the under parts are yellow.

Habits and habitat.—The adults hide beneath flat stones in the water-soaked mud and sand of brook-sides, slithering and jumping out with amazing rapidity when disturbed. The larvæ, distinguishable by their gills, grow nearly as long as the adults and stay in the same places, whence they dash out with flash-like suddenness when the stones are moved.

Food.—They live mainly upon water insects, worms, and small crustaceans, seeking these by daylight in the shallow water.

Breeding habits.—They lay their eggs as early as April and as late as the middle of August, on the undersides of stones in flowing water. There may be as few as a dozen or two or as many as sixty hanging from one stone, each one fastened to it by a separate stalk of jelly.

Life history.—The change from larval to adult form is very gradual; the salamanders may be at least two years old before it is completed. The larvæ are about 2 inches long before they lose their gills. In some regions the adults leave the brooks in the fall and hibernate under stones near the stream. They are often abundant along the borders or in the beds of shallow brooks.

Size.—Length of adult 3 to 4 inches, sometimes smaller.

Range.—From Maine to Florida and westward to Louisiana.

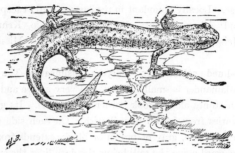

FIG. 294.—Adult purple salamander, *Gyrinophilus porphyriticus.*

Purple salamander, Gyrinophilus porphyriticus.—Full-grown purple salamanders are light reddish with mottled shadowings of a darker tone (Fig. 294).

Habits, food.—They stay in small cold streams and little runnels all their lives, hiding in hollows beneath stones and feeding on the riffle organisms (p. 21) which continually gather around them.

Breeding habits.—Neither their breeding habits nor their eggs are well known although the adults are abundant in certain streams. Adults, and larvæ evidently two years old or more, are found in the same places.

Size.—Adults 6 inches long.

Range.—Locally common, eastern states; westward to Kentucky and Tennessee.

Mud-puppies— *Necturidæ.*

Mud-puppy, water-dog, Necturus maculosus.—A mud-puppy looks like a frog-puppy, or a dachshund in a froggy

Fig. 295.—Mud-puppy, *Necturus maculosus.*

masquerade. Its long body is low-slung on futile looking legs and the dog-like head is flanked by bushy "ears" or gills, which swing rhythmically back and forth as it breathes (Fig. 295). Its mottled brown body is blotched with blue-black on the sides and back, the whole color scheme matching the stream bottom so well that a mud-puppy easily goes unnoticed, especially when its red gills are not expanded, as is often the case in a stream where there is plenty of oxygen.

Habits, food.—Mud-puppies live in the water all their lives, in rivers and creeks, crawling about mostly at night in protected places among stones and débris, feeding upon the yield of the stream bottom—water insects, snails, fish eggs, and small fishes.

Breeding habits.—Mating probably occurs in the fall and sperm cells can be found then in the cloacal chamber of the females. In the following late spring or early summer, mud-puppies lay their eggs, gluing them on flattened stones and guarding the place until after the young larvæ have hatched.

Size.—Commonly a foot long.

Range.—Mud-puppies are very common in certain rivers and lakes. In the upper waters of many streams which flow into the Atlantic Ocean; valleys of the Great Lakes and the Mississippi; Lake Champlain and the upper Hudson; southward into northern Alabama and Arkansas.

Toads and Frogs.—*Anura.*

Toads and frogs are tail-less amphibians with four legs (Fig. 296). Toads are heavy bodied and awkward, their skins

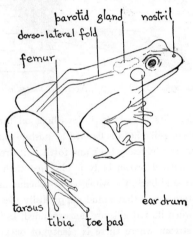

FIG. 296.—Diagram showing the external structures of toads and frogs.

are rough and warty, and behind each eye they have a glandular swelling, the parotid gland.

Toads—*Bufonidæ*

American toad, Bufo americanus.—The American toad is the familiar amphibian throughout the eastern states. On quiet summer evenings it comes out from under verandas and sits on warm door-stones or it patrols the garden for insects.

Between long silences it utters its single "wheep," high and sudden, like an exclamation.

This toad has a thick-set, chunky body and is short-legged and broad-toed; its skin is conspicuously warty and the head·

FIG. 297.—American toad, *Bufo americanus*.

crests are wide and kidney-shaped (Fig. 297). In some localities it is confused with Fowler's toad, which is more slenderly built and has a smoother skin, especially on the under parts (Fig. 298). In a few localities as on Long Island, New York, Fowler's toad takes the place of the American toad. The color of the American toad varies from light to darker brown according to its own temperature and activity. It is usually predominantly red-brown with patches and bands of lighter brown; the warts and parotid glands are likely to be a rich red-brown. The male is smaller than the female and her throat is grayish white while his is nearly black.

Breeding habits.—In early April, American toads come out of their winter burrows, beneath flat stones or logs, and begin their evening migrations to the ponds. By the middle of that month numbers of them appear in the ponds, and their sweet, tremulous calls sound forth uncertainly here and there. The full toad chorus does not begin till the last week in April or the first in May, and then it goes on in daytime or evening, but after the middle of May, the day voices cease though the evening notes may be heard till midsummer. Males reach the ponds slightly earlier than the females, but mating occurs as soon as both sexes have arrived.

Life history.—Toads lay their eggs in May, almost always in quiet water. They are in two long, curling tubes of jelly, each containing a single row of black eggs, four to twelve thousand of them from one toad. In the water the jelly swells and gathers dirt, and pond bottoms are often covered with these dirty, twisted ropes, containing myriads of developing toads (Pl. XX). The eggs hatch into black tadpoles within five to twelve days, depending upon the temperature.

From the middle of June to late July, shallow waters swarm with tadpoles, transforming into toads. Young toads gather on the shores, hopping up the banks and into the grass, meeting their enemies—birds, snakes, frogs—and being eaten by thousands. But the survivors persevere, and forage along the stream side, finally departing for higher ground.

In July and August the old toads leave the ponds and scatter into the gardens and fields, feeding there until they go into hibernation for the winter.

Size.—Male 2 to 3 inches; female larger.

Range.—In most regions east of the Rocky Mountains from Mexico to Great Bear Lake; southern states.

Fowler's toad, Bufo fowleri.—In some parts of New England, Fowler's toad is commoner than the American toad or takes its place. It comes out of hibernation much later; Dickerson says of it, "In late May and June the toad chorus in Rhode Island consists mainly of the voices of Fowler's toad, with only an occasional sweet note from the American toad. In July it is rarely that we hear any voice but that of Fowler's toad."

Its slender legs make it a good jumper, almost as agile as a frog. It is drab, yellowish, or greenish gray with irregular spots of black or dark brown; its under parts are smooth

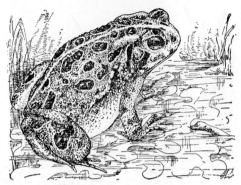

FIG. 298.—Fowler's toad, *Bufo fowleri*.

skinned and white, seldom spotted as they often are in the American toad (Fig. 298). It has a harsh short trill while the American toad's call is a prolonged and musical one.

Habitat.—It frequents the same gardens and ponds as the American toad.

Breeding habits.—Its breeding season is from two to three weeks later than that of the American toad. The mating call is a weird and mournful metallic droning.

Life history.—The eggs are laid in tangled tubes of jelly, like those of the American toad (Pl. XX), but they are often in double rows. The young develop quickly, and before fall the small toads in the garden show all the markings characteristic of their parents.

Size.—Male 2 to 3 inches; female slightly larger.

Range.—Central New England to Georgia, westward to Michigan, common in regions of Rhode Island, Massachusetts, Connecticut, New York, Long Island.

Burrowing Toads—*Pelobatidæ*

Hermit spadefoot, spadefoot toad, Scaphiopus holbrooki.—Although spadefoot toads live in nearly every part of eastern North America, they are not very well known because of their

Fig. 299.—Spadefoot toad, *Scaphiopus holbrooki*, and 1, foot enlarged.

shyness and persistent habit of digging into the ground. When kept in boxes of damp earth they hide themselves in their burrows, coming out only at night, or occasionally on dark days.

They can pull their prominently bulging eyes down on a level with the surface of their heads. The pupil of the eye is a vertical slit like a cat's; in all other frogs and toads it is round. The upper parts of their bodies are dark brown streaked with longitudinal bands of yellow; their undersides are white or pink (Fig. 299).

Breeding habits.—Spadefoots come out of their burrows at the end of April or later and are in the ponds or near them until August, their migrations almost always occurring after a long rain storm. Large numbers come simultaneously into the pond. They stay there only two or three nights, but during that time the males keep up a chorus of loud calls, whose sound is increased by the resonator throat sac three times the size of the head. Spadefoots leave the pond as soon as the eggs are laid, and go back to their old burrowing habits.

Size.—Length 2½ inches; female not much larger than male.

Range.—Common; all of eastern North America, Gulf States and Texas and northward into Arkansas.

Frogs

Like toads, frogs are tail-less amphibians, but they are stronger, more active jumpers, with moist skins and without rough, warty swellings (Fig. 309).

Tree Frogs—*Hylidæ*

Tree toad, common tree frog, Hyla versicolor.—As the scientific name suggests, the colors of the tree toad are changeable and it may be white or gray or green or brown. It has a dark irregularly star-shaped spot on the back, oblique dark stripes on the head, and dark cross bands on the legs, but all

Fig. 300.—Tree toad, *Hyla versicolor*, with vocal sac inflated.

of these may be indistinct or invisible (Pl. XXI). Its white under parts are washed with bright orange-yellow, especially the folds of the hind legs. Like the spring-peeper and other climbing frogs, it has sticky pads on the tips of its toes (Fig. 301).

Habits, habitat.—This is a tree climber whose long, reedy tremolo is familiar on summer evenings, and in the sultry hush before afternoon thunderstorms. Its favorite perch is in the crotch of a limb, where it can hardly be told from the gray bark. Sometimes tree frogs rest on leaves of low shrubs, where they may scarcely be discovered except by accident, so closely do they match the color of leaves. They are very much at home about houses, even climbing into veranda flower boxes, and they can live comfortably in a glass-covered fernery if the air is kept damp and they are occasionally fed with small worms and insects.

Fig. 301.—Tree toad with its body pressed against the glass side of a fernery.

Breeding habits.—By the last of April or first of May tree toads have come out of their winter hiding places on land and are on their way to their breeding ponds. By the middle of May their high resonant voices are raised in full chorus; they begin calling in the early afternoon, especially on warm, moist days, and keep it up well into the night. The gnome-like males sitting on the lily pads with their vocal sacs ballooned out into pearly translucent globes will go on singing in the full flare of a flashlight (Fig. 300). Probably they come to the ponds before the females. In a week's thorough search during the earliest part of the breeding season, Wright found males each evening, but never saw any females. Tree toads usually mate at night. By the first of June they begin to lay their light brownish eggs which are attached in small groups to plant stems, always at or near the surface of the water.

Life history.—The scarlet-tailed tadpoles grow very rapidly, and about three weeks from the date when the eggs are laid their hind legs are beginning to show, and in seven weeks the little frogs, now about half an inch long, are ready to leave the water.

Size.—2 inches, but half-grown ones about an inch long are common.

Range.— Throughout eastern North America, west to Kansas.

Fig. 302.—Spring peeper, *Hyla crucifer*, with vocal sac inflated.

Spring peeper, Hyla crucifer (formerly H. pickeringi).— The best field marks of the spring peeper are its small size, and the dark multiplication sign on its back (Pl. XXI). Its general color varies from light fawn to dark brown. The whole body is delicately translucent and the under parts are white, washed with yellow, though in the male the throat is brown.

Habits, habitat.—Spring peepers cling to dead grass-blades by the pond-side uttering their shrill peeping, one of the earliest calls of spring in the ponds and marshes. They begin to sing in March, when the spotted salamander, *Ambystoma maculatum*, is laying its eggs, and they continue till the end of their own breeding season, often late in May. After that they scatter through swamps and meadows and are only occasionally seen.

Food.—They eat worms and small insects, their diet being similar to that of other frogs, but simpler.

Breeding habits.—Pond shallows and wet hillocks of grass about the margins are favorite breeding places. There on warm evenings in early May their high-pitched, clear chorus can be heard for half a mile. As one approaches, the chorus ends, but after a brief silence voices start up here and there, and if it is quiet enough, a voice finally rises from the grass hillock at one's feet. The flashlight may not reveal the frog at first, but after continued scrutiny, his white vocal sac shines forth in the light (Fig. 302). Clinging there, swollen up like a pouter pigeon, he will keep on uttering his call in the full glare of the light so long as no sound or movement disturbs him. After one peeper is found, a dozen more are usually discovered in all positions, one in the center of a lily flower, others on the floating pads or half-way up the iris leaves.

The males come to the breeding ponds before the females, and always seem to be more numerous. Peepers begin to mate about April 1, continuing till the first or second week in May. They deposit their eggs singly, never in masses, among leaves and grass in shallow water. When peepers are in captivity they sometimes lay their eggs in small clusters.

Life history.—Spring peeper tadpoles begin transforming and coming on land in July when they are little half-inch frogs. The adults leave the water earlier, scattering into moist shadowy places, and nothing is heard of them except a few single notes uttered in autumn, before they disappear into hibernation.

They will live all winter in damp ferneries or moss-gardens, climbing the glass sides of the fernery, often singing a few notes in the evening.

Size.—The male is about an inch long, the female slightly larger.

Range.—Common, eastern and central North America; westward to Manitoba; southward to South Carolina and Louisiana.

Cricket frog, Acris gryllus.—The cricket frog is a tree frog which has such small toe pads that it cannot climb trees, but it can take far higher leaps in air than any crickets can. Its

FIG. 303.—Cricket frog, *Acris gryllus.*

body is usually less than an inch long, brown or grayish colored above, with a bright green stripe running down the middle of the back (Fig. 303). There are dark brown obliquely pointed spots on either side of the green stripe and dark brown cross bands on the hind legs. Its throat and under parts are creamy white. The color tones vary with the frog's activity; it may be quite brown and the back stripe more yellowish than green.

Habits, habitat.—Grass grown, muddy margins of ponds are the special haunt of the cricket frog. There it forages for insects through the day,—easily captured larvæ and pupæ or crickets and grasshoppers, and craneflies and other flying insects, which it can catch by long leaps in air such as few other frogs can make.

Like whirligig beetles, cricket frogs are easily coaxed out of hibernation and they become active in every warm spell of winter.

Breeding habits.—They lay their eggs in late April or May, attaching the single eggs (sometimes small clusters) to submerged grass blades. In that season the males join in a chorus of sharp chirping calls rapidly repeated and often compared to the quick striking together of two pebbles.

Size.—Its body is not more than an inch long.

Range.—Eastern North America, southward to Florida and

westward to Texas, Kansas, and the Northwest. It has not been reported north of southern New York and Connecticut.

F ɪ ɢ. 304.—Swamp cricket frog, *Pseudacris triseriata.*

Swamp cricket frog, Pseudacris triseriata.—The fullgrown swamp cricket frog is about one inch long, ashy brown, varying from light to dark, with three parallel dark stripes which run the length of its back (Fig. 304). The middle one extends along the midline of the back and often forks at the end. There is a distinct dark spot on each eyelid. The under parts are yellowish white. Like the cricket frog this is a tree frog whose toe pads are so small that they are of little help in climbing.

Habits.—These frogs live in wet marshes through the summer, foraging upon insects, like the cricket frog.

Breeding habits.—While searching for *Ambystoma jeffersonianum*, Wright and Allen (*Chorophilus triseriatus.* Bibliography, p. 423) found swamp cricket frogs breeding in ponds in the outskirts of Buffalo about the first of April. The frogs which they observed were shy and easily silenced but the captured ones in their bags and pockets soon began to chirp and started up the chorus again. The egg masses containing from a couple of dozen to 100 eggs are attached to twigs or grass stems.

Range.—Locally abundant in early spring, from Oswego, New York, along Lake Ontario to Utah.

Frogs—*Ranidæ*

Leopard frog, meadow frog, Rana pipiens.—The leopard frog is green or olive green and bronze above, and on its back, sides, and legs there are prominent dark spots rimmed with

FIG. 305.—Leopard frog, *Rana pipiens*.

white. The skin folds or ridges along its back are yellowish or bronzy; it is pure white beneath (Fig. 305). The pickerel frog sometimes confused with this one is washed with bright yellow beneath.

Habitat.—This is one of the most beautiful of frogs, and the common one of the marshes, pond sides, and cat-tail pools. It hibernates in the bottom mud of pools and under the plant litter of brooks where it is often found in winter.

Breeding habits.—The leopard frog choir is the second one to enter the swamp chorus in spring. By the last of April, leopard frogs have assembled in the ponds and their low, guttural croaking can be heard clearly contrasted with the shrill notes of the peeper. From mid-April to early May it is easy to observe their croaking, either at night or in the daytime. The male frogs, lounging half-submerged in the water, appear to take a long breath, after which they suddenly inflate the large vocal sac over each shoulder, which swells

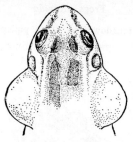

Fig. 306.—Head of male leopard frog with his vocal sacs distended.

larger and larger, as the croak resounds (Fig. 306). When one of them is singing in chorus it repeats the croak four or five times, keeping its sacs distended, suddenly collapsing them as the air is drawn down into the lungs again. Like other frogs, leopards can croak beneath as well as above the water. During the breeding season, they are easily captured, and mating pairs can be collected and kept in jars provided with enough water for the eggs which are likely to be laid there within a few hours.

Life history.—The eggs are laid in masses, attached to sticks or grasses, and are commonly found in marshes and cat-tail pools; each egg mass, containing four to five hundred eggs, is only 1 or 2 inches across when it is first laid, but the jelly soon swells until it is 3 to 5 inches thick.

In late July and August recently transformed leopard frogs populate the margins of the ponds. They are both shy and agile, and at the least alarm, will leap wildly into the water. They are long-nosed and slender, brown or green, often without any spots at all. These young leopard frogs soon join the old ones which have left the water before them and forage with them through the marsh grass, feeding on grasshoppers and leaf insects until October frosts begin, when they go into the streams to hibernate for the winter.

Economic importance.—The leopard frog is the frog of the

laboratories. Thousands of them are used yearly for dissection and experimentation in universities, colleges, and high schools. Although its average weight is not more than two ounces, the leopard frog is the mainstay of the edible frog industry. In 1908, 250,000 pounds of frogs' legs were sold in the United States markets. A firm in the Oneida Lake region of New York conducting a gross business of $15,000 per year in frogs sold one customer over $1,600 worth of frogs' legs between June, 1915, and March, 1916. "An expert can dress between 1,500 and 1,600 frogs per hour, but an average rate is about 1,000 per hour" (Adams, C., and Hankinson, T. L.: *Trans. Amer. Fish. Soc.*, Vol. 45:163).

Size.—The body of the male measures about 3 inches; the female is larger.

Range.—Very common in the whole of eastern and central North America.

Fig. 307.—Pickerel frog, *Rana palustris*.

Pickerel frog, Rana palustris.—The pickerel frog resembles the leopard frog in general shape and color, but is browner; its spots are more regular and rectangular than those of the leopard frog and are not rimmed with white (Fig. 307). The under part of the body is white in front washed with bright orange behind and on the hind legs.

Habits, habitat.—Like the leopard, the pickerel frog hibernates in streams, under stones. Wright trapped many of them at the mouths of ravines, as they were migrating downstream to their spring breeding places in the swampy valley below. Their spring call is similar to that of the leopard frog, is pitched low, and has a distinct snoring quality.

Breeding habits, life history.—Although pickerel frogs are inclined to be shy and solitary at other times, they are gregarious enough during the breeding season, and easy to approach. They lay their eggs in shallow water attached to submerged sticks, often several bunches to one stick. The tadpoles transform in late summer.

Size.—The body is about 2 inches long; the female is a little larger.

Range.—Eastern North America from the Atlantic to the Great Plains.

Fig. 308.—Eastern wood frog, *Rana sylvatica.*

Eastern wood frog, Rana sylvatica.—The upper parts of the wood frog vary from light fawn color to dark brown; beneath it is almost pure white. Its distinctive mark is a prominent dark brown or blackish cheek patch below which a light line extends along the upper jaw to the shoulder (Fig. 308).

Habits, habitat.—Except during the breeding season wood frogs wander far away from the water, foraging among the mosses and fallen leaves of damp woods with which their colors blend well enough to hide them. They hibernate beneath leaves, in stumps, or under logs far away from ponds.

Breeding habits.—Wood frogs come out of hibernation early, usually by late March. They closely follow the spring peeper and arrive suddenly in the woodland pools, generally announcing themselves by a chorus of explosive clucks. There is a protected leaf-strewn forest pond on Mount Tom, in Massachusetts, to which they come earlier than spring peepers do to the ponds of the lower levels. A great company of them remain in the water from one to three weeks; after that only a stray lingerer may now and then be found. During their sojourn in the ponds they sing during the daytime, and at night, too, if it is warm enough. Even in the breeding season wood frogs are shy and their clucking chorus usually ceases as one approaches their pond.

When croaking, the male wood frog sprawls in shallow water with his head above the surface, or swims about during the performance. Mating pairs are easily captured with a water-net, and the females will lay their eggs in captivity. Their rounded egg masses are attached to submerged sticks and to branches which dip into the water (Pl. XX). Two or three masses of wood frog eggs and one or two clusters of spotted salamander eggs (Pl. XX) may be attached to the same twig.

Life history.—In New England the tadpoles transform through midsummer, the first ones being out of the water by the middle of July.

Size.—The body of the male is 2 inches long; the female is 3 inches.

Range.—Common in the east; eastern North America from the Atlantic to the Mississippi River, southward to South Carolina, northward to Quebec.

Pl. XX.—Amphibian eggs: 1, spotted salamander, *Amby-stoma maculatum*; 2, wood frog, *Rana sylvatica*; 3, common toad, *Bufo americanus*.

Photo. by A. H. Morgan

PLATE XX

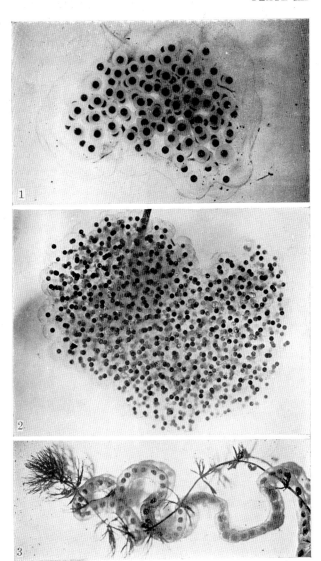

Green frog, Rana clamitans.—The green frog's head and shoulders are bright green, shading to olive or brown at the end of the body (Pl. XXI). It has a lateral skin fold or ridge on each side of its back, the under parts are white with indistinct dark marblings; in the male the throat is washed with yellow. Green frogs might be confused with small bullfrogs except for the lateral folds which are never present in bullfrogs (Pl. XXI and Fig. 309).

Habits, habitat.—Green frogs and bullfrogs live together in swamps and ponds, but the green frog forages along small streams not often frequented by the bullfrog. Green frogs are solitary, only one or two staying in one pool, or in the bends of the stream bank.

They hibernate in the mud of ponds, often staying in springs, wedged between stones or sprawled on the bottom but swimming up into the open water on warm days. A certain covered spring near South Hadley, Massachusetts, is a regular winter resort for green frogs.

Breeding habits.—Green frogs swim about through the ponds very early but they do not begin their low-pitched croaking until much later, and do not mate until the last of May. From then until August they mate and lay their eggs, almost always by night.

Life history.—During June and early July the eggs are very common and the egg masses are spread out like a film nearly a foot across, over beds of *Chara* or other submerged water plants or in the shallow water near shore where they are destroyed in great numbers by drying. The water is usually warm and the eggs often hatch into tadpoles in less than a week.

Green frog tadpoles which hatch in June do not transform to frogs until the following spring or early summer.

Size.—Body of the female 5 inches long, the male is smaller.

Range.—Common in eastern and central United States and southern Canada.

Pl. XXI.—Frogs: from above downward, spring peeper, *Hyla crucifer*, dark and light color phases; "tree toad," *Hyla versicolor*, light color phase; green frog, *Rana clamitans*, male with large and female with smaller ear-drum.

PLATE XXI

Fig. 309.—Bullfrog, *Rana catesbiana*.

Bullfrog, Rana catesbiana.—Bullfrogs are green or greenish brown with white slightly mottled under parts, and yellow throats. They look like larger editions of the green frog except that they never have skin folds on each side of the back (Fig. 309).

Habits, habitat.—Their favorite haunts are in ponds where the shallows are overgrown with pickerel weed and arrowhead, well populated with snails and nymphs of dragonflies and mayflies. They devour great numbers of these as well as worms, tadpoles, and little frogs of their own or any other species. Though less common in small streams than large ones, there are certain little brooks inhabited by burrowing mayflies from whose banks two or three bullfrogs are never missing. Bullfrogs are even more aquatic than green frogs and they never go far away from the water; usually they are in it. They get all their food there, and they are apt to hibernate in the same pond where they spent their summer.

Breeding habits.—The bullfrog is the last of the frog and toad procession to come out of hibernation, and it does not begin croaking in the ponds until nearly June. From then through midsummer, especially on moist evenings, it repeats its famous call, "be drowned, better go round," and as boldly now as in former years it says "jug-o-rum, more rum." During the breeding season bullfrogs, often a dozen or so mating pairs, gather in ponds and at night it is comparatively easy to capture them. They float partly outstretched at the surface and when the light is flashed on them they appear paralyzed though their paralysis is far from dependable. The way to catch them by hand is to seize them very firmly by both hind legs, for a bullfrog "in the hand" is strong and apparently much larger than the same one in the pond.

Life history.—Bullfrogs usually lay their eggs at night, during the last of June or in July. The egg mass, a film of jelly containing 10,000 to 20,000 small eggs, is nearly two feet across and floats near the surface, anchored and half hidden by brush or caught on plant stems.

The tadpoles are two years old or more before they transform into frogs, spending two winters, sometimes a third, in the tadpole stage, finally becoming frogs in late August. All of the large tadpoles so common in pools in late fall or early spring are either green frog or bullfrog tadpoles; there are apt to be many more of the green frogs. But any tadpole over three and a half inches long is pretty surely a bullfrog; one year old bullfrog tadpoles seldom show their hind legs.

Size.—Body of the male 7 to 8 inches long, the female the same.

Range.—North America, east of Rocky Mountains, and introduced west of the Rockies.

CHAPTER XIX

TURTLES AND SNAKES

Found In or Near Water

Turtles

Our native fresh water reptiles are nearly all turtles (*Testu-dinata*). The only snakes which stay consistently by the water or in it are the brown water snakes which sun themselves in shallow stream beds or rest on bushes overhanging the water.

There are many reptiles which live on land but relatively few in the water, and even these aquatic ones have hardly any structures or habits which are thoroughly distinctive of water life. Reptiles are scaly, cold-blooded vertebrates like the fishes, but fishes breathe by gills while reptiles have lungs and generally use them. They do not transform as they grow up like the gilled tadpoles which change to frogs. Newly hatched turtles have lungs, breathe air, and look like their parents. All of the fishes either lay their eggs or bring forth their young in the water, and most amphibians lay their eggs in it, but among the reptiles, even the turtles, which spend their whole lives in the water, come out on land to lay their eggs.

Turtles have an upper and a lower bony shell covered by horny plates, the upper part being known as the carapace and the lower one as the plastron. From the strongholds of these shells turtles thrust out their heads, legs, and tails, those with less shell, like the snapping turtle, having greater freedom of action but less protection. A turtle's backbone connects the neck and tail, as it does in any other vertebrate —fish, cow, or monkey—but it is largely hidden beneath the shell and rigidly joined to it.

Habits, habitat.—Turtles live in quiet ponds and the protected backwaters of streams. Water snakes also prefer quiet places but they usually lie in shallow rills seldom visited by turtles. Turtles have a keen sense of smell under water as well as in air and they can scent their food at considerable distances.

Food.—Turtles and snakes are both generally carnivorous. Turtles feed upon a miscellaneous assortment of animal food, dead and alive—small fish, tadpoles, snails, and insects. To this diet the wood and the painted turtles add water plants and seeds (Fig. 21).

Breeding habits.—Male and female turtles are sometimes but not always distinguishable. The tail of the male may be longer than that of the female; the lower shell or plastron is apt to be slightly convex in the female and concave in the male. In some turtles there are differences in the lengths of the shells, the male wood turtle having a shorter plastron than the female. When turtles are dissected there is no doubt of the sex, for the ovaries of the female are large and conspicuous, with yellow, yolked eggs like those of birds.

Turtles which frequent the water usually mate there, but so does the wood turtle which outside of its breeding period seldom goes into the water. When mating, the male wood turtle grasps the shell of the female, holding to it by his claws, head, and tail. The female does all of the swimming but both animals twist and turn, the female often struggling to get to the surface for air. While this struggle is going on the male discharges large numbers of sperm cells into the reproductive passages of the female. These find their way up the oviducts and meet the eggs as they come down the tubes. Turtle eggs look like bird eggs except that the shells are always clear white or pinkish. Some species, such as the painted turtle, have soft shelled eggs; others, like the snapper, have hard shelled ones. They are hidden in soil or rotting wood and leaves, and usually take a long time to incubate, about eighty days for those of the spotted turtle.

Life history.—Newly hatched frogs are fishlike and young flies look like worms, but just-hatched turtles are small editions of their parents. They have lungs and breathe air; they walk on the same feet which they use in their old age, going through no marked transformation as they grow up. Although fresh water turtles, like land and marine ones, live to a considerable age, their bony shells are never shed, but each plate or shield grows larger and thicker until it reaches adult size. The painted turtle, *Chrysemys picta*, sheds the outer horny transparent layer of its shell periodically and for some time afterwards its colors appear very bright. If a good sized piece of a turtle's shell is broken or crushed, the broken part will slough off, new shell will grow, and after several months only a scar will mark the injury.

Snapping Turtles—*Chelydridæ*

Snapping turtle, Chelydra serpentina.—The snapper is a water turtle but there are more than equal chances that it will be found on land, for it explores the streamsides and adjoining fields in May and June when humanity is also out walking. It is the largest of our fresh water turtles, yet on land it is a swift walker, and can lunge and jump completely off the ground. Snapping turtles may weigh 40 pounds or more but they commonly weigh 25 or 30 pounds and are over 2 feet long. Their shells are comparatively small, allowing free action of the legs and the long neck and head, the latter so large that it can be pulled only part way into the shell (Fig. 310). On the upper side of the tail there is a row of low tubercles forming a crest like the one on an alligator's tail; in very young snappers there are three such elevations

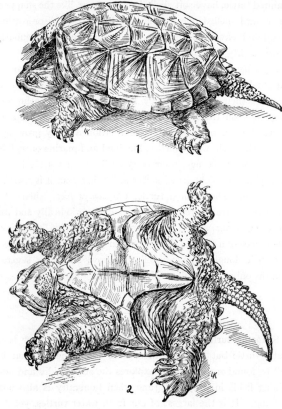

Fig. 310.—Snapping turtle, *Chelydra serpentina;*
1, from above; 2, ventral side showing the small
plastron which allows free action of the legs and
head.

along the middle of the carapace but these do not show very
much in older turtles.

Habits, habitat.—Except around the egg-laying season
snapping turtles stay in ponds and meandering marsh
streams, patrolling the bottom or hanging relaxed in the water

with only their nostrils out of it. Although they appear sluggish and awkward, they can thrust forth their heads and snap their strong hooked jaws with lightning rapidity. They are quick enough to capture swift moving animals—fish, frogs and flies—but they will also devour anything available —insects, snails, crayfishes, mice, small birds, and occasionally dead animals. They very commonly catch ducklings by the legs when they are swimming on meadow ponds, and they sometimes attack full sized ducks. When frightened or maltreated, most turtles retreat into their shells, but snappers protect themselves by snapping and biting, doing so at the slightest excuse. When snappers are caught, they should be carried by the tail, head downward, so that they cannot spring or stretch their necks far enough to bite.

Breeding habits.—The female snapper takes her spring rambles on land, in search of a nesting place. She selects soft, damp earth, scoops a hole in it, digging with her hind legs till her body is nearly hidden, then she lays twenty or more round hard-shelled eggs about an inch in diameter. A vivid story of the egg-laying of the snapping-turtle is told by Dallas Lore Sharp in the chapter " Turtle Eggs for Agassiz" in his volume called "The Face of the Fields." The enemies of the snapper are numbered chiefly among the animals which eat its eggs—mink, weasels, and skunks.

Size.—Length of fullgrown turtle, 2 feet or more; very large ones are nearly 3 feet long and weigh about fifty pounds.

Range.—Common, United States east of the Rocky Mountains.

Box Turtles—*Kinosternidæ*

Musk turtle, stinkpot, Sternotherus odoratus.—Like the snapper the musk turtle lives in the water, coming on land only to lay its eggs. It is one of our smallest turtles, and the whole animal is only 4 or 5 inches long. Its carapace is highly arched, smooth, brown; the plastron is yellowish, small, cross-shaped, and notched behind (Pl. XXII). Two narrow yellow stripes extend along each side of the head and neck, one above and one below the eye. The male has a longer and stronger tail than the female and a "patch of rough scales in the bend between the thigh and the leg." Musk turtles give off a penetrating odor of musk from the musk glands near the bases of the hind legs and near the axils of the forelegs. Their dispositions are consistently vicious. They stretch out their heads very slowly before snapping and the expression of the whole performance is surly and premeditated.

Habits, habitat.—In color, musk turtles match the muddy bottoms of the ponds and sluggish streams where they live, which partly accounts for their being so little known (Pl. XXII). They are bottom foragers that crawl over the mud, stretching their necks out very slowly before snapping at their prey—small fish, worms, insects, or tadpoles. Although having lungs like all other turtles, they are able to stay below the surface of water a very long time; Ditmars kept them for weeks in tanks where they could not get to the air. "Digging in" is about the only activity of musk turtles when they are in captivity; one kept in the Mount Holyoke Zoology Laboratory through a winter and spring would burrow into the dirt as often as it was pulled out. After a long sojourn in the dirt it was thin and shrunken but would appear greatly refreshed as soon as it had been "soaked up" in water.

Breeding habits.—Its 3 to 7 smooth, white, elliptical eggs are laid in late June, in rotting stumps and logs or clumps of reeds. The newly hatched young are about half an inch long.

Size.—The average length of the whole animal is 5 to 6 inches.

Range.—Southern Canada to Florida, westward to Missouri and Texas.

Mud turtle, Kinosternum subrubrum.—Although many persons know all pond turtles as "mud turtles," only this

FIG. 311.—Mud turtle, *Kinosternum subrubrum;*
1, dorsal and 2, ventral view showing the plastron
with hinged ends which can be drawn up against
the carapace.

one small species is the real mud turtle. It is not found north
of New York and even within its range it is far from common.
Its upper shell or carapace is plain dull brown and the broad
oval plastron is yellowish, the two ends of it being hinged so
that they can be drawn up closely against the carapace, the
trait which gives this family the name box turtles (Fig. 311).

Pl. XXII.—Musk turtle, *Sternotherus odoratus*, a box turtle whose plastron is only slightly flexible at the ends, one of our smallest turtles: 1, dorsal and 2, ventral view.

PLATE XXII

The head is brown with yellow fleckings along the sides of the neck but without the distinct yellow lines which mark the musk turtle's head (Pl. XXII). The male has a longer tail than the female and there is a horny point at the end of it.

Habits, habitat.—The mud turtle lives in muddy bottoms similar to the haunts of the musk turtle but it is less fond of the water. It also has a better disposition. Just after it first appears from hibernation it is coated with dried mud paste from its burrow, usually made in moist earth only fifty yards or so distant from a marsh. At the end of hibernation it is in the same shrunken condition as the musk turtle. Its habit of absorbing water at this time is described by Wetmore and Harper in their account of its hibernation: "The turtle that we found was taken home and placed in a basin of water. For several minutes it made no movement save to emit a series of bubbles from its nostrils, or to close and open an eye. Then it proceeded to extend and retract its neck slowly. The jaws were opened and closed slowly. In a short time movement of the jaws ceased, but the turtle continued to draw water into the mouth and then expel it. . . . In a few moments the turtle became more alert and swam and walked about, thrusting its head to the surface."

Breeding habits.—In the Okefinokee Swamp in Georgia, Wright found a nest of the mud turtle in rotten wood, containing three elliptical eggs buried about three inches below the surface.

Size.—The carapace of adults is about 4 inches long.

Range.—Probably not common anywhere. New York, southward to the Gulf of Mexico and westward to the Mississippi Valley.

Pond and Land Turtles—*Testudinidæ*

Painted turtle, Chrysemys picta.—In New England the painted turtle is the most common of all the fresh water turtles. Its only rivals are the spotted turtles which bask with it in the sun, along the same pond banks and floating logs (Pl. XXIII).

Its flattened carapace is very smooth, and the plates are olive brown with borders of pale yellow; these form a narrow light band across the back between the first and second rows of plates. The small marginal plates are red with black and yellow markings, most of the color being on the underside; the plastron is light yellow. There are two bright yellow streaks behind each eye, and stripes of yellow which give place to scarlet on the throat, legs, and tail. Its whole coloration suggests a dark-painted vehicle with gay running gear.

Habits, habitat.—The favorite haunts of painted turtles are the partly overgrown ponds where there are large populations of small water animals (Fig. 21). They swim in and out among the plants, displaying their scarlet rims at each leisurely dip of their bodies, or they climb out of the water to bask upon logs, only to slide back again at the least alarm. They eat almost anything which they find under water but they seem quite unable to swallow if they are out of it. By examining the stomachs of painted turtles, Surface found that their diet included algæ, grasses, moss, insects, little mollusks, and pieces of larger animals evidently eaten when half decayed. In October they begin digging into the muddy pond bottoms for their winter hibernation.

Breeding habits.—They lay their elliptical eggs between the middle and last of June, always in late afternoon or evening. The turtle selects a nest site in soil not far distant from water, digs a hole with her hind feet, and lays the four to eight or more pinkish eggs. Without turning around she pushes each one down into the hole with her hind feet, covering them so well that she leaves little or no trace of her work.

Size.—Length of adult carapace about 6 to 8 inches.

Range.—Eastern North America, northward to southern Canada, southward to Georgia. West of the Alleghanies it is wholly replaced by the closely related western painted turtle, *Chrysemys marginata*.

Spotted turtle, Clemmys guttata.—Spotted turtles are the yellow polka-dotted turtles which sun themselves in companies on floating logs or islands of reeds and grasses. They climb up on to a log, crowding and piling one upon another, but the least alarm sends them all tumbling back into the water together. Such basking companies are often made up of both painted and spotted turtles. The spotted turtle has a smooth, low carapace, black scattered over with yellow or orange spots (Pl. XXIII); the middle of its plastron is dull yellow and on the underside the edges of the carapace are marked with yellow. The male has a tail nearly twice as long as that of the female.

Habits, habitat.—It seems to take all its food under water, yet it travels considerable distances overland. Spotted turtles are very good natured, and they thrive in captivity on a diet of chopped raw meat. This is the species which Yerkes used for studies of habit-formation and found that it does remarkably little aimless wandering, possessing keen senses of smell and sight and appearing to learn from experience. It eats plant stems and leaves as well as insects and crustaceans.

Breeding habits.—It lays its elliptical eggs in the same season as the painted turtle, in late afternoon or evening, from the middle to the last of June. They are a long time incubating; Babcock buried some of them in sand on June 16 and they did not hatch until September 6. At that time the young turtle had a carapace about one inch long.

Size.—The carapace of the male is about 5 inches long, that of the female an inch shorter.

Range.—Through the eastern states from Maine to Florida and westward to Indiana and Michigan.

Wood turtle, sculptured turtle, Clemmys insculpta.—Wood turtles are the familiar "carved" or "sculptured" turtles is wholly replaced by the closely related western painted turtle, *Chrysemys marginata*.

Pl. XXIII.—Two common pond turtles: 1, spotted turtle, *Clemmys guttata*; 2, painted turtle, *Chrysemys picta*.

PLATE XXIII

Fig. 312. Wood turtle, *Clemmys insculpta;* 1, dorsal view showing the sculptured carapace; 2, ventral side.

usually found in fields and open woodlands. They are so called because of the roughly sculptured concentric ridges on each plate of the carapace and these markings alone are enough to identify them (Fig. 312). Their heads and feet are rusty black and brown and all of the other soft parts are dull salmon red. These colors and the gray brown of the carapace hide them in backgrounds of dead grasses and fallen leaves.

Habits, habitat.—During late spring and summer wood turtles wander through pastures and woodland and over upland fields far from the water. The food they gather along the way is not very different from that of the ground-feeding birds—blackberries, partridge berries, mushrooms—but in the water they live on the regular turtle diet of small aquatic animals. They hibernate in muddy stream bottoms.

Breeding habits.—Wood turtles always mate in the water and as readily in tanks or artificial pools as in their native ponds. The usual season is through May and June but Wright found a pair mating in a woodland stream on the first of October. Ordinarily the wood turtle lays her eggs in June, depositing about a dozen in a hollow of the ground, and after covering them, leaves them to hatch as other turtles do.

Size.—Length about 8 inches.

Range.—From Canada southward through New Jersey and Pennsylvania to Maryland and westward to Michigan and Wisconsin.

Soft-shelled Turtles—*Trionychidæ*

Spiny soft-shelled turtle, Amyda spinifera.—There is no mistaking the soft-shelled turtles. In place of the bony shells of most turtles, they have a carapace and a plastron which can be bent between the fingers like rubber. They are thoroughly aquatic animals, swift swimmers with broadly webbed feet (Fig. 313).

The spiny soft-shelled turtle is flat bodied with a yellowish brown carapace and pure white plastron and under parts. The young turtles, 3 or 4 inches long, with polka-dots of black on the carapace, are often sold in the pet shops and by aquarium dealers. The soft-shell bends its long neck in an S-shaped curve; its narrow head is prolonged into a leathery snout with the nostrils at the tip. It usually floats just below the surface of the water, with its nostrils thrust out into the air.

FIG. 313.—Spiny soft-shelled turtle, *Amyda spinifera*, which has a leathery or soft shell: 1, from above; 2, ventral view showing the small soft plastron and webbed feet.

Habits, habitat.—This turtle lives in shallow, muddy-bottomed water, never leaving it except to lay its eggs. It is a scavenger as well as a voracious feeder upon aquatic animals, even good-sized mussels. It thrives in an aquarium, but lies much of the time half buried in the sand. Although this turtle has lungs and no gills, it can stay under water a long time, securing oxygen from the water which it takes into its mouth. Its mouth and throat have a thin lining richly supplied with fine blood-vessels, and an exchange of gases, oxygen and carbon dioxide, takes place just as it does in the gills of fishes.

Breeding habits.—Clumsy and awkward as these turtles are on land, they persevere in crawling out of the water to lay several white, round eggs in the moist sand of the shore.

Size.—Length about 14 inches.

Range.—Along the Mississippi River and its tributaries eastward into Pennsylvania and New York, northward to Lake Champlain.

Fig. 314.—Northern water snake, *Natrix sipedon*, subspecies *sipedon*.

Colubrine or Harmless Snakes—*Colubridæ*

Northern water snake, "moccasin," banded water snake, Natrix sipedon, subspecies sipedon.—This common water snake of the northern states lives in sunny hollows watered by little streams, generally lying partly on the bank and partly across the stream bed. Sometimes it is found on the borders of larger streams and ponds.

It is a heavily built snake, dingy dark brown, sometimes reddish, and of morose appearance; its undersides are spotted with reddish and black. In young snakes and those which have recently shed their skins, the back is crossed by broad brown bands separated by narrower bands of light brown; on the sides the dark bands taper and the light ones become broader (Fig. 314).

Habits, habitat.—One snake or a group of two or three often basks in the sunshine, hanging from bushes over the water, dropping into it when disturbed or slipping in to capture fish or frogs. In warm days of early March water snakes begin sunning themselves along small streams. They are cold then and move slowly, even allowing themselves to be picked up without protest, but when they are brought into the warmth of a house they soon become agile enough to display their natural ugliness of disposition. They will strike viciously at anything which comes near them, and although they are not poisonous they should be kept in a securely screened box. Although this snake is sometimes called "water moccasin" it is not related to the poisonous true water moccasin or "cotton mouth" of the south.

Food.—Water snakes live very largely upon fish, frogs, toads and water insects but they do not neglect the meadow mice and shrews.

Breeding habits.—In the latter part of August or early in September they give birth to living young, the average number being about two dozen to a litter. However, a litter of forty-four has been observed by Ditmars.

Size.—Fullgrown adults are 2½ to 4 feet long and have a girth of about 2 inches; the average length is 3 feet or less.

Range.—From Maine and southern Canada to North Carolina and westward to Kansas and Wisconsin. Common in New England and the Middle States.

BIBLIOGRAPHY

GENERAL REFERENCES

Carpenter, K. E. 1928. Life in Inland Waters. Macmillan Co.

Chapman, R. N. 1925. Animal Ecology. Burgess-Brooke, Inc., Minneapolis. Contains extensive bibliographies which include many technical papers.

Copeia. 1913. A magazine containing notes on fish, amphibians, and water reptiles. Pub. by Kingsbury Box and Printing Co., Northampton, Mass.

Jordan, D. S. 1929. Manual of the Vertebrate Animals of the Northeastern United States. 13th ed. World Book Co., Yonkers, N. Y.

Needham, J. G., and Lloyd, J. T. 1916. Life of Inland. Waters. Comstock Pub. Co., Ithaca, N. Y.

Needham, J. G., and Needham, P. R. 1927. A Guide to the Study of Fresh-water Biology. With Special Reference to Aquatic Insects and other Invertebrate Animals. The Amer. Viewpoint Soc., 13 Astor Place, New York, and Albany. Includes keys with figures of each form mentioned and suggestions for studies of aquatic communities.

Pratt, H. S. 1923. Manual of the Common Invertebrate Animals. Exclusive of Insects. A. C. McClurg & Co., Chicago.
1923 a. Manual of Land and Fresh Water Vertebrates of the United States. P. Blakiston's Son & Co., Phila.

Shelford, V. E. 1913. Animal Communities in Temperate America. Univ. of Chicago Press.

Ward, H. B., and Whipple, G. C. 1918. Fresh-Water Biology. John Wiley & Sons. The most inclusive American fresh water biology. Illustrated keys and descriptions.

Whipple, S. C. 1927. The Microscopy of Drinking Water. (Revised by Fair, G. M., and Whipple, M. C.) John Wiley & Sons.

CHAPTER II

LIFE IN PONDS AND STREAMS

General References: Needham and Lloyd, 1916; Whipple, 1927.

Forbes, S. A. 1925. The Lake as a Microcosm. Bull. Illinois Nat. Hist. Survey, Vol. 15, Art. 9, Urbana.

Needham, J. G. 1922 A Biological Reconnaissance of Lake George. Biol. Survey of Lake George, N. Y. State of N. Y., Conservation Com., Albany.

Seasonal succession of life.

General References: Shelford, 1913, Animal Communities in Temperate America; See successions in lakes and ponds.

Allee, W. C. 1911. Seasonal Succession in Old Forest Ponds. Trans. Illinois State Acad. Sci., Vol. 4: 126–131.

Shelford, V. E. 1918. Physiological Problems in the Life-Histories of Animals, with Particular Reference to Their Seasonal Occurrence. Amer. Nat., Vol. 52: 129–154.

1919. Nature's Mobilization. Nat. Hist., Vol. 19: 205–210.

1929. Laboratory and Field Ecology. Williams & Wilkins Co., Baltimore.

CHAPTER III

COLLECTING AND PRESERVING WATER ANIMALS

Aquatic Life. A magazine devoted to aquarium life. It contains names and addresses of supply dealers. Roth, A. Baltimore.

BIBLIOGRAPHY

Bishop, S. C. 1927. The Amphibians and Reptiles of Allegheny State Park. N. Y. State Mus., Handbook, No. 3, Albany.

Casino, S. E. The Naturalists' Directory. Salem, Mass. Names, addresses and special subjects of study of professional and amateur naturalists of the United States, Canada, and other countries, including South America. (Addresses of collectors and some dealers; biennial.)

Eggeling, O., and Ehrenberg, F. 1912. The Freshwater Aquarium and Its Inhabitants. Henry Holt.

Gordon, M. 1927. Keeping Native Fishes in Aquaria. Cornell Rural School Leaflet, Vol. 21, No. 1, Ithaca, N. Y.

Lutz, F. E. 1927. How to Collect and Preserve Insects. Amer. Mus. Nat. Hist., Guide Leaflet Series, No. 39, New York.

Smith, E. 1902. The Home Aquarium and How to Care for It. E. P. Dutton & Co.

CHAPTER IV

SIMPLER PLANTS AND ANIMALS

General References: **Needham and Needham,** 1927; **Ward and Whipple,** 1918; **Whipple,** 1927; or Chapter V, *Higher plants,* **Kerner and Oliver,** 1895.

Brown, H. E. 1908. Algal Periodicity in Ponds and Streams. Bull. Torrey Botanical Club, Vol. 35: 223–248.

Conn, H. W. 1905. A Preliminary Report on the Protozoa of the Fresh Waters of Connecticut. Conn. State Geol. and Nat. Hist. Survey, Bull. No. 2, Hartford.

Hausman, L. A. 1917. Observations on the Ecology of the Protozoa. Amer. Nat., Vol. 51: 157–172.

Hylander, C. J. 1928. The Algæ of Connecticut. Conn. State Geol. and Nat. Hist. Survey, Bull. No. 42, Hartford.

Kahn, M. C. 1920. Microscopical Trouble-makers in the Water Supply. Nat. Hist., Vol. 20: 83–90.

BIBLIOGRAPHY

Mann, A. 1921. The Dependence of the Fishes on the Diatoms. Ecology, Vol. 2: 79–83.

Matheson, R., and Hinman, E. H. 1928. Chara fragilis and Mosquito Development. Amer. Jour. Hygiene, Vol. 8: 279–292.

Platt, E. L. 1915. The Population of the "Blanket-Algæ" of Fresh-water Pools. Amer. Nat., Vol. 49: 752–762.

Smith, G. M. 1924. Ecology of the Plankton Algæ in the Palisades Interstate Park, Including the Relation of Control Methods to Fish Culture. Roosevelt Wild Life Bull., Vol. 2, No. 2, Syracuse Univ.

Stokes, A. C. 1918. Aquatic Microscopy for Beginners. 4th ed. John Wiley & Sons (out of print).

CHAPTER V

HIGHER PLANTS

General References: **Ward and Whipple,** 1918.

Arber, A. 1920. Water Plants. Cambridge Univ. Press.

Britton, N. L., and Brown, A. 1913. Illustrated Flora of the Northern United States, Canada, and the British Possessions. 2nd ed. Charles Scribner's Sons.

Claassen, P. W. 1921. Typha Insects; Their Ecological Relationships. Cornell Univ. Agri. Exp. Sta., Mem. 47, Ithaca, N. Y.

Coulter, J. M. 1904. Plants, a Text-book of Botany. 3rd ed. D. Appleton & Co.

Grout, A. J. 1905. Mosses with a Hand-lens. 2nd ed. O. T. Louis Co., New York.

Hegner, R. W. 1926. The Interrelations of Protozoa and the Utricles of Utricularia. Biol. Bull., Vol. 50: 239–270. 1926 a. The Protozoa of the Pitcher Plant, Sarracenia purpurea. Biol. Bull., Vol. 50: 271–276.

Kerner, A., and Oliver, F. W. 1895. The Natural History of Plants, Their Forms, Growth, Reproduction, and Distribution. 4 vols. Holt & Co.

1904. The Natural History of Plants. 2 vols. Gresham Pub. Co., London.

Miner, R. W. 1928. A Drama of the Microscope. The New Rotifer Group. Nat. Hist., Vol. 28: 500–514.

Moore, E. 1915. The Potamogetons in Relation to Pond Culture. Bull. Bur. Fish., Doc. 815, Vol. 33: 251–291.

Pearse, A. S., and Terrell, C. B. 1920. Aquatic Preserves. Nat. Hist., Vol. 20: 103–106.

Pond, R. H. 1905. The Biological Relation of Aquatic Plants to the Substratum. Rep. U. S. Com. of Fish and Fisheries for 1903: 483–526.

Power, S. 1903. The Possibilities of Peat. Outlook, Vol. 73: 172–175.

CHAPTER VI

SPONGES

General References: **Ward and Whipple,** 1918, Chap. 10, Potts, E., Sponges (Porifera).

McNair, G. T. 1923. Motor Reactions of the Fresh-Water Sponge Ephydatia fluviatilis. Biol. Bull., Vol. 44: 153–166.

Morgan, A. H. 1929. Fresh-Water Sponges in Winter. Sci. Mo., Vol. 28: 152–155.

Potts, E. 1887. Fresh-water Sponges; a monograph. Proc. Acad. Nat. Sci., Phila., Vol. 39: 158–279.

Smith, F. 1921. Distribution of the Fresh-Water Sponges of North America. Bull. Illinois Nat. Hist. Survey, Vol. 14: 9–22, Urbana.

CHAPTER VII

THE HYDRAS, FRESH WATER JELLYFISHES

General References: **Ward and Whipple,** 1918, Chap. II, Smith, F., Hydra and Other Fresh-Water Hydrozoa; **Pratt,** 1923.

BIBLIOGRAPHY

Clemens, W. A. 1922. Hydra in Lake Erie. Science, Vol. 55, No. 1426: 445.

Gudger, E. W. 1927. Hydras as Enemies of Young Fishes. Nat. Hist., Vol. 27: 270–274.

Hickson, S. J. 1925. Hydra and the Tadpoles. Nature, Vol. 115: 802.

Scourfield, D. J. 1904. Hydra and the Surface Film of Water. Jour. Quekett Micr. Club, Nov. 1904.

Welsh, P. S., and Loomis, H. A. 1924. A Limnological Study of Hydra oligactis in Douglas Lake, Mich. Trans. Amer. Micr. Soc., Vol. 43: 203–235.

CHAPTER VIII

FREE-LIVING FLATWORMS

General References: **Ward and Whipple,** 1918; Chap. 12. Stringer, C. E., Free-living Flatworms; **Pratt,** 1923.

Bardeen, C. R. 1901. On the Physiology of the Planaria maculata with Especial Reference to the Phenomena of Regeneration. Amer. Jour. Phys., Vol. 5: 1–53.

Carpenter, K. 1928. On the Tropisms of Some Freshwater Planarians. Brit. Jour. Exp. Biol., Vol. 5, No. 3: 196–203.

Pearl, R. 1902. The Movements and Reactions of Freshwater Planarians. Quart. Jour. Micr. Sci., Vol. 46: 509–714.

Walter, H. E. 1907. The Reactions of Planarians to Light. Jour. Exp. Zool., Vol. 5: 35–162.

CHAPTER IX

WHEEL ANIMALCULES (Rotifera)

General References: **Needham and Needham,** 1927; **Ward and Whipple,** 1918, Chap. 17, Jennings, H. S., Wheel. Animalcules.

Harring, H. K. 1913. Synopsis of the Rotatoria. U. S. Nat. Mus., Bull. No. 81.

BIBLIOGRAPHY

Jennings, H. S. 1900. Rotatoria of the United States with Special Reference to Those of the Great Lakes. Bull. U. S. Fish Com. for 1899: 67–104.

1901. Synopses of North American Invertebrates. XVII. The Rotatoria. Amer. Nat., Vol. 35: 725–777.

Mueller, H. O. 1925. The Rotifer Group. Nat. Hist., Vol. 25: 223–232.

Myers, F. J. 1925. What is a Rotifer? Nat. Hist., Vol. 25: 211–223.

CHAPTER X

MOSS ANIMALCULES (Bryozoa)

General References: **Pratt,** 1923; **Ward and Whipple,** 1918, Chap. 28, Davenport, C. B., Moss Animalcules (Bryozoa).

Davenport, C. B. 1890. Cristatella: The Origin and Development of the Individual in the Colony. Bull. Mus. Comp. Zool., Harvard College, Vol. 20: 101–152.

1904. Report on the Fresh-water Bryozoa of the United States. Proc. U. S. Nat. Mus., Vol. 27: 211–221.

Landacre, F. 1901. Sponges and Bryozoa of Sandusky Bay. Ohio Nat., Vol. 1: 96–97.

CHAPTER XI

THREADWORMS (Nematodes) AND BRISTLEWORMS
(Oligochætes)

General References: **Pratt,** 1923; **Ward and Whipple,** 1918, Chap. 19, Smith, F., Aquatic Earthworms and other Bristle-bearing Worms.

Darwin, C. 1900. Vegetable Mould and Earthworms. D. Appleton & Co.

Galloway, T. W. 1911. The Common Fresh-water Oligochæta of the United States. Trans. Amer. Micr. Soc., Vol. 30: 285–317.

May, H. G. 1919. Contributions to the Life Histories of Gordius robustus Leidy and Paragordius varius Leidy. Illinois Biol. Monographs, Vol. 5, No. 2.

Montgomery, T. H., Jr. 1899. Synopses of North American Invertebrates. II. Gordiacea (Hairworms). Amer. Nat., Vol. 33: 647–652.

Smith, F. 1900. Notes on North American Oligochæta. Bull. Illinois State Lab. Nat. Hist., Vol. 5: 441–478, Urbana. Also same, Vol. 7: 45–51, 1905.

Walton, L. B. 1906. Naididæ of Cedar Point, Ohio. Amer. Nat., Vol. 40: 683–706.

Welch, P. S. 1914. Studies on the Enchytræidæ of North America. Bull. Illinois State Lab. Nat. Hist., Vol. 10: 123–212, Urbana.

CHAPTER XII

LEECHES

General References: **Pratt,** 1923; **Ward and Whipple,** 1918, Chap. 20, Moore, J. P., Leeches.

Moore, J. P. 1901. The Hirudinea of Illinois. Bull. Illinois State Lab. Nat. Hist., Vol. 5: 479–546, Urbana.
1923. The Control of Blood-sucking Leeches with an account of the Leeches in the Palisades Interstate Park. Roosevelt Wild Life Bull., Vol. 2, No. 1, Syracuse Univ.

Nachtrieb, H. F., Hemingway, E. E., and Moore, J. P. 1912. Report on the Leeches of Minnesota. Geol. and Nat. Hist. Survey of Minn., Zool. Series, No. 5; Part III, Classification of the Leeches of Minnesota, by J. P. Moore.

CHAPTER XIII

CRUSTACEA

Andrews, E. A. 1904. Breeding Habits of Crayfish. Amer. Nat., Vol. 38:165–206.

Calman, W. T. 1911. The Life of Crustacea. Macmillan Co.

Embody, G. C. 1912. Distribution, Food, and Reproductive Capacity of Some Fresh-water Amphipods. Internat. Revue der gesamten Hydrobiologie und Hydrographie. Biol. Suppl. No. 3.

1914. Crustacea. A Key to the Common Genera Occurring in the Fresh Waters of the Eastern United States. Cornell Univ., Ithaca, N. Y.

Forbes, E. B. 1897. A Contribution to a Knowledge of North American Fresh-Water Cyclopidæ. Bull. Illinois State Lab. Nat. Hist., Vol. 5: 27–82, Urbana.

Harris, J. A. 1903. An Ecological Catalogue of the Crayfishes Belonging to the Genus Cambarus. Kans. Univ. Sci. Bull., Vol. 2: 51–187.

Hay, O. P., and Hay, W. P. 1889. A Contribution to the Knowledge of the Genus Branchipus. Amer. Nat., Vol. 23: 91–95.

Hay, W. P. 1896. The Crawfishes of the State of Indiana. Rep. Ind. Geol. Survey, Vol. 20: 475–506.

Pearse, A. S. 1910. The Crawfishes of Michigan. Mich. State Biol. Survey, Vol. 1: 9–22.

Scourfield, D. J. 1896. Entomostraca and the Surface Film of Water. Jour. Linnean Soc., Zool., Vol. 25: 1–9.

1900. Note on Scapholeberis mucronatus and the Surface Film of Water. Jour. Quekett Micr. Club, Series 2, Vol. 7: 309–312.

Shantz, H. L. 1905. Notes on the North American Species of Branchinecta and Their Habits. Biol. Bull., Vol. 9: 249–264.

Turner, C. L. 1926. Crayfishes of Ohio. Ohio State Univ. Bull., Vol. 30.

CHAPTER XIV

WATER-MITES (Hydrachnida)

General References: **Ward and Whipple**, 1918, Chap. **26,** Wolcott, R. H., Water-mites.

Marshall, R. 1908. The Arrhenuri of the United States. Trans. Amer. Micr. Soc., Vol. 28: 85–140.

Wolcott, R. H. 1905. A Review of the Genera of the Water-mites. Trans. Amer. Micr. Soc., Vol. 26: 161–243.

CHAPTER XV

AQUATIC INSECTS

General References:

Alexander, C. P. 1925. An Entomological Survey of the Salt Fork of the Vermilion River in 1921, with a Bibliography of Aquatic Insects. Bull. Illinois Nat. Hist. Survey, Vol. 15, No. 8, Urbana. Excellent bibliography arranged by orders.

Comstock, J. H. 1924. An Introduction to Entomology. Comstock Pub. Co., Ithaca, N. Y.

Leonard, M. D. (editor). 1926. A List of the Insects of New York. Cornell Univ. Agri. Exp. Sta., Mem. 101, Ithaca, N. Y.

Lutz, F. E. 1921. Field Book of Insects. G. P. Putnam's Sons.

Miall, L. C. 1912. The Natural History of Aquatic Insects. Macmillan Co.

Needham, J. G., and Lloyd, J. T. 1916. The Life of Inland Waters. Comstock Pub. Co., Ithaca, N. Y.

Needham, J. G., and Needham, P. R. 1927. A Guide to the Study of Fresh-water Biology. With Special Reference to Aquatic Insects and other Invertebrate Animals. The Amer. Viewpoint Soc., 13 Astor Place, New York, and Albany. Includes keys with figures of each form mentioned and suggestions for studies of aquatic communities.

Needham, J. G. 1928, Elementary Lessons on Insects. C. C. Thomas, Springfield, Ill.

Ward, H. B., and Whipple, G. C. 1918. Fresh-Water Biology. John Wiley & Sons. Includes keys.

BIBLIOGRAPHY

Collembola.

Folsom, J. W. 1916. North American Collembolous Insects of the Sub-families Achorutinæ, Neanurinæ, and Podurinæ. Proc. U. S. Nat. Mus., Vol. 50: 477–525.

Plecoptera.

Needham, J. G. 1901. Plecoptera; in Aquatic Insects in the Adirondacks. N. Y. State Mus., Bull., Vol. 47: 412–418, Albany.

Needham, J. G., and Claassen, P. W. 1925. Monograph: Plecoptera or Stoneflies of America north of Mexico. LaFayette, Indiana.

Smith, L. W. 1913. The Biology of Perla immarginata Say. Ann. Ent. Soc. Amer., Vol. 6: 203–211.

Wu, C. F. 1923. Morphology, Anatomy and Ethology of Nemoura. Lloyd Library, Bull., Ent. Series No. 3: 1–81. Cincinnati, Ohio. Complete life history through 22 instars.

Ephemeridæ.

Morgan, A. H. 1911. Mayflies of Fall Creek. (Egg Laying of Bætis.) Ann. Ent. Soc. Amer., Vol. 4: 371–411.
1913. Contribution to the Biology of Mayflies. Ann Ent. Soc. Amer., Vol. 6: 371–413.

Murphy, H. E. 1922. Notes on the Biology of Some of o North American Species of May-flies. Lloyd Libra Bull., Ent. Series, No. 2: 1–46, Cincinnati, Ohio.

Needham, J. G. 1901. Ephemeridæ. N. Y. State M Bull., Vol. 47: 418–429, Albany.
1905. Mayflies and Midges of New York. N. Y. Mus., Bull., Vol. 86: 17–62, Albany.
1908. Notes on the Aquatic Insects of Walnut Rep. Geol. Survey of Mich. for 1907: 252–271.
1920. Burrowing Mayflies of our Larger La Streams. Bull. Bur. Fish., Vol. 36: 265–292.

BIBLIOGRAPHY

Odonata.

Needham, J. G. 1900. The Fruiting of the Blue Flag (Iris versicolor L.) (Lestes and blue flag). Amer. Nat., Vol. 34: 374–375.

1903. Life-histories of Odonata. Suborder Zygoptera, Damselflies. N. Y. State Mus., Bull., Vol. 68: 218–263, Albany.

Needham, J. G., and Heywood, H. B. 1929. A Handbook of the Dragonflies of North America. Charles C. Thomas, Springfield, Ill.

Wilson, C. B. 1920. Dragonflies and Damselflies in Relation to Pond-fish Culture, with a List of those found near Fairport, Iowa. Bull. Bur. Fish., Vol. 36: 185–264.

Hemiptera.

Hungerford, H. B. 1919. The Biology and Ecology of Aquatic and Semiaquatic Hemiptera. Kans. Univ. Sci. Bull., Vol. 11, No. 17. Excellent account of their biology. Extensive bibliography.

Torre-Bueno, J. R. de la. 1905. Notes on Collecting, Preserving and Rearing Aquatic Hemiptera. Can. Ent., Vol. 37: 12–24.

Neuroptera.

Anthony, M. H. 1902. The Metamorphosis of Sisyra. Amer. Nat., Vol. 36: 615–631.

Davis, K. C. 1903. Sialidæ of North America. N. Y. State Mus., Bull., Vol. 68: 442–486, Albany. Life histories and biology of this family.

Needham, J. G. 1901. Neuroptera; in Aquatic Insects in the Adirondacks. N. Y. State Mus., Bull., Vol. 47: 555–557, Albany.

Trichoptera.

Betten, C. 1901. Trichoptera; in Aquatic Insects in the Adirondacks. N. Y. State Mus., Bull., Vol. 47: 501–572, Albany.

BIBLIOGRAPHY

Krafka, J., Jr. 1915. A Key to the Families of Trichopterous Larvæ. Can. Ent., Vol. 47: 217–225.

Lloyd, J. T. 1921. The Biology of the North American Caddice Fly Larvæ. Lloyd Library, Bull., Vol. 21, Ent. Series No. 1, Cincinnati, Ohio.

Marshall, W. S., and Vorhies, C. T. 1905. The Repair and Rebuilding of the Larval Case of Platyphylax designatus Walk. Biol. Bull., Vol. 9: 232–244.

Murphy, H. E. 1919. Observations on the Egg-Laying of the Caddice Fly Brachycentrus nigrisoma Banks, and on the Habits of the Young Larvæ. Jour. N. Y. Ent. Soc., Vol. 27: 154–159.

Noyes, A. A. 1914. The Biology of the Net-Spinning Trichoptera of Cascadilla Creek. Ann. Ent. Soc. Amer., Vol. 7: 251–271.

Vorhies, C. T. 1909. Studies on the Trichoptera of Wisconsin. Trans. Wisc. Acad. Sci., Vol. 16: 647–738, Madison, Wisc.

Lepidoptera.

Forbes, W. T. M. 1910. The Aquatic Caterpillars of Lake Quinsigamond. Psyche, Vol. 17: 219–227. Photographs of Nymphula maculalis, larva, gills, pupal case.

1911. Another Aquatic Caterpillar (Elophila). Psyche, Vol. 18: 120–121. Cases on Lemna leaves.

Lloyd, J. T. 1914. Lepidopterous Larvæ from Rapid Streams. Jour. N. Y. Ent. Soc., Vol. 22: 145–152.

Welch, P. S. 1916. Contributions to the Biology of Certain Aquatic Lepidoptera. Ann. Ent. Soc. Amer., Vol. 9: 159–190. Excellent account of life history of Nymphula maculalis.

Welch, P. S., and Sehon, G. L. 1928. The Periodic Vibratory Movements of the Larva of Nymphula maculalis Clemens (Lepidoptera) and their Respiratory Significance. Ann. Ent. Soc. Amer., Vol. 21: 243–258.

BIBLIOGRAPHY

Coleoptera.

Blatchley, W. S. 1910. An Illustrated Catalogue of the Coleoptera or Beetles (exclusive of the Rhyncophora) Known to Occur in Indiana. Nature Pub. Co., Indianapolis, Ind.

MacGillivray, A. D. 1903. Aquatic Chrysomellidæ and a Table of the Families of Coleopterous Larvæ. N. Y. State Mus., Bull., Vol. 68: 288–327, Albany.

Matheson, R. 1912. Haliplidæ of North America, North of Mexico. Jour. N. Y. Ent. Soc., Vol. 20: 156–193.

Needham, J. G., and Williamson, H. V. 1907. Observations on the Natural History of Diving Beetles. Amer. Nat., Vol. 41: 477–494.

Richmond, E. A. 1920. Studies on the Biology of the Aquatic Hydrophilidæ. Bull. Amer. Mus. Nat. Hist., Vol. 42, No. 1, New York.

Diptera.

Alexander, C. P. 1919. The Crane-Flies of New York, Part I, Distribution and Taxonomy of Adult Flies. Cornell Univ. Agri. Exp. Sta., Mem. 25, Ithaca, N. Y.
1920. Idem, Part II, Biology and Phylogeny. Cornell Univ. Agri. Exp. Sta., Mem. 25, Ithaca, N. Y.

Claassen, P. W. 1922. The Larva of a Chironomid which is Parasitic upon a Mayfly Nymph. Kans. Univ. Sci. Bull., Vol. 15, No. 16.

Johannsen, O. A. 1903. Aquatic Nematocerous Diptera. N.Y. State Mus., Bull., Vol. 68, Ent. 18: 328–441, Albany.

Kellogg, V. L. 1901. Food of Larvæ of Simulium and Blepharocera. Psyche, Vol. 9: 166–167.

Malloch, J. R. 1914. American Blackflies or Buffalo Gnats, U. S. Dept. Agri., Bur. Ent., Bull. No. 26, Tech. Series.

Matheson, R. 1930. Biology of Mosquitoes. Charles C. Thomas, Springfield, Ill.

BIBLIOGRAPHY

Hymenopiera. (Minute wasp-like insects, not included in this book.)

Matheson, R., and Crosby, C. R. 1912. Aquatic Hymenoptera in America. Ann. Ent. Soc. Amer., Vol. 5: 65–71. Excellent figure of the adult wasp swimming.

CHAPTER XVI

SNAILS AND MUSSELS

Baker, F. C. 1918. The Productivity of Invertebrate Fish Food on the Bottom of Oneida Lake, with Special Reference to Mollusks. Tech. Pub. No. 9, N. Y. State College of Forestry, Syracuse Univ.

1928. The Fresh Water Mollusca of Wisconsin. Part I Gastropoda, Part II Pelecypoda. Wisc. Geol. and Nat. Hist. Survey, Bull. No. 70, pt. 1, Madison, Wisc.

Lefevre, G., and Curtis, W. C. 1912. Studies of the Reproduction and Artificial Propagation of Fresh-Water Mussels. Bull. Bur. Fish., Vol. 30, for 1910: 107–201.

CHAPTER XVII

FISHES

General References: Jordan, 1929; Ward and Whipple, 1918, Chap. 30, Eigenmann, C. H., The Aquatic Vertebrates; Copeia; Aquatic Life.

A Biological Survey of the Erie-Niagara System, Sect. VI, Fishes of the Erie-Niagara Watershed. Supp. to the Eighteenth Ann. Rep., 1928, State of N. Y. Conservation Dept., Albany.

Adams, C. C., and Hankinson, T. L. 1928. The Ecology and Economics of Oneida Lake Fish. Roosevelt Wild Life Bull., Vol. 1, Nos. 3, 4, Syracuse Univ. Bibliography.

Embody, G. C. 1915. The Farm Fishpond. Cornell Reading Courses. Country Life Series, No. 3, Ithaca, N. Y.

Forbes, S. A., and Richardson, R. E. 1909. The Fishes of Illinois. Bull. Illinois Nat. Hist. Survey, Vol. 3, Urbana. Bibliography.

Gage, S. H. 1929. Lampreys and their Ways. Sci. Mo., Vol. 28: 401–416.

Greely, J. R. 1927. Some Common Non-Game Fishes of New York. Cornell Rural School Leaflet, Vol. 21: 57–74, Ithaca, N. Y.

Hankinson, T. L. 1909. Field Problems on Stream Fishes for Secondary Classes. School Sci. and Math., Vol. 9: 234–240. Suggestions for field work upon fishes of ponds and small streams,—study of eggs and nests, blunt-nosed minnow, nesting sunfish.

Jordan, D. S., and Evermann, B. W. 1903. American Food and Game Fishes. Doubleday, Doran & Co.

Reighard, J. E. 1920. The Breeding Behavior of the Suckers and Minnows. Biol. Bull., Vol. 38: 1–32.

Schmidt, J. 1912. The Reproduction and Spawning Places of the Freshwater Eel (Anguilla vulgaris). Nature, Vol. 89: 633–636.

1925. The Breeding Place of the Eel. Smithsonian Ann. Rep. for 1924 : 279–316.

CHAPTER XVIII

SALAMANDERS, FROGS, AND TOADS, FOUND IN OR NEAR WATER

General References: **Jordan,** 1929; **Copeia; Aquatic Life.**

Babcock, H. L. 1926. Time Table of New England Frogs and Toads. Bull. Boston Soc. Nat. Hist., No. 38: 11–14.

Bishop, S. C. 1925. The Life of the Red Salamander. Nat. Hist., Vol. 25: 385–389 (eggs).

1926. Notes on the Habits and Development of the Mud-puppy, Necturus. N. Y. State Mus., Bull., No. 268, Albany.

1927. The Amphibians and Reptiles of Allegany State Park. N. Y. State Mus., Handbook, No. 3, Albany.

Boulenger, E. G. 1914. Reptiles and Batrachians. E. P. Dutton & Co.

Dickerson, M. C. 1906. The Frog Book. Doubleday, Doran & Co. Well written accounts of North American frogs and toads, with a study of the habits and life-histories of those of the northeastern states.

Dunn, E. R. 1926. The Salamanders of the Family Plethodontidæ. Smith College, Northampton, Mass.

Gage, S. H. 1891. Life History of the Vermilion-Spotted Newt (Diemyctylus viridescens Raf.). Amer. Nat., Vol. 25: 1084–1110.

Noble, G. K. 1929. Further Observations on the Life-history of the Newt Triturus viridescens. Amer. Mus. Novitates, No. 348, Amer. Mus. Nat. Hist., New York.

Smith, B. G. 1907. The Life History and Habits of Cryptobranchus alleghoniensis. Biol. Bull., Vol. 13: 5–39. 1907a. The Breeding Habits of Amblystoma punctatum Linn. Amer. Nat., Vol. 41: 381–390.

Wright, A. H. 1920. Frogs: Their Natural History and Utilization. Bull. Bur. Fish., Doc. 888: 5–44. 1924. A Key to the Eggs of the Salientia East of the Mississippi River. Amer. Nat., Vol. 58: 375–381. 1929. Synopsis and Description of North American Tadpoles. Proc. U. S. Nat. Mus., Vol. 74: 1–70.

Wright, A. H., and Allen, A. A. 1908. Notes on the Breeding Habits of the Swamp Cricket Frog, Chorophilus triseriatus Wied. Amer. Nat., Vol. 42: 39–42.

CHAPTER XIX

TURTLES AND SNAKES, FOUND IN OR NEAR WATER

General References: **Jordan**, 1929.

Babcock, H. L. 1919. The Turtles of New England. Memoir Boston Soc. Nat. Hist., Vol. 8.

BIBLIOGRAPHY

Bishop, S. C. 1927. The Amphibians and Reptiles of Allegheny State Park. N. Y. State Mus., Handbook, No. 3, Albany.

Blanchard, F. N. 1925. A Key to the Snakes of the United States, Canada, and Lower California. Mich. Acad. Sci., Arts and Letters, Vol. 4, pt. 2.

Boulenger, E. G. 1914. Reptiles and Batrachians. E. P. Dutton & Co.

Ditmars, R. L. 1908. The Reptile Book. Doubleday, Doran & Co. Well illustrated and interesting accounts of the turtles, tortoises, crocodilians, lizards, and snakes which inhabit the United States and northern Mexico.

Sharp, D. L. 1911. The Face of the Fields. (Chapter on "Turtle Eggs for Agassiz.") Houghton, Mifflin & Co. Also 1910. Atlantic Monthly. Vol. 105: 156–164.

Wright, A. H., and Funkhouser, W. D. 1915. A Biological Reconnaissance of the Okefinokee Swamp in Georgia— The Reptiles. Proc. Acad. Nat. Sci., Phila. Vol. 67: 107–139. (Eggs and nest of mud turtle).

GLOSSARY

Algæ, simple chlorophyll-bearing plants most of which live entirely submerged in water.

Anterior, near or toward front or head end.

Asexual, reproducing by other means than eggs and sperm cells, e. g. budding as in Hydra.

Auricle, a chamber of the heart which receives blood **from** the veins; an ear-like lobe on a planarian.

Axolotl, a larva of *Ambystoma tigrinum* which matures sexually without changing its larval form. Found only in the southwestern United States.

Balancers, processes in front of the gills of certain tailed amphibians, as in salamander larvæ.

Barbel, whisker-like feelers about the heads of some fishes, e. g., the common bullhead.

Brackish, water which is partly salt and partly fresh.

ßryozoans, plant-like animals living in colonies, e. g., *Cristatella*.

Calcareous, limy or containing calcium carbonate.

Carapace, hard upper shell of turtles or of crustaceans such as crayfishes and lobsters.

Carnivorous, eating animal food.

Chitin, horny substance of the skeletons of insects and some other arthropods.

Chlorophyll, green coloring matter of plants.

Cloaca, a cavity in the body of vertebrates into which the intestine, urinary, and reproductive tubes open; not found in most mammals.

GLOSSARY

Clypeus, the skeletal plate above the upper lip or labrum, **in** insects.

Cœlenteron, food cavity in hydra and related animals.

Crustaceans, animals with jointed bodies and appendages and an external limy skeleton.

Ctenoid, rough edged, said of the scales of fishes.

Dermis, an inner layer of cells in the skin of vertebrates.

Desmids, single-celled green plants apparently divided into two parts by a light band.

Diatoms, minute single-celled plants which are characteristically golden brown.

Dorsal, on or toward the back.

Elytra, horny front or outer wings of beetles.

Entomostracan, a minute crustacean, e. g., *Cyclops.*

Fertilization, the union of an egg cell and a sperm cell, forming a new individual.

Formalin, a solution of formaldehyde used as a preservative.

Gemmule, a capsule of sponge cells which live over the winter and from which a new colony grows in the spring.

Gills, organs by which animals can breathe in water.

Glochidium, a larval mussel which lives as a parasite on the skin of fishes.

Hæmophilia, an hereditary disease, in which the blood does not clot properly on exposure to air.

Hermaphrodite, having both male and female reproductive organs in one individual; true of hydra, earthworms, and many other animals.

Hibernate, to pass the winter in an inactive dormant state.

Hydranth, one of the individuals which takes food in a colony of hydra-like animals.

Imago, an adult, sexually mature insect.

Internode, the part of a plant stem between the points from which leaves spring forth.

Labrum, the upper lip of insects and of some other arthropods.

Larva, an immature stage in the life of certain animals; in insects, the stage between the egg and the pupa.

Mandible, the bone of the lower jaw; in crustaceans, the third pair of head appendages; in insects, the first or upper pair of jaws.

Mantle, an outer fold of flesh in many animals; in clams and other mollusks it secretes the shell.

Maxilla, one of the pair of lower jaws in insects, also present in other arthropods.

Micropyle, a small opening in the outer covering of an egg cell through which a sperm cell may enter.

Myriapod, a small arthropod with many pairs of legs, as centipedes.

Node, the point on the stem of a plant from which the leaf springs.

Nymph, an immature insect which undergoes only partial change of form as it matures, e. g., mayflies, grasshoppers.

Operculum, a horny cover over the opening of the shell of some snails; the gill cover of fishes.

Ovary, the organ in which egg cells develop.

Pallial line, scar on the inner surface of clam and mussel shells caused by attachment of muscles of the mantle.

Palp, a sensory organ near the mouth, often jointed as in insects.

Parthenogenesis, the development of an egg without fertilization by a sperm cell.

Peduncle, a short stalk, as the stem of a flower, or the stalk of a crayfish eye.

Periostracum, the outer layer of a molluscan shell.

Petiole, the stem of a leaf.

Plankton, the population of minute plants and animals which live in the surface layers of salt or fresh water.

Plastron, the under shell of a turtle.

Pollination, the transference of pollen containing male cells to the surface of the pistil in higher flowering plants.

Posterior, opposite from head end; hind or rear end.

Prawn, a large shrimp-like crustacean.

Predacious, killing other animals for food.

Pronotum, dorsal region of the prothorax of an insect.

Pupate, in insects, to undergo a change from larval to adult form.

Rhizoid, a root-like filament in lower plants.

Scud, a crustacean of the Order *Amphipoda*, e. g., *Gammarus, Hyalella.*

Sessile, fixed to one place; not on a stalk or stem.

Setæ, bristle-like appendages, in some insects extending back as tails.

Silt, a fine earthy sediment carried and deposited by water.

Somite, a segment of the body, especially of worms, crustaceans, and insects.

Spawn, to lay or produce eggs, especially of fishes.

Spermary, sex organ in which the male or sperm cells develop, as in hydra.

Spicules, minute calcareous or silicious bodies forming the skeleton of sponges.

Spiracles, external openings in the respiratory or tracheal systems of insects and some other arthropods.

Spore, an asexual reproductive cell capable of producing a new individual without fertilization; a resistant stage enabling small organisms to survive cold or drought.

Subimago, the nearly mature winged stage of mayflies.

Swimmeret, abdominal appendage of some crustaceans.

Symbiosis, the association of two species of organisms, in an advantageous partnership.

Tarsi, the segmented feet of insects and other arthropods.

Tentacle, a slender, unsegmented, feeler-like process.

Testis, the organ in which the male or sperm cells develop, especially in higher animals.

Thorax, the division of the body posterior to the head; in mammals, the part of the body containing the heart and lungs.

Umbo, the thickening above the hinge on the shell of a clam.

Utricles, little sacks or bladders, as in the bladderwort, *Utricularia*.

Ventral, the under side or front, opposite to the back.

Vivarium, a place for keeping live animals, as aquarium or terrarium.

Whorl, a circular arrangement of leaves around a stem.

Zooecium, the outer shell-like tube of some bryozoans.

INDEX

INDEX